COLLOIDAL
SURFACTANTS

SOME PHYSICOCHEMICAL PROPERTIES

PHYSICAL CHEMISTRY
A Series of Monographs

Edited by

ERNEST M. LOEBL

Department of Chemistry, Polytechnic Institute of Brooklyn
Brooklyn, New York

COLLOIDAL SURFACTANTS

SOME PHYSICOCHEMICAL PROPERTIES

By

KOZO SHINODA

Department of Chemistry
Yokohama National University
Minamiku, Yokohama, Japan

TOSHIO NAKAGAWA

Research Laboratories
Shionogi Pharmaceutical Company
Imafuku, Amagasaki-shi, Japan

BUN-ICHI TAMAMUSHI

Tokyo Women's
Christian College
Suginamiku, Tokyo, Japan

TOSHIZO ISEMURA

Department of Biology
Osaka University
Kitaku, Osaka, Japan

1963

ACADEMIC PRESS · NEW YORK AND LONDON

TP 149
C63

660
C714

ACADEMIC PRESS, INC.
111 Fifth Avenue, New York, New York 10003

United Kingdom Edition published by
ACADEMIC PRESS, INC. (LONDON) LTD.
Berkeley Square House, London W.1

LIBRARY OF CONGRESS CATALOG CARD NUMBER: 62-13114

Second Printing, 1969

PRINTED IN THE UNITED STATES OF AMERICA

PREFACE

In almost all branches of the chemical industry, surface active agents have found wide use. The many interrelations with various fields of science have stimulated rapid progress in research on the extremely interesting properties of these substances.

Surface active agents are of great importance in detergency, in the textile industry, and in biological research. This is due to their following distinctive features: (1) moderate maximum concentration of molecularly dispersed species; (2) surface and interfacial depression in very dilute solution, due to the adsorption and orientation of molecules at the interface, (3) micelle formation above a certain concentration, due to the free energy decrease of the system; and (4) solubilization of water-insoluble substances by micelles.

Considerable research work with surface active agents has been carried out in Japan; this work, however, is not well known in other countries because many of the papers were published in Japanese, and even those written in English for the *Bulletin of the Chemical Society of Japan* are not widely read.

For this reason, one of us (K.S.), together with several colleagues, planned to publish a book on this subject. Fortunately, Professor Eric Hutchinson, the Editor of this series, came to Yokohama National University as Fulbright Exchange Lecturer for the academic year of 1959–1960. Professor Hutchinson's stay in Japan provided a rare opportunity for cooperative activity toward this end and we wish to express our sincere gratitude to him for his encouragement and many helpful suggestions.

We are grateful to the Daiichi Pharmaceutical Company for various surface active agents.

B. TAMAMUSHI
T. ISEMURA
T. NAKAGAWA
K. SHINODA

May, 1962

CONTENTS

CHAPTER THREE. Adsorption

BUN-ICHI TAMAMUSHI

CHAPTER FOUR. Monomolecular Layers

TOSHIZO ISEMURA

COLLOIDAL
SURFACTANTS

SOME PHYSICOCHEMICAL PROPERTIES

CHAPTER ONE

THE FORMATION OF MICELLES

KŌZŌ SHINODA

I. An Outline of the Behavior of Surface Active Agents in Solution

The distinctive features of surface active agents are: (1) their moderate maximum concentration of molecularly dispersed species; (2) surface and interfacial tension depression in very dilute solution, due to the adsorption and orientation of molecules at the interface; (3) micelle formation above a certain concentration, which has been termed the critical micelle concentration (CMC), due to the free energy decrease of the system; and (4) solubilization of water-insoluble substances by micelles.

The great importance of surface active agents in the textile industry, in detergency, biological actions, etc. has resulted from these peculiar properties. The applications of surface active agents have been rapidly increasing, and an understanding of their physicochemical properties is becoming more and more important to scientists in various fields.

Before discussing the dissolution tendency of surface active agents, which are composed of either an ionic or a nonionic hydrophilic group and a hydrocarbon chain, it seems helpful to outline the factors which control the solubility of simple salts and hydrocarbons, respectively, in water.

In the vapor state the calculation of the equilibrium of

$$NaCl \rightleftharpoons Na^+ + Cl^- \tag{1.1}$$

is straightforward. From the statistical thermodynamic relation in general chemical equilibrium (*1*),

$$\frac{N_{Na^+}N_{Cl^-}}{VN_{NaCl}} = \frac{f_{Na^+}f_{Cl^-}}{f_{NaCl}} \exp\left(-\Delta\chi/kT\right) \tag{1.2}$$

where N_{NaCl}, N_{Na^+}, and N_{Cl^-} are the mole numbers of NaCl, Na^+, and Cl^- ions in the vessel; f_{NaCl}, f_{Na^+}, and f_{Cl^-} are the partition functions of NaCl, Na^+, and Cl^-; $\Delta\chi$ is the excess energy of a pair of free Na^+ and Cl^- ions at rest over one NaCl molecule at rest in its lowest vibrational state; V is the volume of the vessel; k is the Boltzmann constant; and T is the absolute temperature. The ratio of the partition functions of the dissociated ions to that of the salt is much larger than 1, and this term contributes to the dissociation. The factor $\exp(-\Delta\chi/kT)$, which is much smaller than 1, restrains the dissociation. In other words, the electrical energy required for the separation of ions decreases the dissociation, and the translational entropy increase due to the separation of ions increases the dissociation.

The mutual potential energy of Na^+ and Cl^- is approximately $\Delta\chi = 8.6 \times 10^{-12}$ ergs/ion pair.

The partition function of these simple particles can be easily calculated assuming that the vibrational partition function is close to 1 at room temperature, which is a reasonable assumption. Substituting these values and expressing the equilibrium concentration C in gram ions (or gram molecules) per liter, the equilibrium constant at $300°K$ in the gas phase is,

$$K = \frac{C_{Na^+}C_{Cl^-}}{C_{NaCl}} \simeq 10^2 \exp(-\Delta\chi/kT) \approx 10^2 \exp(-210) = 10^{-89} \qquad (1.3)$$

Thus, ordinary salt is naturally completely undissociated in the vapor phase. If we regard water merely as a continuous medium (unhydrated) with dielectric constant $D \approx 80$, the energy of separation of the pair of ions would be reduced to roughly $\Delta\chi/D$. We thus obtain in water (1)

$$K_{NaCl} = \frac{C_{Na^+}C_{Cl^-}}{C_{NaCl}} \simeq 10^2 \exp(-2.6) \simeq 7 \qquad (1.4)$$

In the very strong fields near an ion, a saturation effect sets in, which reduces considerably the effective value of D. The correct value of the equilibrium constant must be much less than 7 in the absence of hydration. Nevertheless, the above discussion explains the large dissociation of salts or ionic surface active agents in water. Dissociation is caused by the entropy increase at the expense of the energy required to separate the ions. As the nonelectrical heat of solution of salt in water or in organic solvents is far less than $\Delta\chi$ ($\Delta\chi$ is about 120 kcal/mole), the above discussion is able to explain the large dissociation and solubility of salts in water and the negligible dissociation and solubility in hydrocarbons whose dielectric constants are about 1 or 3.

If we immerse ionic surface active agents, for example sodium dodecyl sulfate, in water, the "gegenion" Na^+ dissolves in water by the same entropy effect. The dissociation of $1:1$ electrolytes into separate ions increases the total entropy considerably. After dissolution of the sodium ion, the solid ionic surface active agent carries a negative charge and this electrical repulsion increases the solvency of the dodecyl sulfate ion in water. The so-called "hydrophilic group" in an ionic surface active agent has the property of being readily soluble in water, but the heat of solution assigned to the hydrophilic group is not necessarily exothermic. It is not the "sympathetic force" (2) of the hydrophilic group, but rather the entropy increase due to dissociation, which enhances the dissolutive tendency of ionic agents. In spite of their great solubility, the heat of solution of many inorganic salts is generally negative.

There is, however, no dissociable group in a nonionic surface active agent. There is some "sympathetic force" between the hydrophilic portion of the molecule and the surrounding water molecules. The oxygen atom in the hydrophilic group of nonionic agents has a relatively large attraction for water molecules, but the increase of solvency due to this portion is small because the ethylene groups in the polyoxyethylene chain cancel the effect. There is also some positive configurational entropy of solution due to the long and large hydrophilic group of the molecule. Both these effects are usually small (3) compared to that of an ionic group, due to dissociation. For this reason, the maximum concentration of molecular dispersion, i.e., the critical micelle concentration, is very much smaller in nonionic surface active agents whose hydrocarbon chain is the same as that of ionic agents. For example, the CMC of sodium dodecyl sulfate is 0.0081 mole/liter, whereas that of dodecyl glucoside is 0.00019 mole/liter (4).

The "antipathy" between the oleophilic portion and the water molecules does not involve an actual repulsive force between the two (2). As the cohesive forces between the water molecules are very strong and the cohesive forces between hydrocarbon-hydrocarbon or hydrocarbon-water are not strong, the separate phase state has a lower energy than the mixed state. Were there no hydrophilic group in the molecule, i.e., in the case of hydrocarbon, the entropy of dilution would have to counterbalance the heat of solution of hydrocarbon. The effect of molecular size, i.e., hydrocarbon chain length on solubility, can be understood by analogy with the regular solution theory developed by Hildebrand (5)

$$\ln a_2 = \ln X_2 + \frac{V_2 \phi_1^2 (\delta_1 - \delta_2)^2}{RT} \tag{1.5}$$

where a_2 is the relative activity of solute and is very close to 1 at saturation if the solubility of component 1 (liquid) in component 2 (liquid) is small; X_2 is the solubility of solute (hydrocarbon) in mole fraction units; V_2 is the molal volume of solute; ϕ_1 is the volume fraction of solvent; and δ_i are the solubility parameters of the components. The second term expresses the contribution of the heat of solution to the solubility. (There are also structural enthalpy and entropy changes in the case of hydrocarbon in water, but they largely cancel out.) When we discuss the solubility of hydrocarbons in a very different solvent, such as water, the difference in the solubility parameter, i.e., heat of

solution per unit volume, is almost constant for any homologous hydrocarbons, and the heat term is proportional to the molal volume, namely,
to the hydrocarbon chain length.   Actually, the logarithm of the solubility
of hydrocarbons or paraffin chain compounds decreases linearly with the
increase of hydrocarbon chain length.

This tendency is opposed by the influence of the hydrophilic portion
in the case of a surface active agent and shows moderate concentration
of single dispersion.   The saturation concentration of singly dispersed
species (CMC) of the surface active agent, of course, changes very much
with the length of hydrocarbon chain, just as the solubility of hydrocarbons or aliphatic alcohols changes very much with the length of hydrocarbon chain.

If no salt is added to the solution, the concentrations of gegenions and
surface active ions which are in an equilibrium with excess charged solid
ionic surface active agent are practically the same.   On the one hand,
electrical attraction between gegenions and the excess solid decreases
the equilibrium concentration of gegenions in the bulk which are in equilibrium with gegenions in the solid phase, and on the other hand, the
electrical repulsion between surface active ions in the bulk and charged
solid increases the dissolution tendency of the surface active ions which
are also in equilibrium with surface active ions in the charged solid.
If salt is added, the concentration of gegenions increases and that of
paraffin chain ion decreases.   The electrical potential on the excess ionic
surface active agent decreases also by the progressive fixing or approach
of gegenions to the solid surface.   This decrease in electrical potential
increases the solvency of gegenions and decreases that of paraffin chain
ions.   It is clear from the above discussion that the saturation concentration of a singly dispersed ionic agent is roughly the geometrical
average of the saturation concentration of the corresponding inorganic
salt and a hydrocarbon of the same chain length; and the concentration
of singly dispersed paraffin chain ions sensitively decreases with an in
crease of the concentration of gegenions, but the CMC of a nonionic
agent is not affected primarily by the addition of salt.

As described above, surface active agents possess a duality and asymmetry of properties.   These opposing tendencies are very asymmetrically
distributed and may be separately and simultaneously satisfied (2).
Therefore, surface active agents have a very strong tendency for adsorption and orientation at the interface from aqueous solution, and the free
energy of the system decreases as a result of adsorption.   As the adsorption of hydrocarbon chains arises from the strong cohesive force
between the water molecules, there is no positive adsorption at hydro-
carbon-air interface except in the case of fluorocarbon compounds which
have smaller intermolecular force than hydrocarbons.

It is this same combination of properties which is responsible for the characteristic surface or interfacial tension depression and the powerful emulsifying, wetting, dispersing, and foaming abilities of their solutions (2). However, in the bulk of the solution, where there are no surfaces on which adsorption can occur, the paraffin chain molecules (ions) will form aggregates above a certain concentration; that is, micelle formation occurs at a certain concentration at which the (electro) chemical potential of paraffin chain molecule (ions) in the solute state is equal to the (electro) chemical potential of paraffin chain molecule (ions) in the micellar state. The introduction of an aggregate of paraffin chains into which water does not penetrate is thus accomplished with a much smaller expenditure of free energy than would be required if the chains were introduced as separated single chains. The compromise between the segregation of water and hydrocarbon chains and the solvency of the hydrophilic portion of the surface active agent is brought about by the aggregation of the oleophilic portions which are so grouped that the exterior of the aggregate is composed of the hydrophilic portions of the molecules. The shorter the chain, therefore, the smaller will be the reduction of free energy of the system resulting from aggregation and the higher the concentration necessary to produce micelle formation. The fact that there is no clear evidence for the existence of micelles in solutions of paraffin chain salts with less than 4 carbon atoms in the chain is due either to the fact that sufficiently high concentrations, about 3 moles/liter or 40 volume per cent in solution, are unattainable or that energy of aggregation is not big enough to suppress the thermal random mixing motion of molecules. A very high solute concentration in the bulk also changes the solvent property in the direction of being more oleophilic, i.e., less favorable for micelle formation. In solutions of weak electrolytes, e.g., of butyric acid (6, 7), micelles still form. Butanol is also not infinitely miscible with water. The solubility of butanol in water is about 0.97 mole/liter.

A liquid state model for the micelle is supported by the fact that the micelle-forming ion can mix with various additives, forming mixed micelles (8), and by solubilization phenomena exhibited by micellar solutions. It is not necessary that the substance dissolved in this way itself be a liquid; solute (liquid or solid) in solution is in the liquid state. Azobenzene and crystalline derivatives of this compound are dissolved in solutions of paraffin chain salts (2). When both solutes are precipitated by cooling, they are usually easily separated by solution of the azobenzene derivative in an organic solvent and do not, therefore, form solid solution or compound crystalline phases. It seems conclusive that the solvent properties of the micelle are due to its liquid nature (2). The remarkable difference between the liquid state and the solid state is that a solute does mix with various solvents of markedly different molecular sizes and exhibits similar partial molal volumes close to the molal volumes of the solute in the pure state (9), but in the solid state the solute can hardly form mixed crystals with molecules of different sizes and shapes.

Hence, it seems probable that the micelle is in a liquid state and that the structure of the interior resembles that of a liquid paraffin. The structure will be more organized, however, than liquid paraffin because of the hydrophilic group anchored on the micelle surface. The structure of a liquid paraffin may itself be rather more highly organized than it has been supposed, for the paraffin chain is not freely rotating but rather vibrating in its *trans* or *gauche* form (10). The *trans* form is about 800 cal/mole more stable than the *gauche* form. Even a small change in bond angle also needs a very large energy. A rather straight zigzag chain structure for hydrocarbons has become more widely accepted nowadays. A completely flexible model is certainly an overestimation of flexibility and configurational number.

It has been assumed generally that solutions of surface active agents behave as singly dispersed systems up to the CMC. Osmotic coefficient measurements clearly support this view (11). The colligative properties of solutions of surface active agents do not deviate by more than about 5% from those of ideal 1 : 1 electrolytes until the CMC is reached (12). But, as revealed by equivalent conductivity measurements (11, 13), there are some surface active agents which show dimerization. The dimerization process may not be a universal phenomenon in solutions of surface active agents, but may depend largely on the molecular type of the surface active agent. If the hydrocarbon chain is sufficiently long, the free energy of the system may decrease as a result of dimerization. The large area of contact between two hydrocarbon chains and a sufficient concentration of singly dispersed species are necessary to balance the electrical energy of approach of two ionic groups and a translational entropy decrease of about 20 eu. Thus, the dimerization will occur more favorably if the hydrocarbon chain is longer. The fraction of dimer increases with increasing bulk concentration up to the CMC, and then it may stay almost constant above the CMC. Dimerization may not be the initiation of micellar aggregation, but the process may rather resemble the coexistence of monomer and dimer in the vapor phase of acetic acid, where the hydrogen bond is a driving force for dimerization. If the vapor pressure reaches the saturation vapor pressure, then liquid acetic acid, which is in equilibrium with monomer and dimer, will separate The formation of micelles will be similar to this phase separation (14), except that it does not lead to an infinite aggregation number for the micelle. Many theories on micelle formation have been based on this model.

It should then follow that the activity of micellar surface active agents should remain almost constant above the CMC. Graphs of surface tension γ vs. concentration clearly show that the activity of the surface active agent does indeed stay constant above the CMC, supporting the above view; namely, in Gibbs's adsorption isotherm,

$$\left(\frac{\partial \gamma}{\partial \ln a_2}\right)_T = -RT\Gamma_2 \tag{1.6}$$

surface excess Γ_2 shows a large constant value, revealed by radiotracer measurements (15, 16). If $\partial \gamma = 0$, then $\partial a_2 = 0$, i.e., $a_2 = $ constant.

We will now discuss the relation between the saturation concentration of singly dispersed species and the solubility of surface active agents. It is well known that the solubility of paraffin chain salts is a rather peculiar function of the temperature, systems of nearly any composition of paraffin chain salts and water becoming homogeneous at a few degrees above a certain temperature which is known as the Krafft point (17). This fact gives rise to the expression "melting point of soap curds." As Murray and Hartley (18) said, "Melting point of curds phenomena mean that we have a sudden, large increase of solubility over a very short range of temperature and it seems to us that this has in all probability a similar explanation of the other sudden transitions."

By analogy with the phase diagram for ice-water, we may suppose that as the temperature is increased the difference between the concentration of the supercooled micelles and the hydrated solid agent decreases. Above the Krafft point, the equilibrium concentration of the micelles is smaller than that of the (hypothetical) superheated hydrated solid agent, and, therefore, the micelle is the thermodynamically preferred form.

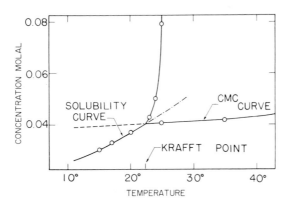

Fig. 1.1. Phase diagram close to the Krafft point.

Only the micelle, and not the solid agent, forms above the CMC, and the saturation concentration stays almost constant (19). We shall have the effect of a very rapid increase of total solubility with increasing temperature once a certain temperature is reached. The sharp rise of solubility which occurs at a certain temperature is attributed to the constancy of the activity of solute above the CMC. The concentration of singly dispersed species may either decrease or increase with an increase of temperature (in the present model). This explanation shifts the emphasis for the anomaly from the temperature to the concentration and affords a simple physical meaning to the Krafft point. Although the melting points of hydrated surface active agents and their Krafft points may be affected by the kinds of gegenions present, as in the case of cetanesulfonates (18), there will exist also a rough parallelism with the melting of hydrocarbon chains, as in the case of soaps found by Krafft (17). Just like the melting point, the Krafft point is lowered by the additives.

It is evident that the liquid state is more stable than the superheated solid state above the melting point, on the basis of the Gibbs free energy, and it seems reasonable to assume a similar relation for the micelles and hydrated solid agent crystals around their melting points. In fact, the heat of fusion of fatty acid or its ester is about 1 kcal/mole of methylene group, and the heat of solution of solid sodium alkyl sulfate to micelle is also 0.9 kcal/mole of methylene group (20).

Slightly above the Krafft temperature, the micelle may be slightly more stable than the infinitely large hydrated surface active agent at low concentration; but the concentration of gegenions increases with the stoichiometric concentration, and under this condition the Krafft point also shifts to the higher temperature and the solid state may again become more stable than the micellar state above the solubility.

In the case of nonionic surface active agents, such as octyl glycol or α-octyl glyceryl ether, the solubility of these compounds exceeds the CMC and there exists some micellar region between the CMC and the solubility at 25°C (21). This condition resembles an aqueous solution of ionic surface active agent slightly above the Krafft point. This micellar region rapidly increases with an increase of the hydrophilic moiety of the molecule, e.g., from octanol to octyl glucoside. The importance of the hydrophilic group in nonionic agents is not mainly to increase the concentration of molecularly dispersed species (CMC), but to increase the micellar region, i.e., solubility (21). Hydrophilic behavior of nonionic agents, however, decreases very much at higher temperatures, accompanied by dehydration; the aggregation number of the micelle increases and the micellar region decreases, and above a certain temperature, known as a cloud point, phase separation does occur.* As most of the

* Refer to Chapter 2.

nonionic agents (hydrated) are liquid at fairly low temperatures, there is no Krafft point in many nonionic agents.

As ionic micelles bear charges on their surface, the kinds and the concentrations of gegenions considerably affect the CMC. The nature of the ionic groups, the number of hydrocarbon chains in the molecule, their length, and the number of ionic groups in the molecules all affect the CMC. As the micelle is in a liquid state and forms mixed micelles, the CMC is also affected by the kinds and amounts of various additives. An exact knowledge of the factors controlling the CMC is very important for the clear understanding of various phenomena caused by surface active agents and of the various effects of additives. The importance of CMC is also clearly shown in the figures of Ekwall (22) or Preston (23), which show abrupt changes in many physicochemical properties with concentration at the CMC.

II. Methods of Measuring the Critical Micelle Concentration

There are a number of methods which have been applied to the determination of the critical micelle concentration of surface active agents. Most of the physicochemical property changes can be used for the determination of the CMC, provided the measurements of the particular property can be carried out accurately. The experimental methods whereby the CMC of solutions of surface active agents may be determined are briefly described below. For detailed descriptions, the reader is referred to original papers and books (24, 25).

1. *Electrical Conductance*

The measurement of conductance for ionic surface active agents can be performed accurately and does not involve any special problems except the application of external electrical forces. The accuracy decreases at higher added salt concentrations. Since the mobility of the ions when present as single species resembles that of dissociated salts and differs markedly from that of the aggregated ions, there is an abrupt change in equivalent conductivity at the CMC. Many careful studies of electrical conductance of ionic agents solutions have been made (11, 26–32). In terms of accuracy and of quantity, conductance data outweigh all other measurements of the properties of colloidal surface active agents.

2. *Transference Number*

As a result of aggregation the mobility of the micelle-forming ion changes, and, consequently, its transport number changes. Hoerr and Ralston (33), Hartley (34) and Shirai and Tamamushi (35) have made direct measurements of transport numbers from which CMC values are readily determined.

3. *Dye Absorption*

The early observations by Hartley (*36*) and Sheppard and Geddes (*37*) that the fluorescence of some dyestuffs changes considerably, depending on whether the dyestuff is in the bulk or is adsorbed by the micelle, have been used with considerable success by Corrin and Harkins (*38*) and Kolthoff and Stricks (*39*). The dyestuff is maintained at constant concentration (about 10^{-5} M), while the concentration of colloidal electrolyte is gradually decreased. At the CMC the color of the solution undergoes a marked change, owing to the changes in the absorption spectrum of the dye. With anionic surface active agents, pinacyanol chloride and rhodamine G may be used; and with cationic surface active agents, sky blue FF, eosin, fluorescein, and dichlorophenolindophenol may be used. Many other dyestuffs which can be used to detect the CMC have been reported (*40, 41*). The CMC is, of course, affected by the presence of dye ions (*42*), but the amount of dyestuff used is too small to change the CMC appreciably. If careful observations of initial color changes are performed during the dilution process, using varying amounts of dyestuff, and if these are extrapolated to zero dye concentration, CMC values agreeing with other results are obtained. The preparation of a series of solutions slightly above and below the CMC improves the accuracy of the end point determination. The end points shift gradually to the more concentrated solution over about half an hour (*43, 44*). The disadvantage of this method is the ambiguity of CMC determinations at high salt or alcohol concentrations. The advantage of this method, however, is that it provides rather accurately the small change or difference in the CMC (as in the case of a mixture of surface active agents), provided comparisons of the color changes are carried out for a series of solutions under the same conditions (*44*).

Nonionic surface active agents, as well as ionic agents, have an influence on the spectra of codissolved dyes, and certain dyestuff-nonionic detergent pairs show a color change at the CMC. The method has been extended to nonionic surface active agents, using pinacyanol chloride (*45*), erythrosin (*46*), iodine (*47, 48*), or benzopurpurin 4B (*49*), and to nonaqueous solutions, using rhodamine G (*50*) as the indicator. Existence of an isosbestic point in the absorption spectra is evidence that dissolved dyestuff or iodine in the bulk is in an equilibrium with that in the micelle and that only one type of adsorbed state is possible in the solution.

4. *Solubilization (24)*

The saturation limit of solubilization of liquid by a solution of surface active agents may be followed conveniently in terms of the optical density of the solution. Excess organic liquids are readily emulsified by surface active agents and utilized to show when saturation is reached (at the end of several hours efficient stirring; may be by supersonic vibration). The end point may be determined instrumentally either by transmission measurements (51) or by light scattering (52). A solid dyestuff which is water insoluble is more convenient to determine the CMC. After sedimentation of dye, transmission measurements either by spectrophotometer or colorimeter give the amount of solubilization. The solubility of either hydrocarbon or dyestuff remains almost constant until the concentration of surface active agent attains the CMC and then increases rather rapidly and almost linearly at the beginning. The CMC value thus determined by solubilization is lower than those obtained from other measurements because of the presence of added hydrocarbon or dyestuff. This method is also applicable either in aqueous solution of nonionic surface active agent (45, 53) or in nonaqueous solution (54–62).

5. *Surface Tension*

The surface tension of aqueous solutions of surface active agents decreases very rapidly until the CMC is reached and then stays constant above the CMC. Accordingly, the CMC can be determined from the inflections of the surface tension vs. log concentration curves (63–67). The method is applicable fairly successfully to purified nonionic surface active agents (21, 46, 68). If the sample contains impurities, however, the inflections in the surface tension vs. log concentration curves become more ambiguous and show minima (69–71). The advantage of the use of this method for the CMC determination is that the accuracy of determining the inflection (or CMC) is nearly the same for longer chain substances as for shorter chain substances because the surface tension value changes over nearly the same magnitude. On the other hand, the accuracy of the other techniques, i.e., electrical conductivity, refractive index, osmotic pressure, partial molal volume, etc. decreases almost inversely proportionally with the CMC values. Using the Gibbs adsorption isotherm equation, the surface excess can be obtained conventionally from surface tension vs. log concentration curves. Adam and Shute (72) and Nutting, Long, and Harkins (73) correlated the sudden change in the time effect at a definite concentration with the appearance of micelles in the bulk of the solution.

6. *Partial Molal Volume*

The usual method involves the accurate measurement of the density of the solution and the determination of concentration. Any change in the partial molal volume of surface active agent will be reflected in the density of the solution. It is necessary to conduct very careful measurements, under accurate temperature control. Several investigators have used this method (74-78).

Instead of making the precise determinations of density and composition required in the usual method, a simple and direct dilatometric procedure has proved to be very efficient and accurate in determining the partial molal volume (9, 79). The dilatometers consists of cylindrical glass bulbs of 100–150-cc capacity, each containing a large glass ball. The stem is a uniform, calibrated capillary with an internal diameter of 1.8–2.0 mm. The dilatometer is placed in a thermostat at constant temperature and filled with solvent extending into the lower part of the stem. A weighed amount of surface active agent (solid or liquid) is sealed into a long, thin-walled glass capsule, narrow enough to slip down through the stem into the bulb. There it is broken, and the solute (surface active agent) is dissolved by twirling the glass ball. The change in the level of the liquid after equilibrium is reached, corrected for the volume of the glass fragments and divided by the number of moles of solute dissolved, gives its partial molal volume. Accurate temperature control within 0.001°C is of course essential. This method is applicable to any type of surface active agent in either aqueous or nonaqueous solution. This method is also useful for the partial molal volume measurement of solubilizate.

7. Refractive Index

The use of refractive index in the determination of CMC has been demonstrated by Hess et al. (80). Klevens (81) and Thiele (82) have applied the method as a means of determining the CMC for a number of ionic surface active agents. As this method does not involve the addition or the application of a strong external field of force, no change in CMC can occur throughout the experiments. The method is applicable to any type of surface active agent and any kind of solvent. Again, careful temperature control and accurate determination of the concentration of the solution are indispensable for this method.

8. Light Scattering

This method has been investigated by several authors for the determination of aggregation number (83–91). The aggregation of surface active agents is reflected in the increases of scattered light. The CMC is determined from the abrupt increase in slope of light scattering vs. concentration. If the sample contains even a very small amount of impurities, such as dodecanol, the result obtained changes considerably. Very careful elimination of dust particles from solution is also necessary. Light scattering measurements are attractive in the sense that they afford the aggregation number. They also afford a measure of dissymmetry of a particle (92) and of the amount of charge on the micelle from the slope of scattered light vs. concentration (87, 88). Filtration through carefully cleaned glass filters was found to affect the measurement by displacing Na^+ in the solution with H^+ on the glass. Small amounts of organic vapors present in the room sometimes affect the measurements (93). Nakagawa et al. (94, 95) have measured the CMC's and the aggregation numbers of nonionic agents in aqueous solution by light scattering techniques.

9. *Freezing Point*

Freezing point measurements can sometimes be applied to the CMC determination (12, 96). Although the osmotic coefficient is thermodynamically important to measure, many of the surface active agents are too insoluble at the freezing point of the solvent. Krafft points of many common surface active agents are higher than 0°C. The CMC or osmotic coefficient thus obtained from freezing point measurements are made at temperatures close to the freezing point of the solvent, i.e., under conditions which are different from those of general practical interest. Many surface chemical properties, such as foaminess and foam stability, etc., change considerably with temperature.

10. *Osmotic Pressure*

The measurement of osmotic pressure is direct and important for the study of the CMC and the properties of solutions of surface active agents if everything is successfully carried out. Hess and Suranyi (97) have attempted to overcome the difficulties of finding a suitable semipermeable membrane in which the solution is placed in a container and the solvent is constrained in a capillary or in a series of capillaries, such as a fritted disc. Hence, the liquid-vapor surface is used as the membrane and the pressure on the solvent is adjusted until vapor equilibrium is attained between solvent and solution; the criterion of equilibrium is the absence of distillation (24).

11. *Vapor Pressure*

Closely related to osmotic pressure is the change in vapor pressure of the solvent as a result of the presence of surface active agent (98). The method is direct and very useful in measuring the change of activity of the solvent. The dew point method using thermistors has been developed and applied (99-102). The method does not give accurate measurements of the change in activity but is sufficient to give the CMC from graphs of vapor pressure depression vs. concentration.

12. *Solubility*

The solubility of ionic surface active agents at lower temperatures shows a steady increase with rising temperature; but, if the solubility becomes equal to the CMC—in other words, if micelle formation has

occurred—there is an abrupt increase in the solubility-temperature relation. (*17–19, 103–108*a). The temperature at which this abrupt change
occurs is known as the Krafft point (*17*), and the concentration at which
it occurs is the CMC at that temperature. The method provides the
CMC at the Krafft temperature. As the heat of micellization and the
heat of crystallization are quite different, it is difficult to calculate the
CMC at any other temperature accurately from the value thus obtained.[*]

13. *Electromotive Force*

Several investigators have measured the properties of surface active
agents by means of electromotive force (*108*b–*111*). Hutchinson and
Winslow (*112*) for example, were able to measure the effects of changes
of temperature and added hydrochloric acid on the CMC of dodecylammonium chloride. The method is rather accurate and convenient,
provided a suitable junction is found. The CMC can be observed very
sharply in this type of experiment and can be plotted in its relationship
to salt concentration and other parameters of the system. The method
necessitates the presence of some amount of electrolyte.

14. *Sound Velocity*

The velocity of sound in a liquid medium can be related theoretically
to the molecular weight by an equation which involves the density and
refractive index of the medium and two empirically derived constants
(*113*). This relationship can be modified to apply to binary solutions of
liquids and has been used to estimate the micellar weight of decylpoly-
glycol ether in methanol and in water. The micellar weight of sodium
oleate in each of these solvents has also been calculated from similar
measurements (*114*). The CMC can be determined also from the break
point of the velocity vs. concentration graph (*115*).

15. *Polarographic Determination*

Colichman (*116*) confirmed that the limiting diffusion current in the
polarograph exhibits a sharp change at the CMC for a number of materials and found that in a number of cases there is agreement between
the CMC determined in this way and that found by other methods.
This effect, accordingly, may be used to determine the CMC. It should
be pointed out, however, that the polarographic method necessitates the
presence of a large amount of supporting electrolyte. Therefore, the
CMC value is very much smaller compared with a solution of surface
active agent with no added salts. The maximum suppress point seems
to be different from the CMC (*117*).

16. *Diffusion*

The rate of micellar diffusion is related to the size and shape of

---

[*] Refer to Fig. 1.1.

the hydrated micelle. Mysels and Stigter (*118*) and Stigter *et al.* (*119*) measured the diffusion coefficient by tagging the micelle with water-insoluble radioactive dye. This method again provides the CMC value if the micellar diffusion is plotted against the concentration of the detergent. The viscosities and diffusion coefficients have been measured for a number of nonionic detergents and the data have been correlated with CMC (*94, 120*).

17. *Viscosity*

A number of studies have been made of the viscosity of solutions of surface active agents (*80, 121–126*). These studies may be used to evaluate the CMC of a solution. The method may be more reliable for solutions of nonionic surface active agents where no electroviscous effects arise.

18. *Dialysis*

Another method which may be used to determine or demonstrate the CMC involves dialysis either through a cellophane membrane (*127, 128*) or nitrocellulose (*20*).

19. *Electrophoretic Mobility*

The electrophoretic mobility of micelles was measured by Stigter and Mysels (*129*). Electrophoresis of polyvinyl acetate emulsions in the presence of various emulsifying agents and salts has been studied. Discontinuities in the curve of migration vs. concentration occur at the CMC (*130*).

20. *Ultraviolet and Infrared Absorption*

It is noteworthy that the ultraviolet absorption spectrum of the paraffin chain quaternary ammonium iodides in aqueous solution undergoes an abrupt change at the CMC, even in the absence of any other solutes (*131*). Although the behavior of the change of the spectra was different from that in aqueous solution, the CMC of alkyl ammonium carboxylates in organic solvents was also determined from the concentration dependence of the ultraviolet and infrared absorption spectrum (*132, 133*).

21. *Fluorescence Depolarization*

The depolarization of fluorescence of a suitable dye which has been solubilized by the micelle undergoes a change at the CMC and can be used to calculate the CMC and estimate micelle size (*50, 58, 60, 134*).

22. *Miscellaneous*

Kolthoff and Johnson (*135*) have shown that H^+ ions associated with the micelles of dodecanesulfonic acid catalyze the reaction between acetone and iodine much more effectively than free H^+ ions. This difference affords an unusual method for determining the CMC of dodecanesulfonic acid by plotting the catalytic effect against the concentration.

It has also been reported that the Wien effect can be used to detect the CMC (136).

The CMC's of sodium dodecyl sulfate, sodium oleate, and dodecylamine hydrochloride were determined from the concentration dependence of high frequency conductivity at frequencies of 15 and 30 Mc/sec (137). The dielectric constant of the solutions showed a considerable increase beyond the concentration for micelle formation (138).

Change in slope of the optical rotation vs. concentration curve in optically active surface active agents such as alkyl-D-glucosides may correspond to the CMC.

Osmosis through charged permeable membranes has been used to determine the micellar charge and to estimate the activity coefficients of both anionic and cationic agents (139, 140). This measurement again reflects the CMC.

Botre *et al.* (141) determined the activity of gegenions in aqueous solutions of cationic and anionic detergents by means of membrane electrodes. The method has been found useful in determining the CMC.

III. The Size and Shape of Micelles

Although there is general agreement on the presence of micelles in solutions of surface active agents, there is disagreement as to their kinds, shapes, and mechanism of formation (24, 142–144).

McBain (145) assumed two kinds of micelles, as shown in Figs. 1.2 and 1.3. The one is a spherical ionic micelle of not more than 10 like ions retaining their charges, formed in dilute solution before the CMC is reached; the other is a micelle with little or no ionic charge, formed just beyond the CMC, so that the solution contains both highly conducting and practically nonconducting lamellar micelles: the combination of the two explain the shape of the conductance curve.

The neutral micelle has been identified by McBain (146) with the lamellar micelle which has been postulated in order to account for the X-ray diffraction patterns obtained on solutions of amphipathic electrolytes by a number of workers (147–150). The lamellar micelle is described as being composed of alternate layers of water and double amphipathic molecules. These latter layers consist of the paraffin chains arranged parallel to each other, in liquid rather than in crystalline packing. The depth of the layer is equal to the length of two fully extended paraffin chains placed end-to-end.

1. THE FORMATION OF MICELLES

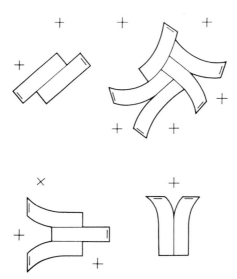

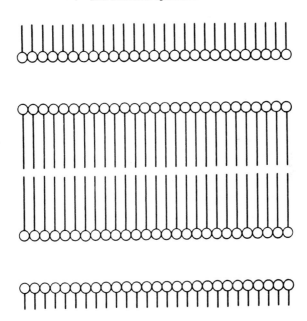

The McBain spherical ionic micelle.

The McBain lamellar micelle.

The simpler model is undoubtedly that of Hartley (*2*, *151*), who in 1939 published a useful summary of his picture of the state in aqueous solutions of paraffin chain salts. Up to the critical concentration, he considers that a paraffin chain salt is a strong electrolyte, completely dissociated and unaggregated. At the CMC, aggregation of the amphipathic ion begins with the formation, at first, of relatively small micelles which grow rapidly over a very limited concentration range to a size which for a given paraffin chain salt remains approximately constant with further increase in concentration, as shown in Fig. 1.4. From light

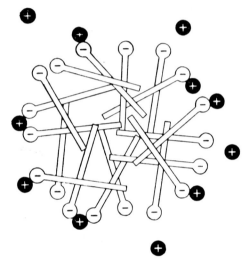

The Hartley spherical micelle.

scattering measurements we can now say that micelles of about 73 aggregates form at the CMC in a solution of sodium dodecyl sulfate and remain approximately constant with further increase in concentration (*91*). The aggregation number, of course, increases with the addition of salts and to a lesser extent with the gradual increase in concentration of surface active agent. Hartley believes that the micelles are liquid and essentially spherical and that their interior approximates the random distribution state of liquid paraffin, but with the hydrophilic end of the ion constrained to remain at the surface of the micelle. After a constant micellar size has been attained, the addition of further solute leads to an increase in the number of micelles with little, if any, increase in the number of unaggregated surface active ions. Hartley thus postulates only one type of micelle, of approximately constant size for a given amphipathic electrolyte in aqueous solutions at all concentrations above the CMC.

Harkins and Mittelmann (*152*) agree with Hartley's concept of one type of micelle, but from their X-ray results consider it to have some regularity of structure and picture it as disc-shaped or cylindrical. Their micelle is similar to the lamellar micelle proposed by McBain, but also resembles Hartley's micelle in respect to its conductibility.

In some other solutions (*85, 153*), however, even in the absence of added electrolyte, and probably in all cases where electrolyte is added, the particle weight of the micelle is such as to exclude a spherical model. Debye and Anacker (*85*) have interpreted the results of angular light scattering studies as indicating that neither a sphere nor a disc-shaped micelle is formed, but rather a rodlike micelle having the general shape of a stack of coins, as shown in Fig. 1.5. Such a model, derived from

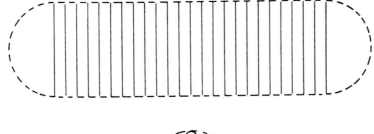

The Debye rodlike micelle.

asymmetry studies, is not only in agreement with light scattering data but would also fit reasonably well into the kind of structure suggested by X-ray measurements of more concentrated solutions.

The Debye micelle, which can be considered to be formed by the lateral distention of a Hartley micelle, may be expected to give rise to considerable viscous resistance, owing to its asymmetry. The gel formation of very dilute solutions (about 1 weight per cent) of long-paraffin chain (longer than 15 carbon atoms) salts can be explained by the formation of a network structure of almost infinitely grown rod- or fiber-like aggregates. The viscosity will then be very much larger, but the mobility of simple ions may be as free as in dilute solution. The soap gel is as good a conductor as the solution (*154, 155*). Moreover, the paraffin chain salt network will be a very good conductor.

TABLE 1.1

SIZE OF MICELLES IN AQUEOUS SOLUTIONS OF IONIC SURFACE ACTIVE AGENTS

Compound	Medium	Micellar weight	Aggregation number	Method	Reference
R_8SO_4Na	H_2O	4,600	20	Light scattering	(160)
$R_{10}SO_4Na$	H_2O	13,000	50	Light scattering	(160,161)
$R_{12}SO_4Li$	H_2O	17,100	63[a]	Light scattering	(91)
$R_{12}SO_4N(CH_3)_4$	H_2O	25,800	76[a]	Light scattering	(91)
$R_{12}SO_4Na$	H_2O	17,800	62[a]	Light scattering	(91)
$R_{12}SO_4Na$	0.02 N NaCl	19,000	66	Light scattering	(162)
$R_{12}SO_4Na$	0.03 N NaCl	23,500	72[a]	Light scattering	(91)
$R_{12}SO_4Na$	0.20 N NaCl	29,500	101[a]	Light scattering	(91)
$R_{12}SO_4Na$	0.50 N NaCl	41,000	142[a]	Light scattering	(91)
$R_{12}SO_4Na$	H_2O	23,200	80	Electrophoretic mobility	(129)
$R_{12}SO_4Na$	0.01 N NaCl	25,600	89	Electrophoretic mobility	(129)
$R_{12}SO_4Na$	0.03 N NaCl	28,700	100	Electrophoretic mobility	(129)
$R_{12}SO_4Na$	0.05 N NaCl	30,100	105	Electrophoretic mobility	(129)
$R_{12}SO_4Na$	0.10 N NaCl	32,200	112	Electrophoretic mobility	(129)
$R_{12}SO_4Na$	H_2O	25,600	89[b]	Diffusion	(119)
$R_{12}SO_4Na$	0.03 N NaCl	29,500	102[b]	Diffusion	(119)
$R_{12}SO_4Na$	0.10 N NaCl	31,600	110[b]	Diffusion	(119)
$R_{14}SO_4Na$	0.10 N NaCl	43,500	138	Light scattering	(161)
R_8SO_3Na	H_2O	6,000	28	Light scattering	(161)
$R_{10}SO_3Na$	H_2O	9,900	40.5	Light scattering	(161)
$R_{12}SO_3Na$	H_2O	14,700	54	Light scattering	(161)
$R_{14}SO_3Na$	H_2O	24,000	80	Light scattering	(161)
$R_{10}N(CH_3)_3Br$	H_2O	10,200	36.4	Light scattering	(84)
$R_{12}N(CH_3)_3Br$	H_2O	15,400	50	Light scattering	(84,161)
$R_{14}N(CH_3)_3Cl$	H_2O	18,600	64	Osmotic pressure, conductivity	(166a)
$R_{14}N(CH_3)_3Br$	H_2O	23,500	75	Light scattering	(84)
$R_{16}N(CH_3)_3Br$	0.013 N KBr	61,700	169	Light scattering	(84)
$R_{12}NH_3Cl$	H_2O	12,300	55.5	Light scattering	(84)
$R_{12}NH_3Cl$	0.0157 N NaCl	20,500	92	Light scattering	(84)
$R_{12}NH_3Cl$	0.0460 N NaCl	31,400	142	Light scattering	(84)
$R_{16}C_5H_5NCl$	0.0175 N NaCl	32,300	95	Light scattering	(163)
$R_{16}C_5H_5NCl$	0.0584 N NaCl	39,800	117	Light scattering	(163)
$R_{16}C_5H_5NCl$	0.438 N NaCl	45,900	135 ± 1	Light scattering	(163)
$R_{16}C_5H_5NCl$	0.730 N NaCl	46,600	137 ± 1	Light scattering	(163)
$R_{12}N(CH_3)_3\frac{1}{2}SO_4$	H_2O	17,900	65	Light scattering	(161)
$R_8SO_3\frac{1}{2}Mg$	H_2O	10,400	51	Light scattering	(161)
$R_{10}SO_3\frac{1}{2}Mg$	H_2O	24,300	104	Light scattering	(161)

Compound	Medium	Micellar weight	Aggregation number	Method	Reference
$R_{12}SO_3\frac{1}{2}Mg$	H_2O	28,600	107	Light scattering	(161)
$(R_{12})_2(CH_3)_2NCl$	0.003 N NaCl	43,600	209	Light scattering	(161)
R_9COONa	0.013 N KBr	7,400	38	Light scattering	(81)
$R_{11}COOK$	H_2O	—	73	Diffusion	(164)
$R_{11}COOK$	H_2O	11,900	50	Light scattering	(160)
$R_{11}COOK$	15—30% (solution)	—	63 ± 8	X-ray small angle	(165)
$R_{11}COOK$	{0.8 N KBr, 0.1 N K$_2$CO$_3$	27,000	110	Diffusion-viscosity	(157)
$R_{11}COOK$	{1.6 N KBr, 0.1 N K$_2$CO$_3$	87.000	360	Diffusion-viscosity	(157)
$R_{11}COONa$	0.013 N KBr	12,400	56	Light scattering	(84)
$R_{13}COONa$	0.013 N KBr	23,800	95	Light scattering	(84)
$R_{13}COOK$	{0.4 N KBr, 0.1 M K$_2$CO$_3$	48,000	180	Diffusion-viscosity	(157)
$R_{13}COOK$	{0.6 N KBr, 0.1 M K$_2$CO$_3$	181,000	680	Diffusion-viscosity	(157)
$R_{13}COOK$	{0.7 N KBr, 0.1 M K$_2$CO$_3$	270,000	1,000	Diffusion-viscosity	(157)
$R_{13}COOK$	{0.8 N KBr, 0.1 M K$_2$CO$_3$	430,000	1,600	Diffusion-viscosity	(157)
$R_{13}COOK$	{1.0 N KBr, 0.1 M K$_2$CO$_3$	860,000	3,200	Diffusion-viscosity	(157)
$R_{15}COONa$	0.013 N KBr	47,300	170	Light scattering	(84)
Na dibutyl-benzenesulfonate	H_2O	66,600	229	Light scattering	(159)
Na dibutyl-naphthalenesulfonate	H_2O	20,000	59	Light scattering	(159)
Na dibutyl-naphthalenesulfonate	0.1 N Na$_2$SO$_4$	27,700	81	Light scattering	(159)
Na m-dodecyl-benzenesulfonate	H_2O	19,900	57	Light scattering	(166b)
Na p-dodecyl-benzenesulfonate	H_2O	8,200	24	Light scattering	(166b)
Na dihexyl sulfosuccinate	H_2O	9,300	24	Diffusion-viscosity	(123)
Na dihexyl sulfosuccinate	H_2O	10,100	26	Osmotic pressure, conductivity	(166a)
Na dioctyl sulfosuccinate	H_2O	21,300	48	Osmotic pressure, conductivity	(166a)

a   Refined treatment.

b   Calculated on the assumption of monolayer hydration.

The size, shape, and charge of micelles have been studied mostly by light scattering and diffusion techniques. Sedimentation date have also been used in conjunction with diffusion data, and micelle shapes ranging from the spherical through the cylindrical to the prolate ellipsoid have been deduced from the results (156, 157).

The most powerful single method for estimating micellar size (and

TABLE 1.2
MICELLAR CHARGE ESTIMATED BY VARIOUS METHODS

Compound	Medium	Fraction of charge	Method	Reference
$R_{12}SO_4Li$	H_2O	0.225	Light scattering	(91)
$R_{12}SO_4N(CH_3)_4$	H_2O	0.184	Light scattering	(91)
$R_{12}SO_4Na$	H_2O	0.168	Light scattering	(91)
$R_{12}SO_4Na$	0.03 N NaCl	0.285	Electrophoresis	(129)
$R_{12}SO_4Na$	0.03 N NaCl	0.142	Light scattering	(91)
$R_{12}SO_4Na$	0.05 N NaCl	0.295	Electrophoresis	(129)
$R_{12}SO_4Na$	0.20 N NaCl	0.155	Light scattering	(91)
$R_{12}SO_4Na$	0.10 N NaCl	0.324	Electrophoresis	(129)
$R_{12}SO_4Na$	0.50 N NaCl	0.154	Light scattering	(91)
$R_{12}NH_3Cl$	0.017—0.1% solution	0.63—0.30	Electrophoretic mobility	(167)
$R_{12}NH_3Cl$	0.017—0.1% solution	0.58—0.34	Transference number	(167)
$R_{12}NH_3Cl$	H_2O	0.12	Transference number	(84)
$R_{12}NH_2Cl$	0.0157 N NaCl	0.084	Transference number	(84)
$R_{12}NH_2Cl$	0.0237 N NaCl	0.079	Transference number	(84)
$R_{12}NH_2Cl$	0.46 N NaCl	0.076	Transference number	(84)
$R_{12}NH_3Br$	0.017—0.1% solution	0.56	Electrophoretic mobility	(167)
$R_{12}NH_3Br$	0.1% solution	0.27	Electrophoretic mobility	(167)
$R_{12}NH_3I$	0.02% solution	0.40	Electrophoretic mobility	(167)
$R_{12}NH_3I$	0.1% solution	0.19	Electrophoretic mobility	(167)
$R_{14}NH_3Cl$	0.006% solution	0.78	Electrophoretic mobility	(167)
$R_{14}NH_3Cl$	0.02% solution	0.42	Electrophoretic mobility	(167)
$R_{14}NH_3Cl$	0.02% solution	0.40	Transference number	(167)
$R_{16}NH_3Cl$	0.002% solution	0.83	Electrophoretic mobility	(167)
$R_{16}NH_3Cl$	0.002% solution	0.80	Transference number	(167)
$R_{16}NH_3Cl$	0.005% solution	0.40	Electrophoretic mobility	(167)
$R_{16}NH_3Cl$	0.005% solution	0.33	Transference number	(167)
$R_{10}N(CH_3)_3Br$	H_2O	0.224	Light scattering	(88)
$R_{10}N(CH_3)_3Br$	0.013 N KBr	0.221	Light scattering	(88)
$R_{12}N(CH_3)_3Br$	H_2O	0.193	Light scattering	(88)
$R_{12}N(CH_3)_3Br$	0.013 N KBr	0.173	Light scattering	(88)
$R_{12}N(CH_3)_3Br$	0.034 N KBr	0.156	Light scattering	(88)
$R_{14}N(CH_3)_3Br$	H_2O	0.130	Light scattering	(88)
$R_{14}N(CH_3)_3Br$	0.013 N KBr	0.124	Light scattering	(88)
$R_{14}N(CH_3)_3Br$	H_2O	0.249	Osmotic coefficient	(171)
$R_{14}N(CH_3)_3Br$	H_2O	0.321	Conductivity	(171)

Compound	Medium	Fraction of charge	Method	Reference
$R_{16}N(CH_3)_3Br$	0.013 N KBr	0.091	Light scattering	(88)
$R_{16}N(CH_3)_3Br$	H_2O	0.11	Osmotic coefficient	(168)
$R_{16}C_6H_5NCl$	H_2O	0.11	Osmotic coefficient	(168)
$R_{16}C_6H_5NCl$	0.0175 N NaCl	0.137	Light scattering	(163)
$R_{16}C_6H_5NCl$	0.0584 N NaCl	0.137	Light scattering	(163)
$R_{16}C_6H_5NCl$	0.438 N NaCl	0.207	Light scattering	(163)
$R_{16}C_6H_5NCl$	0.730 N NaCl	0.256	Light scattering	(163)
$R_{16}C_6H_5NCl$	H_2O	0.314	Conductivity	(172)
$R_{16}C_6H_5NCl$	H_2O	0.210	Osmotic coefficient	(100)
$R_{11}COONa$	0.210 N NaCl	0.36	Osmotic coefficient	(198)
Na diisooctyl sulfosuccinate	H_2O	0.39	Osmotic coefficient	(123)
Na diisohexyl sulfosuccinate	H_2O	0.336	Osmotic coefficient	(123)
Na diisohexyl sulfosuccinate	H_2O	0.39	Conductivity	(123)

shape) is the light scattering technique developed by Debye. The procedure is relatively simple and is described in several papers (83–89). Results obtained by various authors are summarized in Table 1.1 for ionic agents and in Table 2.11 for nonionic agents. The presence of salts decreases the CMC and increases the micellar size (84, 91, 119, 129, 158, 159). The micellar size of ionic agents gradually decreases with temperature. On the contrary, that of nonionic agents increases with temperature and particularly increases enormously near the cloud point of the nonionic agent (95).*

The charges of the micelle have been estimated by light scattering (86–91), electrophoretic mobility (129, 167), colligative properties (168, 169), osmosis (140), and various other properties (166a, 170). The values obtained are not as accurate as for micellar size. Some of the results obtained are summarized in Table 1.2.

It appears to the author that the properties of solutions of surface active agents can be adequately explained by the postulate of only one type of micelle. The interior of the micelle is in the liquid state, but each paraffin chain molecule cannot have the random configuration of a string of beads. Liquid paraffins may have a quasi-crystalline structure at ordinary temperatures. The structure of the interior of a micelle may be more organized because the polar groups are anchored on the surface. As Hartley, who suggested the spherical micelle, points out, the chains cannot be arranged radially, although their length has been taken as the radius of the sphere, because the density throughout must remain that of a hydrocarbon (whose partial molal volume does not change very

* Refer to Chapter 2, Table 2.13.

much from one state to the other), and the axes of the hydrocarbon chain cannot approach each other more closely than about 5 Å, since this is the distance of closest approach between two molecules. Hartley's picture of a spherical micelle does not satisfy these conditions. The structure of the micelle proposed by Harkins, which is something between the Hartley micelle and the Philippoff version (Fig 1.6) of the McBain lamellar micelle (173), seems most reasonable to the author.

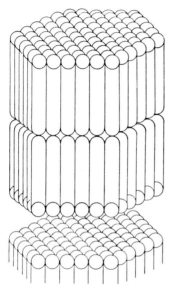

The Philippoff version of the McBain lamellar micelle.

This quasi-crystalline structure does not imply a small entropy change between solid and liquid (micellar) states. The structure of a fatty acid or its ester slightly above the melting point may be close to the solid structure (174), yet the entropy (or heat) of fusion is about 3 eu (or 1 kcal) per methylene group (175, 176). The increase in the heat of solution to form micelles from the pure solid is about 0.9 kcal/methylene group (20), which is close to the increase in the heat of fusion of paraffin chain compounds, about 1 kcal/methylene group.

Apart from the potential and free volume per molecule having different values for the liquid and the crystal, there is a difference due to the change from a localized to a mobile state and excess configurational entropy. Suppose a particle consists of 38 atoms of double layer structure, then the partition function for the one micelle will be of the form $\{f_{(T)}\}^{38}/38!$ where $f_{(T)}$ denotes the partition function of a single molecule, and the division by 38! is required for the mobile (liquid) state of micelle. But each aggregated molecule can move anywhere in the micelle as long as it does not overlap another molecule, and so has an effective free volume 38ν. Thus, the partition function of one micelle will contain the factor $(38\nu)^{38}/38!$. In the (hydrated) crystal, on the other hand, each molecule has its own equilibrium position, and the molecules are localized systems. Consequently, the partition function of the whole crystal is simply $\{f'_{(T)}\}^{38}$, where $f'_{(T)}$, the partition function for the single molecule, now contains only a volume factor ν because the molecule is constrained to remain in the neighborhood of a single fixed equilibrium position. Thus, the partition function of the whole particle in the localized state contains the factor ν^{38} This leads to an excess molecular entropy in the mobile (micellar) state of $k \ln(38^{38}/38!) \approx 38\,k$, i.e., a 2 eu increase per mole of atoms of the same structure and same free volume. This conclusion tells us that a quasi-crystalline structure is a reasonable speculation.

In the micelle proposed by Harkins the total surface does not differ much from the spherical micelle. The shape is roughly spherical and may become an oblate spheroid due to the increase in aggregation number. In this case, the shape and size of micelle can continuously change from a spherical micelle to a lamellar micelle and to an infinitely large crystal We have to remember that the shape and the size of micelle depend on the concentration, temperature, the molecular structure of the respective surface active agents, the kinds of intermolecular force, and the kinds of additives.

IV. The Theory of Micelle Formation

1. *Pseudophase Model for Micelles*

A model that treats micelle formation as a phenomenon similar to phase separation, in which the CMC is a saturation concentration, can be supported by the following phenomena.

If we were dealing with the addition of a salt to a certain amount

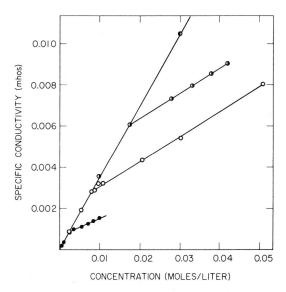

Fig. 1.7. The specific electrical conductance of aqueous solutions of surface active agents plotted as a function of concentration: ◑, R_9SO_3Na; ◐, $R_{11}SO_3Na$; ○, $R_{12}SO_3Na$; ●, $R_{14}SO_3Na$.

of water, the conductivity would at first increase linearly with the amount added (assuming complete dissociation), but, when the saturation concentration was reached, the conductivity would abruptly cease to increase at all, and consequently the differential equivalent conductivity would be nearly constant up to the saturation concentration, and would then fall instantaneously to the constant value zero. The sharp break in the specific conductivity vs. concentration graph (i.e., the sharp transition in differential equivalent conductivity) (Fig. 1.7) in colloidal electrolyte solutions suggests that something similar to a phase separation is oc-

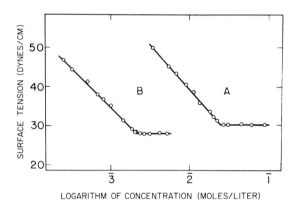

Fig. 1.8. The surface tension in aqueous solutions of octyl (A) and decyl (B) glucosides plotted as a function of concentration at 25°C.

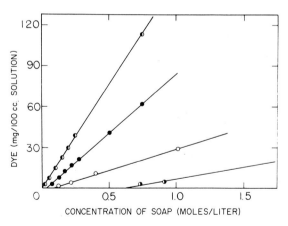

Fig. 1.9. Weight of dye (1-o-tolylazo-β-naphthol) solubilized as a function of soap concentration and chain length: ◑, $R_{13}COOK$: ●, $R_{11}COOK$; ○, R_9COOK, ◑, R_7COOK.

curring in the solution (2). As the micelle is partially dissociated, the specific conductivity still increases above the CMC. The increase in specific conductivity above the CMC can be attributed mainly to the dissociated gegenions (168). A similar discussion can be based on the surface tension or colligative properties vs. concentration graphs (Fig. 1.8). The solubility of additives vs. concentration of surface active agent also suggests that something is occurring which is similar to a phase separation in the solution. Solubilization (Fig. 1.9) is a process similar to the dissolution of additives in a separate phase (177). The effect of various additives on the CMC can be understood also as a phenomenon similar to the effect of additives on the solubility of ordinary substances. (44, 178). The aggregation number of most micelles, $30\sim2000$, is not quite large enough to treat the micelle as a phase, though it seems adequate to call it a pseudophase (14).

To what extent then does the micelle formation show an abrupt change? Bury and collaborators (6, 179) showed that a fairly abrupt transition was to be expected from the application of the mass law to the equilibrium between single species and micelles composed of a fairly large number of monomers. However, the most serious limitation upon the validity of the theory of micelle formation, and the most frequent cause of misunderstanding, has been the neglect of the activity coefficients, which have usually been taken as unity throughout. The activity of single species and aggregated species should be defined for the same standard state. In a nonelectrolyte of total concentration X_2, existing partly as single molecules in concentration $_1X_2$, and partly as micelles composed of n molecules $_nX_2$, the mass law takes the form

$$\frac{_1f_2^n \cdot {_1X_2^n}}{_nf_2 \cdot {_nX_2}} = K = 1 \qquad (1.7)$$

or

$$\frac{_1f_2 \cdot {_1X_2}}{(_nf_2 \cdot {_nX_2})^{1/n}} = K' = 1 \qquad (1.7')$$

where K or K' is the equilibrium constant of the aggregation process, and $_1f_2$ and $_nf_2^{1/n}$ are the activity coefficients of singly dispersed and micellar molecules.

From the fundamental relation in statistical mechanics and thermodynamics, the chemical potential of the single molecule is equal to that of the aggregated molecule under equilibrium conditions. Therefore, K or K' is always one at the association equilibrium. Thus,

$$_1f_2 \cdot {_1X_2} = {_1a_2} = {_na_2} = (_nf_2 \cdot {_nX_2})^{1/n} \qquad (1.8)$$

As the activity of the surface active agent is almost constant above the CMC and the change in concentration of the micelle is difficult to determine, a concentrated solution is a better standard state to choose. If we choose such a concentrated solution as a standard, the activities of singly dispersed agent and micellar agent are both unity at the chosen concentration. The activity coefficient of surface active agent in the micellar state, which resembles the pure liquid state of the agent, is unity and that of the singly dispersed molecule is approximately 1/CMC (CMC in mole fraction units). Introducing these values, we obtain

$$_1f_2 \cdot {_1}X_2 = (_nX_2)^{1/n} , \quad (_1f_2 = 1/\text{CMC}) \tag{1.9}$$

As $_1X_2 + n \cdot {_n}X_2 = X_2$, we obtain

$$_1X_2 + n(_1f_2 \cdot {_1}X_2)^n = X_2 . \tag{1.10}$$

If we know the aggregation number of the micelle and the activity coefficient of the single molecule, we can calculate the concentration of single species $_1X_2$ and aggregated species $_nX_2$ as a function of the total concentration; $_1X_2 = X_2$ at the CMC if the aggregation number is infinitely large. As n is large (about 50~200), if $_1f_2 \cdot {_1}X_2$ has a value appreciably less than 1, then $_nX_2$, the fraction of the solute in the aggregated form, will be negligible; and only when $_1f_2 \cdot {_1}X_2$ becomes comparable with 1 will the concentration of micelles become appreciable. When $_1f_2 \cdot {_1}X_2$ becomes very close to 1, then $_nX_2$ will increase very rapidly with an increase in $_1X_2$. The more or less well-defined concentration at which the transition occurs is termed the critical concentration for micelles, i.e., the CMC (*180*).

The larger the value of n, the more abrupt should be the change in any physical property occurring at the transition concentration. The meaning of the term CMC as used by Williams, Phillips, and Mysels (*31*) and by many investigators is clearly the concentration of solute at which the concentration of micelles would become zero if their concentration continued to change at the same rate as it does at a higher concentration of solute. Practically, then, the CMC is determined as the point of intersection of two lines (the one closely represents a property of complete single dispersion as a function of concentration, and the other closely represents a property of complete aggregation of excess solute above a certain concentration), extrapolating the measured properties of the solution from below and from above the region in which a rapid change of slope is observed. Needless to say, there will be a very small fraction of micelles at the CMC thus defined.

Where we are dealing with aggregation of paraffin chain ions, we shall certainly have a high proportion of gegenions adhering electrostatically to the micelle. If X_2' is the total concentration of salt; $_1X_2'$, the concentration of single surface active ions in equivalent units; $_nX_2'$, the concentration of micelle in units such that $_1X'_2 + n \cdot {}_nX'_2 = X'_2$; and n and n-p, are the aggregation numbers of micelle-forming ions and gegenions per micelle, respectively; Eqs. (1.7) and (1.7') become

$$(_1f'_2 \cdot {}_1X'_2)^n(_1f''_2 \cdot {}_1X''_2)^{(n-p)} = (_nf'_2 \cdot {}_nX'_2)(_{n-p}f''_2 \cdot {}_{n-p}X''_2)^{(n-p)/n} \qquad (1.11)$$

and

$$(_1f'_2 \cdot {}_1X'_2)(_1f''_2 \cdot {}_1X''_2)^{(n-p)/n} = (_nf'_2 \cdot {}_nX'_2)^{1/n}(_{n-p}f''_2 \cdot {}_{n-p}X''_2)^{(n-p)/n2} \qquad (1.11')$$

Murray and Hartley (18) have considered by means of Eq. (1.11) that the change in the curve of a physical property vs. concentration will be made more abrupt by taking into account this association of the gegenions with the micelle. The abruptness of the change which occurs when micelle formation begins, and the type of the curve to be expected, will also depend on the relative contributions of the solute in the micellar and single form to the physical property being considered.

2. Relation between the CMC Values of Ionic Agents and Nonionic Agents

Let us now discuss the abruptness and approximate correlation between CMC values of nonionic agents and ionic agents which have the same oleophilic group and a similar hydrophilic group except in regard to dissociation.

If $_1f_2 \cdot {}_1X_2$ in Eq. (1.9) is close to $_1f'_2 \cdot {}_1X'_2(_1f''_2 \cdot {}_1X''_2)^{(n-p)/n}$ in Eq. (1.11), the abruptness of aggregation will be nearly equal for the same n value, and the CMC value of a nonionic agent will be roughly the square of the value for an ionic (181). Actually, the CMC values of nonionic agents are very much smaller, as shown in Table 1.3. The consideration

TABLE 1.3

COMPARISON OF CMC VALUES OF IONIC AGENTS AND NONIONIC AGENTS

Compound	CMC (mole fraction)	$-\log_{10}$CMC	$-1.5 \log_{10}$CMC	Reference
Octyl glucoside	4.5×10^{-4}	3.35	—	(21,68)
Octyl glyceryl ether	1×10^{-4}	3.98	—	(21)
R_8SO_4Na	2.3×10^{-3}	(2.64)	3.96	(223)
$R_8C_5H_5NBr$	4.3×10^{-3}	(2.37)	3.55	(68)
Dodecyl glucoside	3.4×10^{-6}	5.47	—	(4)
$R_{12}SO_4Na$	1.5×10^{-4}	(3.82)	5.73	(31)
$R_{12}O(CH_2CH_2O)_nH$	$2-9 \times 10^{-6}$	5.3—5.9	—	(53)

of the role of gegenions in the process of aggregation, therefore, does not affect the sharpness of the change of a physical property but explains the large CMC value of ionic agents.

As the ratio of gegenions to paraffin chain ions in the micelle is not unity, the logarithm of CMC for a nonionic agent is not exactly twice the logarithm of CMC for an ionic agent. From experiments involving added salts, however, we know that the CMC decreases roughly in inverse proportion to the one-half power of the concentration of univalent gegenions. Extrapolating this experimental fact, we can estimate that the CMC of an ionic agent in the presence of a swamping excess of gegenions will be the one and one-half power of the CMC in the absence of added salt. If the micelle is completely neutralized under this condition, the product of the concentration of paraffin chain ions and that of gegenions which is equal to unity should be close to the CMC value of a nonionic agent of similar molecular structure. Actually, the one and one-half power of the CMC of an ionic agent lies close to the CMC value of nonionic agents, as shown in the fourth column of Table 1.3. If, instead of extrapolating to the presence of swamping excess of salt, we assume, based on experimental fact, that gegenions have an effect proportional only to the one-half power of their concentration, the product of the concentration of paraffin chain ions and the one-half power of the concentration of gegenions leads to the same conclusion.

I would like to quote here Fowkes's discussion. "··· One might also note that for micelles of equal aggregation number, twice as many ionic particles are required to make up a micelle and the tendency to form micelles is proportional to the square of the concentration of ionic detergent but only the first power of the concentration of non-ionic material. If the equilibrium constant were the same for both micelles, (K is always equal to 1), a CMC of 10^{-2} mole/l. for ionic substances would correspond to 10^{-4} mole/l. for non-ionic" (*181*).

3. Enthalpy and Entropy of Micellization

If the micelle is treated as a phase, the CMC may be regarded as the saturation solubility of single species, which, if exceeded, leads to the production of a new phase. Stainsby and Alexander (182) have calculated the change in heat content and in entropy at micellization from the temperature dependence of the CMC of surface active agent. Ignoring deviations from ideality,

$$\Delta H_m = -RT^2\left(\frac{\partial \ln \text{CMC}}{\partial T}\right)_p \tag{1.13}$$

and

$$\Delta H_m = T\Delta S_m \tag{1.14}$$

where ΔH_m and ΔS_m are the conventional heat and entropy of micellization, respectively. In the case of an ionic agent (electrolyte), the heat of micellization should be given conventionally by

TABLE 1.4

DIRECT AND CONVENTIONAL HEAT OF MICELLIZATION

Compound	Medium	Temperature (°C)	$\triangle H_m$ (kcal/mole)	Method	Reference
R_8SO_4Na	H_2O	25	0.8	Calorimetry	(184)
R_8SO_4Na	0.694 N NaCl	25	0.3	Calorimetry	(184)
$R_{10}SO_4Na$	H_2O	25	0.5	Calorimetry	(184)
$R_{12}SO_4Na$	H_2O	5	0.8	Temperature dependence	(187)
$R_{12}SO_4Na$	H_2O	25	0.6	Temperature dependence	(187)
$R_{12}SO_4Na$	H_2O	25—30	−1.0	Temperature dependence	(63)
$R_{12}SO_4Na$	H_2O	35—45	−1.8	Temperature dependence	(63)
$R_{12}SO_4Na$	H_2O	40—60	−1.9	Temperature dependence	(187)
$R_{12}SO_4Na$	H_2O	60—80	−5	Temperature dependence	(63)
$R_{12}SO_4Na$	5.03% R_3OH	5	2.5	Temperature dependence	(187)
$R_{12}SO_4Na$	5.03% R_3OH	25	−0.5	Temperature dependence	(187)
$R_{12}SO_4Na$	5.03% R_3OH	45	−2.8	Temperature dependence	(187)
$R_{12}SO_4Na$	5.71% 2-Propanol	5	2.3	Temperature dependence	(187)
$R_{12}SO_4Na$	5.71% 2-Propanol	25	0	Temperature dependence	(187)
$R_{12}SO_4Na$	5.71% 2-Propanol	45	−2.8	Temperature dependence	(187)
$R_{14}SO_4Na$	H_2O	35−45	−1.5	Temperature dependence	(63)
$R_{14}SO_4Na$	H_2O	60—80	−5.5	Temperature dependence	(63)
$R_{10}SO_3Na$	H_2O	25—35	−0.5	Temperature dependence	(81)
$R_{10}SO_3Na$	H_2O	35—45	−1.4	Temperature dependence	(81)
$R_{10}SO_3Na$	H_2O	60—80	−3	Temperature dependence	(81)
$R_{12}SO_3Na$	H_2O	35—45	−1.8	Temperature dependence	(81)
$R_{12}SO_3Na$	H_2O	60—80	−4	Temperature dependence	(81)
$R_{12}SO_3H$	H_2O	15	1.2	Temperature dependence	(189)
$R_{12}SO_3H$	H_2O	25—30	0	Temperature dependence	(189)
$R_{12}SO_3H$	H_2O	70	−2.4	Temperature dependence	(189)
R_7COOK	0.033 N KOH	15	2.3	Temperature dependence	(186)

Compound	Medium	Temperature (°C)	$\triangle H_m$ (kcal/mole)	Method	Reference
R_7COOK	0.033 N KOH	20	1.6	Temperature dependence	(186)
R_7COOK	0.033 N KOH	25	1.5	Temperature dependence	(186)
R_7COOK	0.0417 N KOH	25	1.7	Calorimetry	(184)
R_7COOK	1.802 N KCl 0.042 N KOH	25	1.5	Calorimetry	(185)
R_7COOK	0.033 N KOH	30	1.4	Temperature dependence	(186)
R_7COOK	0.033 N KOH	35	0.9	Temperature dependence	(186)
R_7COOK	0.033 N KOH	40	0.2	Temperature dependence	(186)
R_7COOK	0.033 N KOH	45	−0.5	Temperature dependence	(186)
R_7COOK	0.033 N KOH	50	−1.4	Temperature dependence	(186)
R_7COOK	0.033 N KOH	50	1.0	Calorimetry	(186)
R_7COOK	0.033 N KOH	55	−2.3	Temperature dependence	(186)
$R_{11}COOK$	H_2O	25	2.6	Temperature dependence	(189)
$R_{11}COOK$	H_2O	25—35	−1	Temperature dependence	(81)
$R_{11}COOK$	H_2O	35—45	−2.4	Temperature dependence	(81)
$R_{11}COOK$	H_2O	50	0	Temperature dependence	(189)
$R_{11}COOK$	H_2O	60—80	−5	Temperature dependence	(81)
$R_{11}COOK$	H_2O	70	−2.4	Temperature dependence	(189)
$R_{13}COOK$	H_2O	25—35	−1	Temperature dependence	(81)
$R_{13}COOK$	H_2O	35—45	−1	Temperature dependence	(81)
$R_{13}COOK$	H_2O	60—80	−2	Temperature dependence	(81)
$R_{12}NH_3Cl$	H_2O	35	−1.3	Temperature dependence	(112)
$C_7H_{15}COO$- -$(CH_2CH_2O)_{7.6}CH_3$	H_2O	10	2.4	Temperature dependence	(190)
$C_7H_{15}COO$- -$(CH_2CH_2O)_{7.6}CH_3$	H_2O	25	2.4	Temperature dependence	(190)
$C_7H_{15}COO$- -$(CH_2CH_2O)_{7.6}CH_3$	H_2O	38	2.4	Temperature dependence	(190)
$C_{10}H_{21}O(CH_2CH_2O)_{12}$- -$CH_3$	H_2O	10	3.3	Temperature dependence	(95)
$C_{10}H_{21}O(CH_2CH_2O)_{12}$- -$CH_3$	H_2O	25	3.3	Temperature dependence	(95)
$C_{10}H_{21}O(CH_2CH_2O)_{12}$- -$CH_3$	H_2O	40	3.3	Temperature dependence	(95)

$$\Delta H_m = -RT^2\left(\frac{\partial \ln \text{CMC}}{\partial T}\right)_p - RT^2\left(\frac{\partial \ln X_i}{\partial T}\right)_p^{K_g} \tag{1.15}$$

where K_g is the constant given by

$$\ln \text{CMC} = -K_g \ln X_i + \text{const}$$

and K_g has a similar physical meaning to $(n - p)/n$; X_i is the concentration of gegenions. When the concentration of gegenions is kept constant, Eq. (1.15) becomes identical to Eq. (1.13).

Matijevic and Pethica (183) have given,

$$\Delta H_m = -nRT^2\left(\frac{\partial \ln \text{CMC}}{\partial T}\right)_p \tag{1.16}$$

where n is 1 for complete ion exchange, and 2 when no ion exchange occurs (i.e., the micelle has the same number of gegenions and paraffin chain ions). When excess salt is present with one in common with the detergent, the concentration of gegenions does not change with the CMC, and the micelle-forming ion will have a constant activity coefficient independent of ion exchange; Eq. (1.16) becomes the same as (1.13). Application of these equations to experimental data generally yield values of ΔH_m which decrease with increasing temperature. In some cases where a fairly wide temperature range has been studied, a minimum has been observed in the curve of CMC against temperature, indicating a zero value of ΔH_m. At higher temperatures, ΔH_m becomes negative. In all cases, ΔH_m has a relatively small value in spite of the very low saturation concentration of surface active agents.

Recently, the heat of micellization in aqueous solutions of various ionic agents has been determined by direct calorimetric measurements of heats of dilution (20, 184–186). As the CMC and the heat of micellization are both small, it is not easy to obtain an accurate value from the direct calorimetric measurements, but it is thermodynamically very important.

The heats of micellization obtained both by direct calorimetric measurements and by temperature dependence of the CMC are summarized in Table 1.4. The values obtained from temperature dependence are not as accurate as the CMC values themselves because of the small change in CMC. The temperature dependence of the logarithm of CMC is usually not linear (188), and it is difficult to obtain accurate slopes. The conventional heat of micellization obtained from the temperature dependence of the CMC needs correction due to (i) the change of activity with the concentration of surface active ions (or molecules), (ii) the change of activity with the concentration of gegenions in the case of ionic agents, and (iii) the change of aggregation number.

A smaller value of heat of micellization in the heat content would be expected in the presence of added salt as a result of the smaller change of activity with the concentration of gegenions and reduced electrical repulsion within the micelles. This is confirmed experimentally in the cases of sodium octyl sulfates (185) and potassium octanoate (186).

Refined Treatment. If we regard the micelle as a pseudophase, the amounts of micellar species do not affect the thermodynamic property of residual solution. Accordingly, if we use $_1X_2$ instead of the stoichiometric concentration X_2, we can treat the solution just like an ordinary solution.

The entropy and the enthalpy change at micellization are related by the equation

$$\frac{\Delta H_m}{T} = \Delta S_m = -\left(\frac{\partial \Delta G_m}{\partial T}\right)_{P,_1X_2} = RT\left(\frac{\partial \ln a_2}{\partial T}\right)_{P,_1X_2} \tag{1.17}$$

As a_2 is a function of $p, T, _1X_2$,

$$\Delta S_m = -RT\left(\frac{\partial \ln a_2}{\partial \ln _1X_2}\right)_{P,T}\left(\frac{\partial \ln _1X_2}{\partial T}\right)_{P,a_2} \tag{1.18}$$

This equation is valid for a solution of nonionic agent. McBain and Hutchinson (24) derived the following equation for heat of micellization

$$-\Delta H_m = -RT^2\left[g_1 + \left(\frac{\partial g_1}{\partial \ln X_2}\right)_{P,T}\right]\left(\frac{\partial \ln X_2}{\partial T}\right)_{P,\text{Sat}} \tag{1.19}$$

where g_1 is the osmotic coefficient of component 1.

These authors derived this equation from the following relation:

$$-\Delta S_m = -X_1\left(\frac{\partial \mu_1}{\partial X_2}\right)_{P,T}\left(\frac{\partial \ln X_2}{\partial T}\right)_{P,\text{Sat}} \tag{1.20}$$

where μ_1 is the chemical potential of component 1.

If we apply the Gibbs-Duhem relation, we obtain

$$\Delta S_m = -\left(\frac{\partial \mu_2}{\partial \ln X_2}\right)_{P,T}\left(\frac{\partial \ln X_2}{\partial T}\right)_{P,\text{Sat}} \tag{1.21}$$

If the aggregation number of the micelle is infinity, then $_1X_2 = X_2$ at the CMC, and Eq. (1.18) agrees with Eq. (1.21). As we already discussed in the preceding section, the concentration of single dispersion $_1X_2$ is close to the total concentration at the CMC, and the ratio of $_1X_2/X_2$ is almost constant for the change of CMC and n, so that we may use X_2 instead of $_1X_2$ in may cases. If we know the aggregation number as a function of the temperature, we can calculate $_1X_2$ and can get more accurate values of the entropy of micellization.

Though the accuracy is not good, the temperature dependence of the aggregation number can in principle be determined experimentally by light scattering or diffusion measurements. Introducing the aggregation number Eq. (1.10), we can numerically calculate the change of the concentration of single species with the aggregation number. This correction of the entropy change seems very small and can be neglected in many cases. Near the cloud point of nonionic agents, the temperature dependence of the aggregation number is very large and will contribute to the heat and entropy of micellization appreciably over a narrow temperature range.

In solutions of ionic agents, the activity of the micelle-forming species is a function of the concentrations of both surface active ions and gegenions. If we denote surface active ions by component 2 and gegenions by 3, we obtain instead of Eq. (1.18):

$$\Delta S_{m_{2,3}} = -\left(\frac{\partial \Delta G_{m_{2,3}}}{\partial T}\right)_{P,X_2,X_3} = -RT\left[\left(\frac{\partial \ln a_{2,3}}{\partial \ln X_2}\right)_{P,T,X_3}\left(\frac{\partial \ln X_2}{\partial T}\right)_{P,a_{2,3}}\right.$$
$$\left. + \left(\frac{\partial \ln a_{2,3}}{\partial \ln X_3}\right)_{P,T,X_2}\left(\frac{\partial \ln X_3}{\partial T}\right)_{P,a_{2,3}}\right] \tag{1.22}$$

Relative activity of nonionic solute may be expressed as*

$$\ln a_2 = \ln X_2 + \frac{\phi_1^2 B}{RT} \tag{1.23}$$

where B is not a function of X_2, and ϕ_1 is the volume fraction of solvent. The first term and the second term express the contribution of the entropy (3,191) and the heat of mixing.

Relative activity of ionic micelle-forming species, $R_-X_+^{(n-p)/n}$, may be expressed as

$$\ln a_{2,3} = \left(\ln X_2 + \frac{\phi_1^2 B'}{RT}\right) + \frac{n-p}{n}\left(\ln X_3 + \frac{\phi_1^2 B''}{RT}\right) \tag{1.24}$$

where B' and B'' are constants and not functions of X_2.

Differentiating Eq. (1.23), we obtain

$$\left(\frac{\partial \ln a_2}{\partial \ln X_2}\right)_{P,T} = 1 - 2\phi_2 \ln \frac{a_2}{X_2} \tag{1.25}$$

below the CMC of nonionic solutes.

Similarly, differentiating Eq. (1.24), we obtain

---

* There are additional entropy and enthalpy changes in aqueous solution of paraffin chain compounds due to the ice structure of surrounding water molecules but both are functions of ϕ_1^2 and largely cancel each other.

$$\left(\frac{\partial \ln a_{2,3}}{\partial \ln X_2}\right)_{P,T,X_3} = 1 - 2(1 - \phi_1) \ln \frac{a_2}{X_2}; \qquad (a_2 \approx 1) \quad (1.26)$$

$$\left(\frac{\partial \ln a_{2,3}}{\partial \ln X_3}\right)_{P,T,X_2} = \frac{n-p}{n}\left\{1 - 2(1 - \phi_1) \ln \frac{a_3}{X_3}\right\}; \qquad (a_3 \approx 1) \quad (1.27)$$

For ionic solutes under a definite concentration of gegenions, the second term in Eq. (1.22) disappears. In a solution of added salts, the latter term contributes approximately $(n - p)X_2/nX_3$ times that of the first term (because $\partial \ln X_3/\partial \ln X_2 = X_2/X_3$). Substituting $a_2 = 1$ and $X_2 = $ CMC in mole fraction units, the concentration dependence of activity can be estimated. The value is, of course, a function of the CMC value and the ratio of molal volumes of solute against solvent. As it turned out from recent experimental facts, the entropy of mixing is not a function of volume but of mole fraction. The excess entropy due to the different molecular sizes was neglected in Eqs. (1.23) and (1.25). Some of the calculated values are shown in Table 1.5. The value

TABLE 1.5

CONCENTRATION DEPENDENCE OF ACTIVITY AT A DEFINITE
CONCENTRATION OF GEGENIONS

Compound	CMC (mole fraction)	$\left(\dfrac{\partial \ln a_2}{\partial \ln X_2}\right)_{P,T,X_1}$ at CMC
R_8SO_4Na	0.00237	(0.64)
$R_{10}SO_4Na$	0.00058	0.88
$R_{12}SO_4Na$	0.000146	0.94
$R_{14}SO_4Na$	0.000036	0.98
$R_8-OCH<(CHOH)_5$	0.00045	0.89
$R_{10}-OCH<(CHOH)_5$	0.00004	0.99
$R_{12}-OCH<(CHOH)_5$	0.0000034	0.999

changes with the amounts of additives and salts. If the CMC value is very small, the change of activity with concentration is equal to unity in the case of a nonionic agent and is equal to $1 + K_g$ in the case of an ionic agent. Thus, Eqs. (1.13), (1.15), and (1.16) are all explained coherently by taking into account the change of activity with concentration.

From Hess's law one may construct the following scheme (182).

$$\Delta_1 H_2$$

Hydrated solid (or liquid) agent   Single species

$$\Delta_n H_2 \qquad\qquad \Delta H_m$$

Micelles

where $\Delta_1 H_2$ or $\Delta_n H_2$ is the heat of solution to form single species or micelles from the hydrated (solid) agent and ΔH_m the heat of micelle formation. The value of $\Delta_1 H_2$ may be obtained from the temperature dependence of solubility below the Krafft point, and ΔH_m may be obtained from the temperature dependence of CMC above the Krafft point; $\Delta_n H_2$ is given as a sum of these values. From this experimental result and also from direct calorimetric measurements, we can conclude that ΔH_m is small compared with $\Delta_1 H_2$ or $\Delta_n H_2$ and the heat of fusion of hydrated solid contributes the greater part of $\Delta_1 H_2$ and/or $\Delta_n H_2$.

An explanation of the small heat effects is made in terms of structural effects exhibited in water, as discussed by Frank and Evans (192). According to these ideas, water molecules tend to form a kind of ice structure around the molecules of nonpolar solutes. With single paraffin chain ions in aqueous solution, this structure formed around the hydrocarbon chain lowers the energy and entropy of the solution and results in an extra specific heat because of the gradual breakdown of the structure with rise of temperature. The enthalpy and entropy changes due to the ice structure around the hydrocarbon are large but largely cancel each other.

It has been shown experimentally (192) that the decrease in heat content on dissolving nonpolar gases in water is much larger than in organic solvents, and this is paralleled by corresponding entropy effects and a higher specific heat of the water solutions. If these views also apply to the hydrocarbon part of the single ions, the water solutions of single ions should show this extra specific heat (184, 187).

4. Theory of the Critical Micelle Concentration

It is, in principle, identical to treat the formation of micelles as a mass action equilibrium or to treat the micelle as a separate phase (193). We have to use the mass action model for micelle formation if the aggregation number is small or if the change in aggregation number affects the thermodynamic functions appreciably. We may apply the phase separation model for the formation of micelles if the aggregation number is very large. Many theoretical papers dealing with the CMC have been published (168, 194–212). As the structural effects for entropy and enthalpy largely cancel the theory predicts the CMC nicely, just as the regular solution theory predicts solubility very well, while the agreement between theory and experiments for the heat or entropy of solution is not nearly so good. As for the CMC, the theory has to explain the distinctive and well-known facts that the CMC changes markedly with (i) paraffin chain length and (ii) number of charges and concentration of gegenions. Most of the theories explain the effect of chain length on the CMC, but only a few explain the effect of the number of charges of gegenions on the CMC (194, 206, 207).

If we treat the equilibrium between molecules, the partial (chemical) potential* of agent in single species is equal to the partial (chemical) potential in the aggregated state (201, 213).

$$\mu_{\text{solute}} = \mu_{\text{micellar}} \tag{1.28}$$

Where we have electrically charged species and the possibility of doing electrical work, the chemical potential is replaced by the electrochemical potential, which contains an additional energy term of the type $Ze\psi$, where Z is the number of charges of the ion, e is the electronic charge, and ψ is the electrical potential (214).

$$\mu'_{\text{single}} = \overline{\mu}_{\text{micellar}} + Ze\psi = \mu'_{\text{micellar}} \tag{1.29}$$

If we use the electrochemical potential of paraffin chain ions in the case of ionic agents, the only difference in the nonionic agent is the extra electrical term. We can forget about the electrochemical potential of the gegenions.
We will begin with the CMC of surface active agents of the most common molecular type, namely, those which have one dissociable group

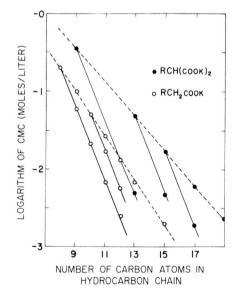

Fig. 1.10. The change in the logarithm of the CMC as a function of the number of carbon atoms in the hydrocarbon chain for a definite concentration of gegenions at 25°C.

---

* Chemical potential per mole and partial potential per molecule.

at one end of the straight hydrocarbon chain. The free energy decrease due to the aggregation of the hydrocarbon chains and the electrical energy accompanying the aggregation of polar dissociated groups are the main factors at micellization (83). From experimental studies of the CMC of homologous paraffin chain salts vs. the length of hydrocarbon chain at the same ionic strength (i.e., a definite concentration of gegenions), the standard free energy change per methylene group is estimated as 1.08 kT (at 25°C) (215). It is always safe to say that addition of one methylene group lowers the CMC about one-third of the initial value. Figure 1.10 illustrates this relation. This value may be compared to the value 0.64–0.71 kcal/mole (1.08–1.2 kT) derived by Langmuir (216) as the heat of adsorption of a methylene group in water. Cassie and Palmer (194) assumed 0.85 kT or 1.2 kT on the basis of the adsorption data of Powney and Addison (63) at the water-xylene interface. Overbeek and Stigter (207) obtained 1.02 kT from the data on sodium dodecyl sulfate at 25°C.

A reasonably high electrical potential on the micelle surface can be inferred from the marked decrease in CMC with added salts (and the high surface potential of ionized monolayers). If it it assumed, therefore, that the double layer thickness is small in comparison with the radius of curvature of the micelle surface or that the surface of a micelle is planar, and that the charge of the micelle is smeared out over its surface, then the gegenions are distributed homogeneously (and parallel to the micelle surface), and the electrical potential is only a function of the coordinate perpendicular to the micelle surface. Now, the Poisson-Boltzmann equation may be applied to the micelle consisting of a plane, uniformly charged surface in contact with a solution of strong 1 : 1 electrolyte (194, 217, 218),

$$\frac{d^2\psi}{dx^2} = -\frac{4\pi}{D} \sum z_i n_i e \exp\left(\frac{-z_i e\psi}{kT}\right) \tag{1.30}$$

where ψ is the electrical potential; x, the direction normal to the surface; D, the dielectric constant of the solution; Z_i, the number of charges of ions; n_i, the number of ions/cc in the bulk of the solution ($n_i = C_i N/1000$ and C_i is the mole number of ions per liter); N, Avogadro's number; k, the Boltzmann constant; and T, the absolute temperature. Considering the following boundary conditions, at

$$x = \infty, \qquad \psi = 0, \qquad \frac{d\psi}{dx} = 0 \tag{1.31}$$

Eq. (1.30) can be integrated:

$$\frac{1}{2}\left(\frac{d\psi}{dx}\right)^2 = \frac{4\pi kT}{D} \sum n_i[\exp\left(-Z_i e\psi/kT\right)-1] \tag{1.32}$$

and therefore,

$$\frac{1}{2}\left(\frac{d\psi}{dx}\right)^2_{x=0} = \frac{4\pi kT}{D} \sum n_i[\exp(-Z_ie\psi_0/kT)-1] \qquad (1.33)$$

The surface charge density σ may be obtained directly from the potential function (217, 218)

$$\sigma = -\int_0^\infty \rho dx = \frac{D}{4\pi}\int_0^\infty \frac{d^2\psi}{dx^2}dx = -\frac{D}{4\pi}\left(\frac{d\psi}{dx}\right)_{x=0} \qquad (1.34)$$

where ρ is the charge density. Introducing Eq. (1.34) into (1.33), we obtain

$$-\left(\frac{4\pi\sigma}{D}\right)^2 = \frac{8\pi kT}{D}\sum n_i\{\exp(-Z_ie\psi_0/kT)-1\} \qquad (1.35)$$

Equation (1.35) gives the electrical potential ψ_0 at the charged surface of the micelle. If the micelle-forming ion is an anion, ψ will be negative, and $-Z_ie\psi_0$ will be positive for cations and negative for anions. As the electrical potential on the micelle surface is usually several times larger than kT, the condition $\exp(-Z_ie\psi_0/kT) \gg 1$ is satisfied, and the contributions of the anions and 1 on the right-hand side of Eq. (1.35) can be neglected.* Thus, the gegenion is of primary importance in varying the electrical potential and therefore in varying the CMC. The similiion has almost no effect. Changing the kinds of gegenion also has only a small effect.

Using these approximations, we obtain for the 1:1 paraffin chain salts,

$$\frac{2\pi\sigma^2}{DkT} = n_i\exp(e\psi_0/kT) = \frac{NC_i}{1000}\exp(e\psi_0/kT) \qquad (1.36)$$

The electrical potential would be given by

$$\psi_0 = \frac{kT}{e}\left\{\ln\frac{2000\pi\sigma^2}{DNkT} - \ln C_i\right\} \qquad (1.37)$$

where C_i is the total concentration of gegenions in equivalents of effective ion per liter.

The integral work of introducing another charge e into the surface of the micelle is given by $e\psi$. A reasonable alternative is to assume that each ion, instead of contributing a charge e to the micelle, would contribute less than this because of the gegenion which accompanies the introduction of another charge (197).

If it is assumed that the effective electrical work is $K_ge\psi_0$, then the electrical work per paraffin chain ion in micelle formation is

---

* In the presence of excess salts, we cannot neglect 1, and Eq. (1.35) becomes $[(\cosh Ze\psi_0/2kT)-1]$.

$$E_{\rm el} = K_g k T \left\{ \frac{\ln 2000 \pi \sigma^2}{DNkT} - \ln C_i \right\} \tag{1.38}$$

where K_g is the experimental constant for the particular surface active agent.

The electrochemical potential of a surface active agent in the micellar state, $\mu'_{\rm micelle}$, and that in the singly dispersed state, $\mu'_{\rm single}$, may be given as follows (201):

$$\mu'_{\rm micelle} = N \left[-\chi - kT \frac{\ln (2\pi mkT)^{3/2} v}{h^3} - kT - kT \ln j(T) + pv_l \right] \tag{1.39}$$

$$\mu'_{\rm single} = N \left[-\chi' + kT \ln \frac{CNkT}{1000} - kT \ln \frac{(2\pi m)^{3/2}(kT)^{5/2}}{h^3} \right.$$

$$\left. + kT \ln j'(T) + pv_s \right] \tag{1.40}$$

where $-\chi$ is the uniform potential of the micelle which is a smoothed value for all relative configurations of the given molecule (ion) and its neighbors, and in this case χ contains the electrical energy; $-\chi'$ is a uniform potential of the solute; v is the free volume of one molecule; $j(T)$ and $j'(T)$ are partition functions for the internal degrees of freedom to be equal in the two phases; h is the Planck constant; and C is the concentration of solute in the bulk of the solution in moles per liter. At ordinary pressures, pv_l and pv_s are negligibly small compared with kT and might be omitted without loss of accuracy (1).

Introducing Eqs. (1.39) and (1.40) into (1.29), we obtain

$$\ln C = \ln \frac{1000}{Nv} - \frac{\chi - \chi'}{kT} - 1 = \ln \frac{1000}{Nv} - \frac{m\omega}{kT} + E_{\rm el} - 1 \tag{1.41}$$

where $\chi - \chi'$ is the free energy difference between the micellar state and the singly dispersed state, due to the cohesive energy change $m\omega$ and the electrical energy change $E_{\rm el}$. The change in hydration energy per molecule is assumed small, but this will simply change the value of the constant in Eq. (1.44) or (1.45).

Introducing Eq. (1.38) into (1.41), we obtain

$$\ln C = -\frac{m\omega}{kT} + K_g \left(\ln \frac{2000 \pi \sigma^2}{DNkT} - \ln C_i \right) + \ln \frac{1000}{Nv} - 1 \tag{1.42}$$

If no salt is added, $C_i = C$, and we obtain

$$\ln C = \frac{1}{1 + K_g} \left(-\frac{m\omega}{kT} + K_g \ln \frac{2000 \pi \sigma^2}{DNkT} + \ln \frac{1000}{Nv} - 1 \right) \tag{1.43}$$

For a homologous series of surface active agents, we obtain

$$\ln C = -\frac{m\omega}{kT} - K_g \ln C_i + K_1 \tag{1.44}$$

or

$$\ln C = -\frac{1}{1 + K_g}\left(\frac{m\omega}{kT}\right) + K_0 \tag{1.45}$$

Equations (1.44) and (1.45) explain the change in CMC as a function of paraffin chain length m and the concentration of gegenions C_i.

Individual factors which affect the CMC will be explained in the following sections.

V.   The Effect of Molecular Type on the Critical Micelle Concentration (219)

1.   Hydrocarbon Chain Length

The number of carbon atoms in the hydrocarbon chain of homologous surface active agents is known to be a determining factor of the CMC (26, 81, 151, 215, 220-223). It has been shown that the CMC decreases logarithmically with an increase in the number of carbon atoms m for various surface active agents, and the dependence is expressed by the equation (223)

$$\log_{10} C = A - Bm \tag{1.46}$$

where A and B are constants for the particular homologous series and temperature.

The values of A are approximately constant for homologs of different numbers of carbon atoms in the hydrocarbon chain and vary with the kinds and number of hydrophilic groups or substituents in the hydrocarbon chain, whereas the values of B are approximately equal to $\log_{10}2$ for all paraffin chain salts having one ionic group, but vary with the number of ionic groups, including nonionic agents. These values are shown in Table 1.6. Equations (1.43) and (1.45) provide a theoretical basis for the empirical equations. Comparing these equations, we obtain

$$B = \frac{\omega}{(1 + K_g)2.303kT} \tag{1.47}$$

where ω is the cohesive energy change transferring one methylene group from a hydrocarbon environment to an aqueous medium. For 1:1-type paraffin chain salts, B is almost constant. This means, according to Eq. (1.47), that K_g, the slope of CMC as a function of the concentration of the gegenions, does not change much for different surface active agents; K_g actually lies between 0.4 and 0.6. The small value of B in 2:1-type paraffin chain salts will be explained in a later paragraph. Though the CMC is dependent mostly on the number of carbon atoms

TABLE 1.6

Slope B and Intercept A of Various Surface Active Agents

Compound	Temperature (°C)	A	B	Determination of CMC	Reference
R_iCOOK	25	1.63	0.290	Dye method, refraction	(224,81)
R_iCOOK	45	1.74	0.292	Refraction	(81)
R_iSO_3Na	40	1.59	0.294	Conductivity, refraction	(81,225)
R_iSO_3Na	50	1.63	0.294	Conductivity, refraction	(81,225)
R_iSO_4Na	45	1.42	0.295	Dye method, refraction	(223)
R_iNH_3Cl	45	1.79	0.296	Conductivity	(226)
$R_iN(CH_3)_3Br$	60	1.77	0.292	Conductivity	(227)
$R_iCH(COOK)_2$	25	1.54	0.220	Dye method, solubilization	(215)
$R_iCH(COOK)$- -$CH(COOK)_2$	25	1.70	0.226	Dye method	(228)
Na 2-n-alkyl- benzenesulfonate	55	—	0.292	Dye method	(229)
Alkyl glucoside	25	2.64	0.530	Surface tension	(4)

in the chain, it also depends on A. The value of A changes with the concentration of gegenions and the kinds of hydrophilic group.

If the length of the various paraffin chain salts, namely, straight chain fatty acid soaps, alkyl sulfonates, alkyl sulfates, and alkyl ammonium chlorides, are compared, all CMC values fall on one line in a plot of ln CMC vs. the length of chain (223). The length is measured from the hydrogen of the ultimate carbon to the charged atom at the hydrophilic end of the paraffin chain. This relation is a fortuitous one. The CMC of the series of surface active agents $R_{16}(OC_2H_4)_iOSO_3Na$, for $i = 0$ to 4, changes only from 0.0004 to 0.00009 moles/liter (230).

The CMC values are close to each other for ionic agents of the same hydrocarbon chain length, and the difference comes from the changes in the degree of dissociation, the size, and the hydration of ionic groups.

As there is no electrical work accompanying the formation of micelles of nonionic agents, the electrical term in Eqs. (1.42) and (1.44) disappears. The change in CMC as a function of the paraffin chain length may be expressed as

$$\ln C = \frac{-m\omega}{kT} + \text{const} \tag{1.44'}$$

Actually, the CMC of nonionic agents or the solubility of paraffin chain alcohols (231) decreases about one-third for each additional methylene group (4, 232). This relation is similar to that of ionic agents under the condition of a definite concentration of gegenions (*215*). As the electrical work per micelle-forming ion is almost equal under this condition, the relation between the CMC and paraffin chain length of ionic agents is also expressed by the same equation.

The relation holds for a wide range of paraffin chain lengths in the case of ionic agents, whereas the relation holds only up to dodecyl compounds in the case of nonionic agents, as shown in Fig. 1.11.

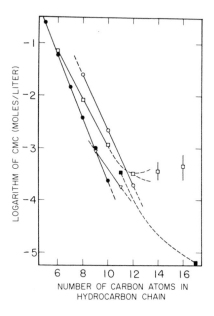

Fig. 1.11.   The relationship between the CMC of nonionic agents and the hydro-carbon chain length at 25°C: ○, alkyl glucoside; □, polyoxyethethylene (≈10) alkyl ether; ●, R_iOH; ■, sucrose monoester; ▽, methoxypolyoxyethylene (≈6) alkyl ester.

There are two conflicting results for longer chain nonionic agents (*232, 233*).

2.   *The Number of Ionic Groups*

Most of the ionic surface active agents investigated heretofore have been 1 : 1-type electrolytes. Consequently, it has become important and interesting to investigate substances which possess two or three ionic groups at one end of the hydrocarbon chains. Recently, the CMC values of potassium alkyl malonate (*215*), $R_iCH(COOK)_2$; potassium alkane tri-carboxylates (*228*), $R_iCH(COOK)CH(COOK)_2$; α-sulfonated fatty acids (salts) and their esters (*234–236*), $RCHSO_3Na \cdot COOH$, $RCHSO_3Na \cdot COONa$, and RCH(SO$_3$Na)COOR have been investigated.

These types of surface active agents show lower Krafft points compared with corresponding surface active agents which have one ionic group. As the hydrophilic property of the molecule increases they have different hydrophilic-oleophilic balance as compared with 1 : 1-type paraffin chain salts. For compounds which have the same H-L (hydrophilic-lyophilic) balance as ordinary soaps, both the hydrocarbon chain and the hydrophilic portion are large, so that they may exhibit quite different properties. The CMC becomes much larger due to the replacement of a hydrogen atom by an ionic group.

The CMC values and the ratio of the CMC to that of the corresponding fatty acid soap are shown in Table 1.7. The large CMC value

TABLE 1.7

CMC OF SURFACE ACTIVE AGENTS WHICH HAVE TWO OR THREE IONIC GROUPS
AND RATIO OF CMC TO THAT OF CORRESPONDING FATTY ACID SOAPS

Compound	CMC (moles/liter)	Calculate CMC (moles/liter)	Ratio of CMC's
R$_8$CH(COOK)$_2$	0.35	0.33	3.5
R$_{10}$CH(COOK)$_2$	0.13	0.12	5.2
R$_{12}$CH(COOK)$_2$	0.048	0.044	7.7
R$_{14}$CH(COOK)$_2$	0.017	0.016	10
R$_{16}$CH(COOK)$_2$	0.0063	0.0058	(15)
R$_{18}$CH(COOK)$_2$	0.0023	0.0021	(23)
R$_6$CH(COOK)CH(COOK)$_2$	0.79	0.73	4.0
R$_8$CH(COOK)CH(COOK)$_2$	0.28	0.26	5.6
R$_{10}$CH(COOK)CH(COOK)$_2$	0.095	0.094	7.3
R$_{12}$CH(COOK)CH(COOK)$_2$	0.034	0.034	(10)
R$_{14}$CH(COOK)CH(COOK)$_2$	0.012	0.012	(15)
R$_{12}$CH(SO$_3$H)(COOH)	0.0024 $\pm$0.0002	—	—
R$_{14}$CH(SO$_3$H)(COOH)	0.0006 $\pm$0.0001	—	—
R$_{14}$CH(SO$_3$Na)COOCH$_2$CH$_2$SO$_3$Na	0.008 ($\pm$0.002)	—	—
R$_{16}$CH(SO$_3$Na)COOCH$_2$CH$_2$SO$_3$Na	0.0025($\pm$0.0005)	—	—

results mainly from the larger electrical repulsive force due to the increase in the number of ionic groups. In the case where no salt is added, $C_i = i$ CMC, where i is the number of ionic groups. The electrical energy per micelle-forming ion becomes i times greater. Introducing these relations into Eqs. (1.44) and (1.45), we obtain

$$\ln C = -\frac{m\omega}{kT} + iK_g \ln i \cdot C_i + K_1 \tag{1.48}$$

$$\ln C = -\frac{m\omega}{(1 + iK_g)kT} + \frac{K_1 + iK_g \ln i}{(1 + iK_g)} = -\frac{m\omega}{(1 + iK_g)kT} + K_2 \tag{1.49}$$

Substituting $i = 1$, 2, or 3, $K_g = 0.56$ for fatty acid soaps and potassium alkyl malonates and 0.37 for potassium alkane tricarboxylates and using the CMC values of fatty acid soaps, the CMC values of $R_iCH(COOK)_2$ and $R_iCH(COOK)CH(COOK)_2$ were calculated theoretically, as show in column 3 of Table 1.7. The relation between the CMC and the chain length of potassium mono-, di-, and tricarboxylates is shown in Fig. 1.12.

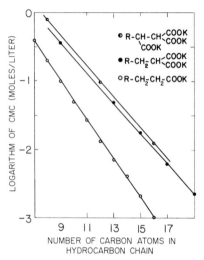

Fig. 1.12. The logarithm of the CMC of potassium mono-, di-, and tricarboxylates as a function of hydrocarbon chain length at 25°C.

The procedures are simply to multiply the number of ionic groups by the electrical work term and the concentration of gegenions. From the good agreement between experiment and theory, we can confirm the following equation

$$\ln C = -\frac{m\omega}{kT} + iK_g \ln \frac{2000\pi\sigma^2}{DNkTCi} + \text{const} \tag{1.50}$$

In the case where no salts are added, $C_i = i\,\text{CMC}$, we obtain

$$\ln C = \frac{1}{1 + iK_g}\left(-\frac{m\omega}{kT} + iK_g \ln \frac{2000\pi\sigma^2}{DNkTi} + K_3\right) \tag{1.51}$$

3. *Surface Active Agents Which Possess Two Hydrocarbon Chains*

Dialkyl sodium sulfosuccinates have shown various desirable properties in many practical applications. As these compounds are industrial products, only limited studies have been carried out using carefully purified materials. The CMC values of these compounds obtained by surface tension measurements after purification by crystallization, ad-

sorption, and foam fractionation are reported and shown in Table 1.8
(237).

It is interesting to note that the experimental points for the straight-chain sulfosuccinates also obey Eq. (1.46) (with a slightly smaller B value). As one would expect, the CMC's for the branched-chain sulfosuccinates occur at higher concentration than for the straight-chain sulfosuccinates, since the free energy decrease due to the aggregation of hydrocarbon chain is less than that of the straight sulfosuccinate containing the same number of carbon atoms.

TABLE 1.8

CMC OF A SERIES OF DIALKYL DIMETHYL AMMONIUM CHLORIDES AND OF
DIALKYL SODIUM SULFOSUCCINATES

Compound	CMC (moles/liter)	Method	Reference
Dibutyl sodium sulfosuccinates	0.20	Surface tension	(237)
Diisobutyl sodium sulfosuccinates	0.20	Surface tension	(237)
Dipentyl sodium sulfosuccinates	0.053	Surface tension	(237)
Dihexyl sodium sulfosuccinates	0.0124	Surface tension	(237)
Dioctyl sodium sulfosuccinates	0.00068	Surface tension	(237)
Di-2-ethylhexyl sodium sulfosuccinates	0.0025	Surface tension	(237)
$(C_8H_{17})_2(CH_3)_2NCl$	0.0266	Conductivity	(239)
$(C_{10}H_{21})_2(CH_3)_2NCl$	0.0020	Conductivity	(239)
$(C_8H_{17})(C_{12}H_{25})(CH_3)_2NCl$	0.0018	Conductivity	(239)
$(C_{12}H_{25})_2(CH_3)_2NCl$	0.00018	Conductivity	(239)

Comparison of the CMC's of (I) (0.0097 M) (238) and (II) (0.0124 M) is also interesting:

$$R_6-CH-SO_4Na \qquad R_6OOC-CH-SO_3Na$$
$$R_6-CH_2 \qquad\qquad R_6OOC-CH_2$$
$$(I) \qquad\qquad (II)$$

We know that the CMC value of an $-SO_4Na$ compound is about 0.8 as large as the corresponding $-SO_3Na$ compound. We estimate the CMC value of (III) as 0.012 moles/liter:

$$R_6CH-SO_3Na$$
$$R_6CH_2$$
$$(III)$$

and we find that the $-COO-$ groups in the latter compound do not contribute appreciably to the CMC.

Ralston et al. (239) measured the CMC's of dialkyl dimethyl ammonium chlorides. The values are also shown in Table 1.8. The CMC of $(R_8)_2N(CH_3)_2Cl$ (0.0266 moles/liter) is close to the CMC of $R_{11}N(CH_3)_3Cl$. No big difference was found between the CMC of $(R_8)(R_{12})N(CH_3)_2Cl$ and that of $R_{10}R_{10}N(CH_3)_2Cl$.

4. *Position of Ionic Group in the Alkyl Chain*

The effect of the position of the ionic group on the CMC was first measured by Winsor (*43*). Evans determined by conductivity the CMC of a large number of sodium alkyl sulfates in which the the total hydrocarbon chain contains 8–19 carbon atoms and the position of the sulfate group ranges from the terminal to the medial position (*238*). The results are given in Table 1.9.

TABLE 1.9

CMC OF SODIUM ALKYL SULFATES OF VARYING HYDROCARBON CHAIN LENGTH
AND VARYING POSITION OF SULFATE GROUP AT 40°C

Position of $-SO_4Na$ group along chain	Number of carbon atoms in chain RCHR'	CMC (moles/liter)	Position of $-SO_4Na$ group along chain	Number of carbon atoms in chain RCHR'	CMC (moles/liter)
1	8	0.136	4	16	0.00172
1	12	0.00865	4	18	0.00045
1	14	0.00240	5	14	0.00675
1	16	0.00058	5	15	0.0034
1	18	0.000165	5	19	0.00033
2	8	0.180	6	11	0.083
2	10	0.0495	6	16	0.00235
2	13	0.00650	6	18	0.00072
2	14	0.00330	7	13	0.0193
2	15	0.00171	7	14	0.00970
2	17	0.00049	8	15	0.00665
2	18	0.00026	8	16	0.00425
3	11	0.0289	9	17	0.00235
3	14	0.00430	10	19	0.00094
3	15	0.00220	15	29	0.00008
4	14	0.00515			

The relation between the number of carbon atoms and the logarithm of the CMC (Fig. 1.13) shows that lines drawn through the points representing homologous series are straight except in the case of short chain compounds. All the straight lines can be represented by equations of the type:

$$\log_{10}C = A - Bm \qquad (1.46)$$

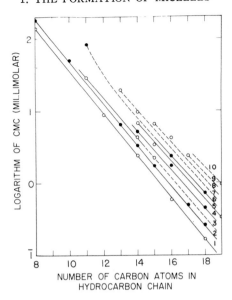

Fig. 1.13. The relationship between the number of carbon atoms and the logarithm of the CMC of sodium alkyl sulfates at 40°C. The numerals for the individual curves denote the position of the -SO₄Na in the chain.

Values of the constants for the separate homologous series are given in Table 1.10. It will be noted that the slope of the lines B decreases somewhat as the sulfate group is shifted towards the middle of the chain, indicating a smaller free energy decrease per methylene group on micellization. The values of A are approximately constant for all homologous series with different sulfate positions. For a series of sodium alkyl sulfates of the same number of carbon atoms, the CMC increases

TABLE 1.10

SLOPE B AND INTERCEPT A OF SODIUM ALKYL SULFATES FOR VARIOUS POSITIONS OF THE SULFATE GROUP AT 40°C

Position of sulfate group	B	A	Position of sulfate group	B	A
1	0.294	4.49	6	0.270	4.72
2	0.286	4.53	7	0.256	4.59
3	0.280	4.55	8	0.251	4.58
4	0.266	4.47	9	0.245	4.55
5	0.258	4.44	10	0.240	4.52

as a result of the change in position of the sulfate group from the terminal to the medial position. In the case of sodium tetradecyl sulfate, for example, the CMC of sodium tetradecyl-7-sulfate (0.0097 moles/liter) is about 4 times higher than that of sodium tetradecyl-1-sulfate (0.0024 moles/liter). This change corresponds to a decrease of approximately two methylene groups in a straight chain sulfate.

5. *Addition of a Benzene Ring in the Oleophilic Portion of the Molecule*

TABLE 1.11

CMC OF SODIUM ALKYL BENZENESULFONATES

Lyophilic group	CMC (moles/liter)	Method	Temperature (°C)	Reference
p-Hexylbenzene	0.037	Dye method	75	(242a)
p-Heptylbenzene	0.021	Dye method	75	(242a)
o-Octylbenzene	0.019	Dye method	55	(229)
p-Octylbenzene	0.015–12	Conductance	60—25	(241)
p-Octylbenzene	0.0147	Conductance	35	(242)
p-Nonylbenzene	0.0065	Dye method	75	(242a)
p-Decylbenzene	0.00381	Conductance	50	(242)
o-Dodecylbenzene	0.0017	Dye method	55	(229)
o-Dodecylbenzene	0.00159	Conductance	30	(166)
m-Dodecylbenzene	0.00146	Conductance	30	(166)
p-Dodecylbenzene	0.00119	Conductance	30	(166)
p-Dodecylbenzene	0.0012	Conductance	60	(241,242)
p-Tetradecylbenzene	0.00066	Dye method	75	(242a)
p-1-Methyldecylbenzene	0.00245	Solubility	19	(242)
p-1-Methyldecylbenzene	0.00253	Conductance	35	(242)
p-1-Methyldodecylbenzene	0.00071	Solubility	27.7	(242)
p-1-Methyldodecylbenzene	0.00072	Conductance	35	(242)
p-1-Methyltetradecylbenzene	0.00050	Solubility	32.6	(242)
p-1-Methyltetradecylbenzene	0.00031	Conductance	40	(242)
p-1-Methylhexadecylbenzene	0.00014	Solubility	45.5	(242)
p-1-Methylhexadecylbenzene	0.00013	Conductance	50	(242)

Although large amounts of surface active agents of this type have been produced commercially, no extensive data using pure materials have been reported for these systems.

Shick and Fowkes have investigated the effect of additives on the CMC of sodium 2-n-alkylbenzenesulfonates (229). Ludlum has measured the CMC of sodium 2-, 3-, or 4-dodecylbenzene-sulfonate (240).

Paquette *et al.* (241) have measured the CMC of sodium p-n-octyl- and p-n-dodecylbenzenesulfonates (with the corresponding alkyl sulfonates). Gershman (242) has measured the CMC of a series of sodium 1-methylalkylbenzenesulfonates. Results are shown in Table 1.11.

From a comparison of the CMC values of these sodium alkyl benzene-

TABLE 1.12

EFFECT OF UNSATURATION AND POLAR SUBSTITUTION ON CMC

Compound	CMC (moles/liter)	Method	Temperature (°C)	Reference
Potassium stearate	0.00045	Refraction	55C	(223)
Potassium stearate	0.0005	Conductivity	60C	(243a)
Potassium oleate	0.0012	Refraction	50C	(223)
Potassium oleate	0.0015	Conductivity	25C	(125)
Potassium elaidate	0.0015	Refraction	50C	(223)
Potassium abietate	0.012	Dye method	25C	(223)
Potassium dehydroabietate	0.027	Dye method	25C	(223)
Potassium 9,10-dihydroxystearate	0.0075	Conductivity	60C	(243a)
Potassium 9.10-dihydroxystearate	0.008	Refraction	55C	(223)
Potassium ricinoleate	0.0036	Refraction	55C	(223)
Potassium ricinelaidate	0.0055	Refraction	55C	(223)
Potassium N-dodecyl-β-alaninate	0.0026	Refraction	35C	(223)
Potassium N-dodecyl-β-alaninate	0.003	Refraction	50C	(223)
Potassium hexadecanote	0.0022	Refraction	50C	(223)
N-Dodecyl-β-alanine hydrochloride	0.010	Refraction	30C	(223)
Dodecylammonium chloride	0.014	Refraction	30C	(223)
$R_{16}SO_4Na$	0.0004	Surface tension	25C	(230)
$R_{16}(OCH_2 \cdot CH_2)_2SO_4Na$	0.00021—22	Conductivity, surface tension, dye method	25C	(230)
$R_{16}(OCH_2 \cdot CH_2)_2SO_4Na$	0.00012-1.34-14	Surface tension, conductivity, dye method	25C	(230)
$R_{16}(OCH_2 \cdot CH_2)_3SO_4Na$	0.00007—12.3	Surface tension, conductivity	25C	(230)
$R_{16}(OCH_2 \cdot CH_2)_3SO_4Na$	0.0001	Dye method	25C	(230)
$R_{16}(OCH_2 \cdot CH_2)_4SO_4Na$	0.00008	Surface tension	25C	(230)
$R_{16}(OCH_2 \cdot CH_2)_4SO_4Na$	0.0001	Dye method	25C	(230)
$R_{18}OCH_2CH_2SO_4Na$	0.00019—11	Surface tension, dye method	25C	(230)
$R_{18}(OCH_2CH_2)_2SO_4Na$	0.00008—7	Surface tension, dye method	25C	(230)
$R_{18}(OCH_2CH_2)_3SO_4Na$	0.00005	Surface tension, dye method	25C	(230)
$R_{18}(OCH_2CH_2)_4SO_4Na$	0.00004	Surface tension, dye method	25C	(230)
$R_{12}CHSO_3HCOOH$	~0.0025	Surface tension, dye method	28—25	(236)
$R_{14}CHSO_3HCOOH$	~0.00068	Surface tension, dye method	28—25	(236)

Compound	CMC (moles/liter)	Method	Temperature (°C)	Reference
$R_{16}CHSO_3HCOOH$	~0.00015	Surface tension, dye method	28—25	(236)
$R_{14}CHSO_3NaCOOCH_3$	~0.00037	Surface tension, dye method	28—25	(236)
$R_{14}CHSO_3NaCOOC_2H_5$	~0.00031	Surface tension, dye method	28—25	(236)
$R_{14}CHSO_3NaCOOC_3H_7$	~0.00010	Surface tension, dye method	28—25	(236)
$R_{16}CHSO_3NaCOOCH_3$	~0.00010	Surface tension, dye method	28—25	(236)
$R_{14}CHSO_3NaCOOCH_2CH_2SO_3Na$	~0.0087	Surface tension, dye method	28—25	(236)
$R_{16}CHSO_3NaCOOCH_2CH_2SO_3Na$	~0.0027	Surface tension, dye method	28—25	(236)

sulfonates with sodium alkyl sulfonates, it is concluded that the addition of the benzene ring in the hydrocarbon chain is equivalent to the addition of about 3.5 methylene groups. From the very recent study of selective adsorptivity of sodium *p*-dodecylbenzene sulfonate against sodium dodecyl sulfate by radiotracer technique (243), the selective adsorptivity being 35-50, we arrived also at the conclusion that the addition of a benzene ring is equivalent to the addition of about 3.5 methylene groups.

6. *Effect of Unsaturation on the CMC*

Data for the unsaturated and corresponding saturated compounds are shown in Table 1.12.

It is evident from these results that the presence of one double bond increases the CMC about 3-4 times compared with the saturated compound. A similar difference in CMC has also been noted in the comparison of the CMC of potassium abietate (0.012 moles/liter) and potassium dehydroabietate (0.027 mole/liter). Klevens (223) noted that the marked differences in solubility between the saturated and unsaturated soaps do not carry over to their association properties, i. e., in the formation of micelles. The difference in the CMC between saturated and unsaturated compounds results from the difference in nonelectrical energy change on micellization, and this difference may be small; but the solubility may be very different, for the Krafft point is different.

7. *Polar Substitution in the Chain*

The effect of substitution of polar groups for hydrogen in the hydrocarbon chain results in a marked increase in the solubility and the CMC of the surface active agents. Some of the results are shown in Tables 1.7. and 1.12. The CMC of potassium 9,10-dihydroxyoctadecanoate is about 16 times higher than that of potassium octadecanoate. One substitution of an –OH group corresponds to a 4 times higher CMC value or a decrease of two methylene groups. The CMC values of *cis*-and *trans*-12-hydroxy-9-octadecanoic acids, 0.0036 and 0.0055, respectively, are 3–3.3 times higher than those of the corresponding 9-octadecanoic acids, as shown in Table 1.12.

It is expected that the CMC value would become higher if the molecule becomes more soluble following unsaturation or polar substitution in the hydrocarbon chain. The change in surface free energy of solution in Eq. (1.45) is reflected in the CMC. If the molecule is n times more soluble, the CMC value is $n^{1/(1+K_g)}$ times larger. (For examle, if the compound becomes 3 times more soluble, the CMC value becomes about 2 times higher.)

8. *Fluorocarbon Chain Compounds*

Arrington and Patterson (*244*) measured the CMC of a series of fluoroalkanoic acids and their ammonium salts of the general formula $H(CF_2)_nCOOH(NH_4)$. The compounds are completely fluorinated except for the terminal hydrogen atom. Klevens and Raison (*245, 245a*) have

TABLE 1.13

CMC OF FLUORINATED SURFACE ACTIVE AGENTS

Compound	CMC (moles/liter)	Method	Reference
$H(CF_2)_6COONH_4$	0.25	Dye method	(*244*)
$H(CF_2)_8COONH_4$	0.038	Dye method	(*244*)
$H(CF_2)_{10}COONH_4$	0.009	Dye method	(*244*)
$H(CF_2)_6COOH$	0.15	Dye method	(*244*)
$H(CF_2)_8COOH$	0.03	Dye method	(*244*)
$C_5F_{11}COOK$	0.5	Dye method	(*245*)
$C_7F_{15}COOK$	0.027	Dye method	(*245*)
$C_9F_{19}COOK$	0.0009	Dye method	(*245*)
$C_5F_{11}COOH$	0.051	Dye method	(*245*)
$C_7F_{15}COOH$	0.009	Dye method	(*245*)
$C_9F_{19}COOH$	0.0008	Dye method	(*245*)
$C_3F_7NH_2$	0.132	—	(*245*)
$C_3F_7NH_3Cl$	1.1	—	(*245*)

measured the CMC's of perfluoroalkanoic acids and their potassium salts. The results are shown in Table 1.13.

As the investigation lacks a quantitative relation between log CMC and log concentration of gegenions, and since the samples were not very pure, it would be premature to draw definite conclusions for the CMC of fluorocarbon compounds. However, the dependence of the CMC upon chain length is analogous to that of hydrocarbon compounds (*246a, b, c, d*). The more rapid decrease in CMC for one addition of $-CF_2-$ group and the smaller CMC value compared with the hydrocarbon compounds of the same carbon atoms are consistent with the lower cohesive energy of fluorocarbon compounds or larger heat of mixing of fluorocarbon with water, i.e., the large ω value in Eqs. (1.44) and (1.45)

There are tenfold, threefold, and onefold differences in CMC in the case of the C_6-, C_8-, C_{10}-perfluoro acids and salts, respectively. This may result at least partly from the incomplete dissociation of fluorocarbon acids at higher concentrations.

9. Types of Hydrophilic Groups

As already stated in Section V, 1, the CMC is expressed by:

$$\log_{10} C = A - Bm \qquad (1.46)$$

For a homologous series of surface active agents, the change in CMC

TABLE 1.14

EFFECT OF DIFFERENT KINDS OF HYDROPHILIC GROUPS ON CMC

Compound	CMC (moles/liter)	Temperature (°C)	Method	Reference
$R_{12}COOK$	0.0125	25	Dye method	(*81*)
$R_{12}SO_3K$	0.009	25	Conductivity	(*32*)
$R_{12}SO_3Na$	0.010	20	Refraction	(*246*)
$R_{12}SO_3Na$	0.0081	25	Conductivity	(*31*)
$R_{12}SSO_3Na$	0.002	—	—	(*249*)
$R_{12}NH_3Cl$	0.014	30	Refraction	(*246*)
$R_{12}-N(CH_3)_3Cl$	0.016, 0.020	30	Dye method, conductivity	(*223*) (*239*)
$R_{12}-N(CH_3)_3Br$	0.016	25	Conductivity	(*227*)
$R_{12}-NC_5H_5Cl$	0.015	30	Refraction	(*223*)
$R_{16}-NH_3Cl$	0.00085	55	Refraction	(*81*)
$R_{16}-N(CH_3)_3Br$	0.0010	60	Conductivity	(*227*)
$R_{16}-N(CH_3)_3Cl$	0.0013, 0.0014	30	Conductivity	(*247,239*)
$R_{16}-N(CH_3)_2(C_2H_4OH)Cl$	0.0012	30	Conductivity	(247)
$R_{16}-N(CH_3)(C_2H_4OH)_2Cl$	0.0010	30	Conductivity	(*247*)
$R_{16}-N(C_2H_4OH)_3Cl$	0.0010	30	Conductivity	(*247*)
$R_{16}-NC_5H_5Cl$	0.0009	30	Conductivity	(*248*)
$R_{16}-NC_5H_5Br$	0.0008	30	Transport number	(*34*)

arises mainly from the difference in hydrocarbon chain length, and the value of A stays constant.

The difference in the CMC of various surface active agents which have the same hydrocarbon chain results mainly from the kinds of hydrophilic group, the number of charges of gegenions, molecular shape, and so on. Some of the A-values are shown in Tables 1.6 and 1.10. The CMC's of various surface active agents which have the same oleophilic group are shown in Table 1.14.

It can be seen from Table 1.14. that the effect of the type of hydrophilic groups on the CMC is generally not large. If we recall the theoretical derivation of the CMC and the mechanism of dissolution of ionic agents, this result is to be expected. The ionic group markedly increases the solvency of ionic agents by dissociation. For all 1 : 1-type paraffin chain salts whose dissociation is complete, and for which, therefore, the electrical work at micellization is of the same order, the contribution of the ionic group to the CMC is approximately the same. Small differences in hydration, in nonelectrical energy of the ionic group at micellization, or in ionic radius affect the CMC but little.

The CMC values of nonionic agents which possess the same hydrocarbon chain are affected by the sizes and the kinds of hydrophilic groups (*21*, *212*, *250-252*). Some of the results are summarized in Table 1.15.

TABLE 1.15

EFFECT OF SIZES AND KINDS OF HYDROPHILIC GROUPS ON
CMC OF NONIONIC AGENTS

Compound	CMC (moles/liter)	Method	Temperature (°C)	Reference
$R_8OCH_2CH_2OH$	0.0049	Surface tension	25	(*21*)
$R_8OCH_2CHOHCH_2OH$	0.0058	Surface tension	25	(*21*)
$R_8OCH<(CHOH)_5$	0.025	Surface tension	25	(*21*)
$R_9COO(CH_2CH_2O)_{7.0}CH_3$	0.0008-0.0010	Solubilization and dye method	27	(*212*)
$R_9COO(CH_2CH_2O)_{16.0}CH_3$	0.0014-0.0018	Solubilization and dye method	27	(*212*)
$R_{11}COO(CH_2CH_2O)_{6.0}CH_3$	0.00015-0.00020	Solubilization and dye method	27	(*212*)
$R_{11}COO(CH_2CH_2O)_{12.5}CH_3$	0.00028-0.00035	Solubilization and dye method	27	(*212*)
$R_{10}O(CH_2CH_2O)_{12}CH_3$	0.0011	Light scattering	29	(*252*)
$R_{10}O(CH_2CH_2O)_8CH_3$	0.0006	Light scattering	30	(*254a*)
$R_{10}O(CH_2CH_2O)_{11}CH_3$	0.00095	Light scattering	30	(*254a*)
$R_{10}OCH<(CHOH)_5$	0.0022	Surface tension	25	(*4*)
$R_{11}COO$-sucrose	0.00034	Surface tension	27.1	(*232*)
$R_{11}OCH<(CHOH)_5$	0.00065 (interpolated)	Surface tension	25	(*4*)

10. *The Number of Charges of Gegenions*

Lottermoser and Püschel (*26*) have reported correspondingly smaller CMC's for the bivalent Cu, Zn, and Mg salts than for the univalent Na,

K, and Ag salts of the alkyl sulfates. Lange (*253*) measured the CMC of sodium and calcium dodecyl sulfates. Lelong et al. (*254*). measured the CMC of a series of magnesium alkyl sulfonates. Miyamoto (*254b*) measured the CMC of dodecyl sulfate salts of seven bivalent cations. The results are summarized in Table 1.16.

TABLE 1.16

CMC OF BIVALENT SALTS OF ALKYL SULFATES AND ALKYL SULFONATES

Compound	CMC (normal)	Method	Temperature (°C)	Reference
$R_{12}SO_4(\frac{1}{2}Zn)$	0.0021	Conductivity	60	(*26*)
$R_{12}SO_4(\frac{1}{2}Cu)2H_2O$	0.0017	Conductivity	40	(*26*)
$R_{12}SO_4(\frac{1}{2}Cu)2H_2O$	0.0020	Surface tension	25	(*254b*)
$R_{12}SO_4(\frac{1}{2}Mg)$	0.0016	Conductivity	25	(*26*)
$R_{12}SO_4(\frac{1}{2}Mg)$	0.0018	Surface tension	25	(*254b*)
$R_{12}SO_4(\frac{1}{2}Ca)$	0.0026	Surface tension	54	(*254b*)
$R_{12}SO_4(\frac{1}{2}Ca)$	0.0029	Dye method	70	(*253*)
$R_{12}SO_4(\frac{1}{2}Sr)$	0.0022	Surface tension	67	(*254b*)
$R_{12}SO_4(\frac{1}{2}Pb)$	0.0020	Surface tension	54	(*254b*)
$R_{12}SO_4(\frac{1}{2}Mn)$	0.0022	Surface tension	25—54	(*254b*)
$R_{12}SO_4(\frac{1}{2}Co)3H_2O$	0.00166	Surface tension	25	(*254b*)
$R_6SO_3(\frac{1}{2}Mg)$	0.6	Dye method	25	(*254*)
$R_8SO_3(\frac{1}{2}Mg)$	0.09[a]	Conductivity	25	(*254*)
$R_{10}SO_3(\frac{1}{2}Mg)$	0.014[a]	Conductivity	25	(*254*)
$R_{12}SO_3(\frac{1}{2}Mg)$	0.002[a]	Conductivity	25	(*254*)

[a] Extrapolated to 25°C.

The electrical potential on the micelle surface for a 1 : 1-type paraffin chain salt was derived theoretically and given in Eq. (1.37). If the gegenion is multivalent, we obtain

$$\psi_0 = \frac{kT}{Z_i e}\left(\ln \frac{2000\pi\sigma^2}{DNkT} - \ln C_i\right) \qquad (1.52)$$

from Eq. (1.35), where Z is the number of charges of the gegenions, and C_i is the concentration of gegenions. If no salt is added, $C_i = \frac{1}{2}$ CMC for bivalent salts of paraffin chain ions; that is, the electrical energy for micellization decreases approximately to one-half compared with 1 : 1-type paraffin chain salts, so that we obtain

$$\ln C = -\frac{m\omega}{kT} + \frac{K_g}{Z_i}\left(\ln \frac{2000\pi\sigma^2}{DNkT} - \ln C_i\right) + K_4 \qquad (1.53)$$

If no salt is added,

$$\ln C = \frac{1}{1 + (K_g/Z_i)}\left(-\frac{m\omega}{kT} + \frac{K_g}{Z_i}\ln \frac{4000\pi\sigma^2}{DNkT}\right) + K_5 \qquad (1.54)$$

Lelong's (254) results agree well with this theoretical relation.

11. Kinds of Univalent Gegenions

The CMC is not markedly dependent on the nature of the gegenions (255). Since the electrical energy for micellization is determined mainly by the concentration, the nature of the gegenion exerts only a secondary effect. Some of the results are summarized in Table 1.17.

TABLE 1.17

EFFECT OF DIFFERENT KINDS OF GEGENIONS ON CMC

Compound	CMC (moles/liter)	Method	Temperature (°C)	Reference
$R_{11}COONa$	0.026	Dye method	25	(223)
$R_{11}COOK$	0.0255	Dye method	25	(223)
$R_{11}COOCs$	0.025	Dye metbod	25	(223)
$R_{12}NH_3Cl$	0.014	Dye method	30	(223)
$R_{12}NH_3Br$	0.012	Dye method	30	(223)
$R_{12}NH_3OCOCH_3$	0.0151	Conductivity	25	(256)
$R_{12}NH_3NO_3$	0.0115	Conductivity	25	(226)
$R_{12}NC_5H_5Cl$	0.015, 0.0174	Dye method, conductivity	25,30	(223,258)
$R_{12}NC_5H_5Br$	0.016, 0.0125	Dye method, conductivity	25,30	(223,258)
$R_{12}NC_5H_5I$	0.0045	Conductivity	30	(258)
$R_{18}NH_3Cl$	0.00055	Conductivity	60	(226)
$R_{18}NH_3OCOCH_3$	0.00040	Conductivity	60	(226)
$R_{18}N(CH_3)_3Cl$	0.00034	Conductivity	25	(257)
$R_{18}N(CH_3)_3OOC-COOH$	0.0001	Conductivity	25	(257)
$R_{18}N(CH_3)_3Br$	0.00031	Conductivity	25	(257)
$R_{18}N(CH_3)_3OCOH$	0.00044	Conductivity	25	(257)
$R_{18}N(CH_3)_3NO_3$	0.00023	Conductivity	25	(257)
$R_{12}SO_4Li$	0.0088	Light scattering	25	(91)
$R_{12}SO_4Li$	0.0105	Conductivity	40	(259)
$R_{12}SO_4Na$	0.0081, 0.0089	Conductivity	25,40	(31,259)
$R_{12}SO_4K$	0.0078	Conductivity	40	(259)
$R_{12}SO_4Cs$	0.0069	—	40	(265a)
$R_{12}SO_4N(CH_3)_4$	0.00555	Light scattering	25	(91)
$R_{12}SO_4$-triethanol-ammonium	0.004	Surface tension	33	(260)
$R_{12}SO_4$-morpholinium	0.003~4	Surface tension	40	(260)

12. Miscellaneous

Sodium cholate solution was studied by Ekwall (22, 261). The CMC was about 0.040–0.044 M as was shown by all the methods used. Some results for abietate are shown in Table 1.12.

VI.   The Effects of Additives and Salts on the Critical Micelle Concentration

As explained in the preceding section, the critical micelle concentration of a surface active agent can be estimated fairly accurately by comparison with the CMC values of analogous compounds and by aid of the theory. It is not very difficult to determine the CMC of a pure surface active agent using the experimental methods described in Section II. There are, however, many systems where we want to know the change in CMC as a function of the amounts of various additives. These CMC values are rather troublesome and time-consuming to measure individually. The CMC change gives us information on the effect of additives on the surface activity of the surface active agent and on the surface activity of the additives, and provides a clearer understanding of the action of surface active agents. The change in CMC also affords information on the role of additives in concentrated solutions. Accordingly, it is desirable to calculate the CMC, knowing the composition of the solution. The effect of additives can be classified as follows: (1) the effect of the concentration and number of charges of gegenions;   (2) the effect of adding a closely related surface active agent;   (3) the effect of added higher alcohols;   (4) the effect of methanol, dioxane, glycol, etc.;   (5) the effect of added nonpolar hydrocarbons;   (6) the effect of pH.

1. *The Effect of Added Salts; the Concentration and Number of Charges of Added Ions*

There are various different effects of added salts on the CMC. Above all, the effect of concentration and the number of charges of gegenions are the most important. The types and the number of charges of similiions have only a small effect, and the types of gegenions affect the CMC but little. The differences of CMC due to the different gegenions result from differences in ionic radius and hydration of the gegenions and in degree of dissociation.

There are several papers on the effect of added salts (*38, 81, 112, 215, 229, 253, 255, 262*). As a result of these experiments, it has been found that the logarithm of the CMC changes linearly with the logarithm of the concentration of gegenion C_i, (Fig. 1.14)

$$\ln C = - K_g \ln C_i + \text{const} \tag{1.55}$$

where K_g is an experimental constant with a value of about 0.4–0.6. For surface active agents which have two ionic groups the slope is twice as great (*215*) (Fig. 1.15).

$$\ln C = - 2K_g \ln C_i + \text{const} \tag{1.56}$$

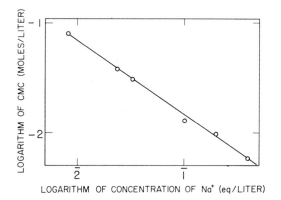

Fig. 1.14. The relationship between the logarithm of the CMC and the logarithm of the concentration of gegenions of sodium dodecyl sulfate at 25°C.

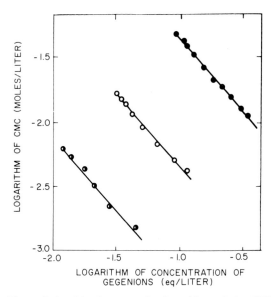

Fig. 1.15. The relationship between the logarithm of the CMC and the logarithm of the concentration of gegenions of potassium alkyl malonate at 25°C: ●, $R_{12}CH (COOK)_2$; ○, $R_{14}CH(COOK)_2$; ◐, $R_{16}CH(COOK)_2$.

Lange (253) has measured the effect of the number of charges of gegenions on sodium and calcium dodecyl sulfates and on dodecylpyridinium chloride. The slope of the logarithm of the CMC of calcium dodecyl sulfate vs. the concentration of calcium ion is approximately one-half that of sodium ion.

$$\ln C = -\frac{K_g}{Z_i} \ln C_{i2} + \text{const} \tag{1.57}$$

The electrical potential on the micelle surface is given as a function of the concentration and the number of charges of gegenions and similions, as follows:

$$\left(-\frac{4\pi\sigma}{D}\right)^2 = \left(\frac{d\psi}{dx}\right)^2_{x=0} = \frac{8\pi kT}{D} \sum n_i\left[\exp\left(-\frac{Z_i e\psi_0}{kT}\right)-1\right] \tag{1.35}$$

Eq. (1.35) gives the electrical potentials in each of the following cases (206).

(A) For paraffin chain salts of the 1:1 type:
    (i) with no added salt

$$\psi_0 = \frac{kT}{e} \ln \frac{2000\pi\sigma^2}{DNkTC_{i1}} \tag{1.58}$$

where $C_{i1} = \text{CMC} = 1000 \, n_1/N$;
    (ii) with added univalent gegenions

$$\psi_0 = \frac{kT}{e} \ln \frac{2000\pi\sigma^2}{DNkTC_{i1}} \tag{1.59}$$

where $C_{i1} = \text{CMC} + C_s$, and C_s is the concentration of added salts;
    (iii) with added bivalent gegenions

$$\frac{2000\pi\sigma^2}{DNkT} = C_{i1} \exp\left(\frac{e\psi_0}{kT}\right) + C_{i2} \exp\left(\frac{2e\psi_0}{kT}\right) \tag{1.60}$$

where $C_{i1} = \text{CMC}$, and C_{i2} is the concentration of added bivalent gegenions in moles/liter;
    (iv) with added trivalent gegenions

$$\frac{2000\pi\sigma^2}{DNkT} = C_{i1} \exp\left(\frac{e\psi_0}{kT}\right) + C_{i3} \exp\left(\frac{3e\psi_0}{kT}\right) \tag{1.61}$$

where $C_{i1} = \text{CMC}$, and C_{i3} is the concentration of added trivalent gegenions.

(B) For paraffin chain salts of the 2:1 type:
    (i) with no added salt

$$\psi_0 = \frac{kT}{2e} \ln \frac{2000\pi\sigma^2}{DNkTC_{i2}} \tag{1.62}$$

where $C_{i2} = \text{CMC}/2$;
    (ii) with added univalent gegenions

$$\frac{2000\pi\sigma^2}{DNkT} = C_{i1} \exp\left(\frac{e\psi_0}{kT}\right) + C_{i2} \exp\left(\frac{2e\psi_0}{kT}\right) \tag{1.63}$$

where C_{i1} is the concentration of added gegenions, and $C_{i2} = CMC/2$;
(iii)   with added bivalent gegenions

$$\psi_0 = \frac{kT}{2e} \ln \frac{2000\pi\sigma^2}{DNkTC_{i2}} \tag{1.64}$$

where $C_{i2} = CMC + C'_{s2}$ and C'_{s2} is the concentration of added gegenions.
For 1:1-or 2:1-type paraffin chain salts, we obtain by combining Eqs. (1.38) and (1.41) with (1.59) or (1.64)

$$\ln C = -\frac{m\omega}{kT} + K_g \ln \frac{2000\pi\sigma^2}{DNkTC_{i1}} + K_s \tag{1.44}$$

$$\ln C = -\frac{m\omega}{kT} + \frac{K_g}{2} \ln \frac{2000\pi\sigma^2}{DNkTC_{i2}} + K_s \tag{1.65}$$

For a surface active agent which has two ionic groups

$$\ln C = -\frac{m\omega}{kT} + 2K_g \ln \frac{2000\pi\sigma^2}{DNkTC_i} + \text{const} \tag{1.66}$$

These relations very successfully explain the experimental results described in Eqs. (1.55), (1.56), and (1.57).

It is expected from Eqs. (1.44) and (1.65) that the logarithm of the CMC should be a linear function of the logarithm of the concentration of gegenions in both types of surface active agents. If the constant K_g is the same for surface active agents whose neutralizing ion is uni- or bivalent, then the slope of the ln CMC vs. ln C_i line is one-half in the latter. Equations (1.58)–(1.64) can be tested with the experimental data obtained by Lange (253). It has been found that the slope of the plot of ln CMC vs. ln C_i is a linear function; the slope is $0.503 = K_g$ for sodium dodecyl sulfate and $0.286 = K_g/2$ for calcium dodecyl sulfate. Substituting CMC's and $K_g = 0.54$ (as the average for sodium and calcium dodecyl sulfate) into Eq. (1.44) and (1.65), we obtain at $T = 343°K$

$$\frac{2000\pi\sigma^2}{DNkT} = 0.654$$

Introducing Eqs. (1.58)–(1.64) into Eq. (1.41) and substituting the above values in it, a comparison between the theoretical and the experimental CMC values as a function of the concentration and the number of charges of gegenions was obtained. The results are shown in Fig. 1.16.
It is apparent from Fig. 1.16 that the calculated CMC values show excellent agreement with the experimental results, using experimental CMC values with no salt added and K_g values. In the case of dodecylpyridinium chloride the agreement is not so satisfactory.

The CMC of a mixture of sodium and calcium dodecyl sulfate can be understood as the effect of the number of charges of gegenions and

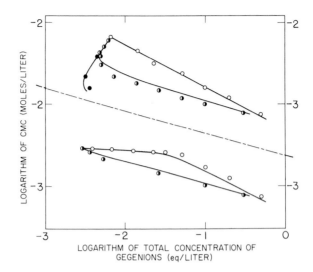

Fig. 1.16. The effect of added NaCl (○), CaCl₂ (◐), and AlCl₃ (●) on the CMC of sodium or calcium dodecyl sulfates at 70°C.

calculated from Eqs. (1.60) and (1.41). In this case, however, the sum of the equivalent concentrations of sodium and calcium ions is equal to the CMC, i.e., $C_{i1} + 2C_{i2} = CMC$. The results of a comparison between the experimental (253) and the calculated CMC (206) values are summarized in Table 1.18.

TABLE 1.18

COMPARISON BETWEEN OBSERVED AND CALCULATED CMC VALUES OF MIXTURES
OF SODIUM AND CALCIUM DODECYL SULFATE AT 70°C

Mole fraction of $R_{12}SO_4(\frac{1}{2}Ca)$	Observed CMC (moles/liter)	Calculated CMC (moles/liter)
0	0.0066	0.0067
0.02	0.0057	0.0056
0.05	0.0053	0.0050
0.1	0.0049	0.0046
0.25	0.0040	0.0037
0.5	0.0034	0.0033
0.75	0.0031	0.0031
1	0.0029	0.0029

The variation of the electrical potential as a function of the concentration and valence of gegenions, expressed in Eqs. (1.58)–(1.64), explains the Schulze-Hardy rule semiquantitatively (206).

The addition of salts to solutions of nonionic agents has a relatively small effect. The effect is not electrical and is probably rather indirect. The volume of salts added, including water of hydration, may change the effective concentration of agents so that the CMC decreases. Sodium chloride has a larger effect than calcium chloride (4). The results are shown in Table 1.19.

TABLE 1.19

EFFECT OF ADDED SALTS ON CMC OF OCTYL GLUCOSIDE AS DETERMINED BY
SURFACE TENSION MEASUREMENTS AT 25°C

Substance	Medium	CMC (moles/liter)
Octyl β-D-glucoside	H₂O	0.025
Octyl β-D-glucoside	0.93 N CaCl₂	0.017
Octyl β-D-glucoside	0.47 N NaCl	0.017
Octyl β-D-glucoside	0.93 N NaCl	0.012
Octyl β-D-glucoside	0.93 N Na₂SO₄	0.009

2. *The Critical Micelle Concentration in Mixtures of Surface Active Agents*

The study of the critical micelle concentrations of detergent mixtures

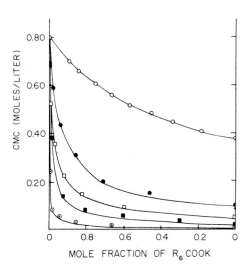

Fig. 1.17. The CMC of soap mixtures at 25°C: ○, potassium heptanoate + potassium octanoate; ●, potassium heptanoate + potassium decanoate; □, potassium heptanoate + potassium undecanoate; ■, potassium heptanoate + potassium dodecanoate; ⊙, potassium heptanoate + potassium tetradecanoate.

(*44, 263-265*) is an interesting subject to clarify our understanding of micelle formation and preferential micelle-forming tendency, on the one hand, and very useful for practical purposes, on the other hand, because commercial surface active agents almost always contain some higher or lower homologs as an impurity.

a. Binary Detergent Mixtures

Data are shown in Figs. 1.17 and 1.18. It is seen in all cases that

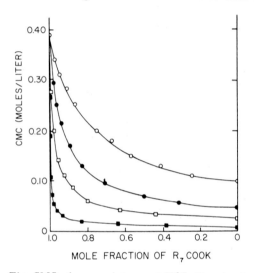

Fig. 1.18. The CMC of soap mixtures at 25°C: ○, potassium octanoate + potassium decanoate; ●, potassium octanoate + potassium undecanoate; □, potassium octanoate + potassium dodecanoate; ■, potassium octanoate + potassium tetradecanoate.

there are no CMC values which do not fall within the range of the pure surface active agents. It can also be seen from Figs. 1.17 and 1.18 that the curves of the CMC of detergent mixtures vs. mole fraction are quite similar when the difference in the number of carbon atoms between the component detergents is the same. The larger the difference in CMC, i.e., in the number of carbon atoms between the component detergents, the greater the change in the CMC of the shorter chain detergent by the addition of the same mole fraction of a longer chain detergent. As the curves seem provisionally to show a great departure from ideal mixing, it was once thought that the mixing of even homologous detergents is nonideal. This departure is explained as follows. The partial vapor pressures of liquids are proportional to their respective mole fractions in ideal solution, and the total vapor pressure changes linearly from one value to the other, provided the vapor pressure is plotted on a mole fraction basis for the condensed phase. However, the stoichiometric concentration or mole fraction in aqueous solutions of detergent mixtures corresponds to the vapor pressure or mole fraction in the vapor phase of the ideal solution because most of the detergents are in a singly dispersed state at the CMC. The single species are in equilibrium with micelles whose composition is quite different, because of selective aggregation, from that in the bulk of the solution; that is, the mole fraction in the plot of a detergent mixture is not the mole fraction of the micelles but that of the dispersed molecules (34).

All phenomena relating to the CMC of mixtures of surface active agents have been explained inclusively by a theory for all mole fraction ranges by Lange (263) and by Shinoda (44, 178) as follows. The CMC's of paraffin chain salts are given as a function of the number of carbon atoms in the paraffin chain m and of the concentration of gegenions in gram equivalents per liter C_i

$$\ln C = -\frac{m\omega}{kT} - K_g \ln C_i + K_1 \tag{1.44}$$

If no salt is added, C_i is equal to the CMC

$$\ln C = -\frac{m\omega}{(1 + K_g)kT} + K_0 \tag{1.45}$$

Consider a mixed micelle of two soaps. If we denote the number of carbon atoms in the respective soaps by m_1 and m_2 and the mole fractions of the soaps by x and $(1-x)$, respectively, the concentrations of these soaps in the bulk of the solution in equilibrium with the mixed micelle are given by Eq. (1.44), assuming an ideal mixing of the homologous soaps in the micelle (where the term ideal mixing implies the athermal mixing of two kinds of molecules sufficiently similar in size and shape).

$$\ln C_{m1,x,c_{mix}} = -\frac{m_1\omega}{kT} - K_g \ln C_{mix} + \ln x + K_1 \tag{1.67}$$

and

$$\ln C_{m2,(1-x),c_{mix}} = -\frac{m_2\omega}{kT} - K_g \ln C_{mix} + \ln(1-x) + K_1 \tag{1.68}$$

From Eqs. (1.44), (1.45), and (1.67), we obtain

$$\ln C_{m1,x,c_{mix}} = (1 + K_g) \ln C_{m1} - K_g \ln C_{mix} + \ln x \tag{1.69}$$

Similarly, from Eqs. (1.44), (1.45), and (1.68), we obtain

$$\ln C_{m2,(1-x),c_{mix}} = (1 + K_g) \ln C_{m2} - K_g \ln C_{mix} + \ln(1 - x) \tag{1.70}$$

Evidently, the CMC of a soap mixture is given by the summation of the concentration of the respective soaps

$$C_{m1,x,c_{mix}} + C_{m2,(1-x),c_{mix}} = C_{mix} \tag{1.71}$$

Introducing Eqs. (1.69) and (1.70) into (1.71), we obtain

$$C_{m_1}^{1+K_g}x + C_{m_2}^{1+K_g}(1-x) = C_{mix}^{1+K_g} \tag{1.72}$$

This equation expresses the CMC of a two-component soap mixture. From this Eq. (1.72), it is evident that there are no CMC values which do not fall within the range of the pure soaps.

From Eqs. (1.67) and (1.68), the ratio of the concentrations of soaps present as single species is,

$$\frac{C_{m2,x,c_{mix}}}{C_{m2,(1-x),c_{mix}}} = \frac{x}{1-x} \exp \frac{(m_2 - m_1)\omega}{kT} \tag{1.73}$$

If we assume that the mole fractions of composite soaps in the single species form are x' and $(1-x')$, we obtain

$$\frac{x'}{1-x'} = \frac{x}{1-x} \exp \frac{(m_2 - m_1)\omega}{kT} \tag{1.74}$$

Introducing the relation (1.74) into (1.72), we derive

$$C_{m1}^{1+K_g} \frac{x'}{x' + (1-x')\exp\left[(m_2 - m_1)\omega/kT\right]}$$
$$+ C_{m2}^{1+K_g} \frac{(1-x')\exp\left[(m_2 - m_1)\omega/kT\right]}{x' + (1-x')\exp\left[(m_2 - m_1)\omega/kT\right]} = C_{mix}^{1+K_g} \tag{1.75}$$

This equation (1.75) expresses the CMC of the two-component soap mixture in terms of the mole fractions of the soaps present as single species. As the majority of the soap molecules are in the form of single species, and as there are few micelles at the CMC, Eq. (1.75) also expresses the CMC of soap mixtures in terms of the mole fraction of the total mixed soaps (the sum of the concentration of soap in the micellar state and in the singly dispersed state).

Introducing $K_g = 0.56$, $\omega = 1.08 \ kT$, and the values of the CMC's of the component soaps, the CMC's of two-component soap mixtures may be calculated. The observed values and the calculated lines are plotted in Figs. 1.17 and 1.18. Experimental results are in good agreement with calculated values. Some difference between the theoretical values and the experimental results was observed when there is a large difference in the chain length of mixed detergents. This small difference can be explained by secondary effects, such as (i) the incomplete penetration of longer chain molecules into the palisade layer of micelle of shorter chain molecules, and (ii) small changes in mole fraction in the bulk due to the preferential aggregation of longer chain ions at the CMC. The earlier observation that, if the CMC's of two paraffin chain salts are quite different, than the paraffin chain salt with the higher CMC value tends to act as a salt toward the other paraffin chain salt (*264*), is also clearly understandable from the theory; that is, the very small tendency of a shorter chain salt to micellize does not much affect the CMC of the longer chain compound, and exerts mainly a gegenion effect in depressing the electrical potential on the micelle surface and therefore the CMC.

b. Ternary Detergent Mixture

The CMC's of ternary soap mixtures have been measured for various combinations of soap mixtures (*178*). One of these is illustrated in Fig. 1.19. In all the cases studied, the CMC of the soap mixture lies between

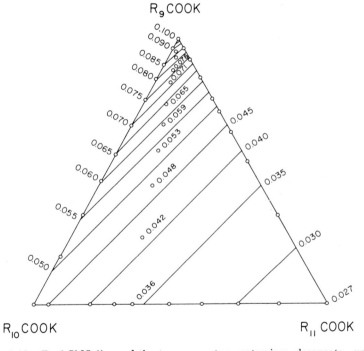

Fig. 1.19. Equi-CMC lines of the ternary system potassium decanoate, undecanoate, and dodecanoate at 25°C.

the highest and lowest CMC value of the individual surface active agents. When the differences in the number of carbon atoms of the mixed soaps are the same, the ratio of the CMC's at the same composition is constant over all mole fraction ranges for the respective ternary mixtures.

Extension of the treatment of binary soap mixtures gives the following equation for the CMC of a multicomponent soap mixture

$$\sum C_{m_i}^{1+K_g} \cdot x_i = C_{\text{mix}}^{1+K_g} \tag{1.76}$$

and

$$\sum C_{m_i}^{1+K_g} \frac{x_i' \exp(m_i\omega/kT)}{\sum x_i' \exp(m_i\omega/kT)} = C_{\text{mix}}^{1+K_g} \tag{1.77}$$

Where x and x' are the mole fractions of mixed soaps in the micelle and in the bulk of the solution, respectively; and C_{m_i} is the CMC of pure surface active agent whose carbon number is m_i. Equations (1.76) and (1.77) explain satisfactorily all the experimental results. It has been also verified theoretically that the equi-CMC plot is linear and therefore can be calculated from the CMC values of binary mixtures (178).

c. *Mixtures of Nonionic Agents*

The CMC of mixtures of nonionic agents have also been investigated (4, 266). The results are summarized in Table 1.20. As there is no

TABLE 1.20

CMC OF MIXTURES OF NONIONIC SURFACE ACTIVE AGENTS

Compound	Mole fraction of latter compound	CMC (moles/liter)	CMC (Calculated)
Octyl glucoside-decyl glucoside	0.089	0.0125	0.013
Octyl glucoside-dodecyl glucoside	0.0084	0.015	0.012
$C_9H_{19}COO(CH_2CH_2O)_{11.9}CH_3$- $C_{11}H_{23}COO(CH_2CH_2O)_{12.5}CH_3$	0.1	0.00034	(0.00034)
$C_9H_{19}COO(CH_2CH_2O)_{11.9}CH_3$- $C_{11}H_{23}COO(CH_2CH_2O)_{12.5}CH_3$	0.7	0.00038	0.00044
$C_9H_{19}COO(CH_2CH_2O)_{11.9}CH_3$- $C_{11}H_{23}COO(CH_2CH_2O)_{12.5}CH_3$	0.6	0.00044	0.00049
$C_9H_{19}COO(CH_2CH_2O)_{11.9}CH_3$- $C_{11}H_{23}COO(CH_2CH_2O)_{12.5}CH_3$	0.4	0.00054	0.00062
$C_9H_{19}COO(CH_2CH_2O)_{11.9}CH_3$- $C_{11}H_{23}COO(CH_2CH_2O)_{12.5}CH_3$	0.3	0.00070	0.00072
$C_9H_{19}COO(CH_2CH_2O)_{11.9}CH_3$- $C_{11}H_{23}COO(CH_2CH_2O)_{12.5}CH_3$	0.22	0.00085	0.00077
$C_9H_{19}COO(CH_2CH_2O)_{11.9}CH_3$- $C_{11}H_{23}COO(CH_2CH_2O)_{12.5}CH_3$	0.1	0.0011	0.00107
$C_9H_{19}COO(CH_2CH_2O)_{11.9}CH_3$- $C_{11}H_{23}COO(CH_2CH_2O)_{12.5}CH_3$	0.00	0.0014	(0.0014)

electrical energy involved in micellization the theoretical treatment is far simpler, and the CMC is given as a function of the mole composition of the mixture.

$$\sum C_{m_i} \cdot x_i = C_{\text{mix}} \tag{1.78}$$

$$\sum C_{m_i} \frac{x' \exp{(m_i \omega / kT)}}{\sum x'_i \exp{(m_i \omega / kT)}} = C_{\text{mix}} = \sum C_{m_i} \frac{x'_i C_{m_i}}{\sum x'_i C_{m_i}} \tag{1.79}$$

3. The Effect of Added Higher Alcohols

The physicochemical properties, such as surface tension (267), CMC, foaminess (268), foam stability (229), and solubilization of hydrocarbon (170, 269), change considerably in the presence of a very small amount of paraffin chain alcohols. We also find very often that the addition of longchain alcohols modifies the properties of emulsion polymers. Most of the surface active agents synthesized from longchain alcohols, such as sodium alkyl sulfates and sulfonates, contain some unreacted alcohol. Hence, the CMC change due to added alcohols is very important both academically and industrially to elucidate the phenomena. Remarkable changes in many properties due to the addition of very small amounts of alcohol result at least partly from its high selective adsorptivity at the surface and in the micelle.

There are several papers on the effect of alcohols on the CMC (14, 229, 257, 270-276). The CMC of a series of fatty acid soaps in the presence of a series of alcohols, which permits a determination of the effect of the chain length of either component, has been determined (178). The effect of alcohols on the CMC of potassium dodecanoate is shown in Figs. 1.20, 1.21, 1.22. The logarithm of the rate of change of

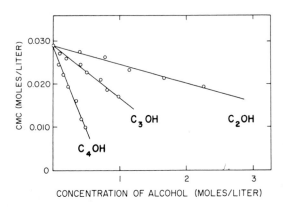

Fig. 1.20. The effect of ethanol, propanol, and butanol on the CMC of potassium dodecanoate at 10°C.

CMC with alcohol concentration $\log_{10}(-dC/dC_a)$ vs. the number of carbon atoms in the alcohol is shown in Fig. 1.23. The relation between $\log_{10}(-dC/dC_a)$ and the number of carbon atoms in the hydrocarbon chain

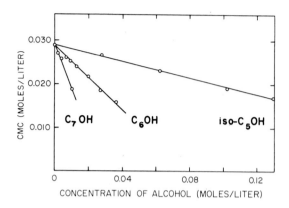

Fig. 1.21. The effect of isopentanol, hexanol, and heptanol on the CMC of potassium dodecanoate at 10°C.

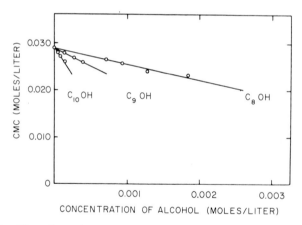

Fig. 1.22. The effect of octanol, nonanol, and decanol on the CMC of potassium dodecanoate at 10°C.

of surface active agent is shown in Fig. 1.24.

It has been found that (*a*) the initial rate of change of CMC with alcohol concentration is constant, i.e., the CMC initially decreases linearly with alcohol concentration; (*b*) the logarithm of the rate of change of CMC with alcohol concentration is a linear function of the number of carbon atoms in the alcohol molecule; and (*c*) the logarithm of the rate of change of CMC with the concentration of a given alcohol is a linear function of the number of carbon atoms in the hydrocarbon chain of the surface active agent. The data fit the equation (*178, 276*)

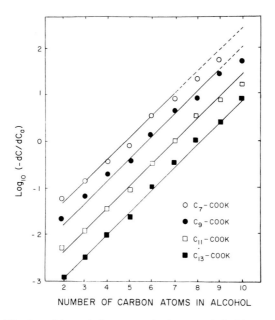

Fig. 1.23. The logarithm of the rate of change of CMC with alcohol concentration [$\log_{10}(-dC/dC_a)$] vs. the number of carbon atoms in the alcohol.

TABLE 1.21

RATE OF CHANGE OF CMC WITH CONCENTRATION OF ALCOHOL
($-dC/dC_a$) FOR VARIOUS ALCOHOLS AND SURFACE
ACTIVE AGENTS

Alcohol	$-dC/dC_a$ when agent is					
	R_5COOK (10°C)	R_7COOK (10°C)	R_9COOK (10°C)	$R_{11}COOK$ (10°C)	$R_{13}COOK$ (18°C)	$R_{12}NH_3Cl$ (25°C)
R_2OH	0.19^a	0.057	0.020	0.0048	0.0010	0.0015^b
R_3OH	0.45^a	0.14	0.065	0.012	0.0032	0.0062^b
R_4OH	1.5^a	0.38	0.19	0.038	0.0098	0.019^b
R_5OH	3.5^a	1.2^a	0.43	0.11^a	0.033^a	—
R_6OH	9.0^a	3.6	1.3	0.37	0.098	0.21^b
R_7OH	—	8.3	4.4	1.0	0.32	0.62^b
R_8OH	—	23	8.3	3.5	1.0	—
R_9OH	—	57	29	8.1	2.6	—
$R_{10}OH$	—	112	55	18	8.1	20.2^b
$R_{11}OH$	—	—	—	—	—	44.5^b

[a] From reference 276.
[b] From reference 273; all the other values are from reference 178.

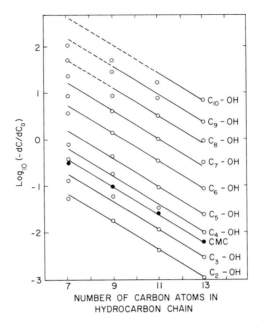

Fig. 1.24. The logarithmic relationship between the rate of change of CMC with alcohol concentration [$\log_{10}(-dC/dC_a)$] vs. the number of carbon atoms in the paraffin chain of soap.

$$\ln(-dC/dC_a) = -0.69\,m + 1.1\,m' + \text{const} \qquad (1.80)$$

where m and m' are the number of carbon atoms in the hydrocarbon chain of the paraffin chain salts and alcohols, respectively. The deviation of $-dC/dC_a$ from the logarithmic relationship for the longer chain alcohols mixed with the shorter chain soaps, as can be seen in Fig. 1.23, indicates incompleteness or difficulty in the penetration of the hydrocarbon chain of the alcohol molecules into the interior of the micelle. The values of $-dC/dC_a$ for various alcohols and surface active agents are summarized in Table 1.21.

It is known that alcohol molecules penetrate the oriented structure of the micelle (8, 277), forming a mixed micelle. An attempt was made to explain the effect of alcohols on the CMC in terms of the decrease of charge density on the micelle surface and the increase in entropy of mixing due to the penetration of alcohol molecule (178). The addition of salt likewise depresses the CMC, but the decrease results mainly from the decreased electrical energy per micelle-forming ion.

The relationship between the CMC and the surface charge density on the micelle has already been given by Eq. (1.42) as follows:

$$\ln C = K_g(\ln \sigma^2 - \ln C_i) + K_6$$

where σ is the surface charge density; and C_i is the concentration of gegenions in gram equivalents per liter and is equal to the CMC in the case when no salt is added.

Let the mole fractions of alcohol and surface active agent in the mixed micelle be x and $(1 - x)$, respectively; then the CMC of this mixed micelle is

$$\ln C' = K_g[\ln (1 - x)^2 \sigma^2 - \ln C_i'] + \ln (1 - x) + K_6 \tag{1.81}$$

The differences between Eqs. (1.42) and (1.81) reside in the change in surface charge density from σ to $(1 - x)\sigma$ and in the addition of the mixing term.

Substituting $C_i = \text{CMC}$, $C_i' = \text{CMC}'$, and $K_g = 0.56$ in Eqs. (1.42) and (1.81), we obtain

$$\ln C' = \ln C + 1.36 \ln (1 - x) \tag{1.82}$$

$$C' = C(1 - 1.36x) \qquad x \ll 1 \tag{1.83}$$

On the other hand, if the energy decrease in the hydrocarbon portion of the alcohol molecule in passing from the aqueous environment into the micelle is proportional to the number of carbon atoms in the alcohol, the following expression of the law of partition may be applied:

$$C_a/x = K_7 \exp(-m'\omega/kT); \qquad C_a \ll 1 \tag{1.84}$$

where K_7 is a constant and ω is the surface energy per methylene group passing from the aqueous phase into the interior of the micelle. Since there are few micelles at the CMC, the fall in alcohol concentration in the aqueous phase due to the penetration of alcohol molecules into the micelle is negligible.

Substituting Eq. (1.84) into (1.83), we obtain

$$C' = C\left(1 - K_8 C_a \exp \frac{m'\omega}{kT}\right) \tag{1.85}$$

From Eq. (1.85), we derive

$$\frac{C - C'}{C_a} = K_8 C \exp \frac{m'\omega}{kT} \tag{1.86}$$

or

$$\ln \frac{C - C'}{C_a} = \ln C + \frac{m'\omega}{kT} + \text{const} \tag{1.87}$$

or, substituting Eq. (1.45) for $\ln C$,

$$\ln \frac{C - C'}{C_a} = -\frac{m\omega}{(1 + K_g)kT} + \frac{m'\omega}{kT} + \text{const} \tag{1.88}$$

Equation (1.88) corresponds to Eq. (1.80). Comparing these equations, the free energy change per methylene group in passing from the aqueous phase into the hydrocarbon environment can be estimated both from the first term and from the second term of Eq. (1.88). The agreement in both terms is excellent, and ω is about 1.08 kT per molecule or 620 cal/mole of methylene groups at 10°C.

The CMC of dodecylammonium chloride in the presence of hexanol (or decanol) and salt (KCl) was measured by Herzfeld et al. (273) and is plotted as a function of alcohol concentration at constant salt concentration in Fig. 1.25. Extension of the theory dealing with the

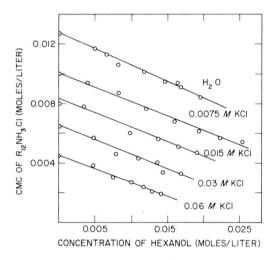

Fig. 1.25. The CMC of dodecylammonium chloride in the presence of hexanol and potassium chloride.

effect of alcohol can also explain these results; C'_s in Eqs. (1.81) and (1.42) is now not equal to the CMC but to the total concentration of gegenions in this case.

4. *The Effect of Added Hydrocarbons*

Hydrocarbons such as benzene or heptane are solubilized in the interior of the micelle (75, 278). Solubilized hydrocarbon increases the micelle size and slightly changes the curvature of the micelle surface and the dimensions of the micelle. This change in curvature may slightly decrease the electrical potential and therefore the electrical work for micellization per micelle-forming ion. The surface free energy decrease in the hydrocarbon chain of the surface active agent on micellization may also slightly increase due to the presence of solubilized hydrocarbon in the interior of micelle. These two factors both tend to decrease the CMC, and about 5–30% decrease in CMC is observed. The effect is far smaller compared to that of salts, longer chain homologs, and alcohols (*279*).

Hutchinson *et al.* (*14*) have measured the effect of cyclohexane, *n*-heptane, and toluene on the CMC of dodecylammonium chloride by electrical conductivity. Lin (*32*) has measured the effect of benzene on the CMC of potassium dodecylsulfonate by the electrical conductivity method. Results are given in Table 1.22. Klevens has measured that

TABLE 1.22

EFFECT OF ADDED HYDROCARBONS ON CMC OF DODECYLAMMONIUM CHLORIDE

Hydrocarbon	Concentration of Hydrocarbon (moles/liter)	CMC (moles/liter)	Decrease in CMC (%)
Cyclohexane	0	0.0145	—
Cyclohexane	0.00154	0.0134	8
Cyclohexane	0.0025	0.0130	10
Cyclohexane	0.00416	0.0120	17
n-Heptane	0.00087	0.0134	8
n-Heptane	0.00212	0.0131	10
n-Heptane	0.00272	0.0128	12
Toluene	0.00078	0.0140	3
Toluene	0.00219	0.0135	7
Toluene	0.00296	0.0131	10

of benzene on various potassium carboxylates and sodium alkyl sulfonates by dye titration (*280*). The results are given in Table 1.23.

TABLE 1.23

EFFECT OF ADDED BENZENE ON THE CMC OF IONIC AGENTS AS DETERMINED BY DYE TITRATION

Compound	CMC (No benzene added)	CMC (Benzene added)	Decrease in CMC (%)
R_7COOK	0.395	0.384	(3)
R_9COOK	0.100	0.093	7
$R_{11}COOK$	0.024	0.020	13
$R_{13}COOK$	0.0063	0.0051	19
$R_{10}SO_3Na$	0.038	0.034	10
$R_{12}SO_3Na$	0.0092(33.5°C)	0.0075	19
$R_{14}SO_3Na$	0.0025(42.5°C)	0.0018	28

The effect of the presence of benzene, cyclohexane, hexane, octane, dodecane, heptadecane, octadecane, hexanol, octanol, dodecanol, octad-ecanol, undecyl chloride, stearonitrile, and stearamide upon the equiva-lent conductivity of aqueous solutions of dodecylammonium chloride has also been determined (281). With the exception of heptadecane and octadecane (no effect), all the compounds investigated lowered the equivalent conductivity and the CMC in the amine salt solutions. The changes in CMC are not quantitatively given in this paper.

5. *The Effect of pH*

It has been reported from surface tension and conductivity studies that there is essentially little or no difference in the CMC of the alkyl sulfates with changes in pH (26, 282, 283). It has been observed that the effects of potassium hydroxide or potassium chloride on the CMC of fatty acid soaps are almost identical. It is also found that the production of an acid soap, for example, by the addition of excess fatty acid or by decrease in pH by the addition of an inorganic acid, will result in a marked decrease in CMC and in enhancement of solubilizing power.

It has been shown that the CMC of the perfluorohexanoic acid is about one-tenth of the corresponding value for the potassium salt (245) Similar but smaller differences have also been reported by Arrington and Patterson (244) for ω-hydroperfluoroalkanoic acid and its ammonium salt. Some of the results were shown in Table 1.13.

Klevens and Raison (245) have measured the effect of pH on the CMC of perfluorohexanoic acid for various mole fractions of acid in mixtures of the acid and its salt. A marked change in CMC with pH

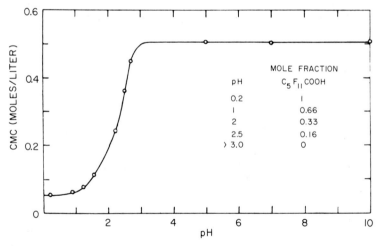

Fig. 1.26. The effect of *pH* on the CMC of perfluorohexanoic acid.

was observed in the case of perfluorohexanoic acid, as can be seen in Fig. 1.26. There was little or no decrease in CMC as the pH was decreased by the addition of hydrogen chloride below that of the pure acid. Even though no definite control of ionic strength was made in these perfluorohexanoic solutions, there appears to be little or no effect of added salt in the region of pH 3. In definite contrast to the decreases observed in CMC with added electrolyte in paraffin chain salt solutions, no such decrease was observed in perfluorohexanoic acid potassium chloride solutions. The apparent constancy of CMC with increase in ionic strength above pH 3, as seen in Fig. 1.26, is in accord with these previous findings. At higher concentrations of alkali, there is a slight diminution of the surface tension as well as a decrease in the CMC. All the alkali above equimolarity present in these systems tends to act like a simple electrolyte, depressing the CMC of the salt. It has been found that, with decrease in the chain length of the surfactant, much higher concentrations of added electrolyte are necessary to produce a decrease in CMC. The various CMC values of the respective paraffin chain acid and salt, or base and salt, are collected in Tables 1.13 and 1.24.

TABLE 1.24

CMC of Various Paraffin Chain Salts and Their
Respective Acids or Bases (245)

Compound	CMC (moles/liter)	Compound	CMC (moles/liter)
R_3COOH	1.1—1.2	R_3COONa	∼3.5
R_5COOH	0.1	R_5COOK	1.5—1.6
R_7COOH	∼0.008	R_7COOK	0.39
4-Hexylresorcinol	0.004	Potassium 4-hexylresorcinol	0.038
$R_{12}SO_4H$	0.0062	$R_{12}SO_4Na$	0.0081
$R_{12}SO_3H$	0.009	$R_{12}SO_3Na$	0.011
R_6NH_2	∼0.04	R_6NH_3Cl	0.9

Alkali above equimolarity of the acid may act like a simple electrolyte, changing the electrical potential of the micelle surface, and this potential is a function of the concentration of gegenions but not of pH. Below equimolarity, the CMC usually decreases remarkably because the dissociation of acid is much smaller than that of the salt, and if the micelle consists mostly of undissociated molecules the effect of the presence of salt may be small; and this agrees with observation. For a very strong acid, such as alkyl sulfonic or sulfuric acid, the CMC will be close to that of the salts, and the effect of added salt will be similar over wide pH ranges. It follows that the contribution of the electrical repulsion to association should be about equivalent in both acid and salt solutions. This would result in essentially equivalent CMC values for both paraffin chain acids and salts of the same lengths, which is essentially what has been observed for these longer chain strong acids and salts.

However, there is every indication from conductivity measurements that both the perfluoro acids and their salts are also completely ionized in dilute solutions (245). Yet the differences between the CMC values of these two systems are at least tenfold in the case of the C_6 compound. Probably, the micelles of perfluoro acids are incompletely dissociated.

6. *The Effect of Added Dioxane, Glycol, Methanol, etc.*

The effect of added dioxane, glycol, methanol, etc. on the CMC, reported by Harkins *et al.* (284) is shown in Fig. 1.27. As stated earlier,

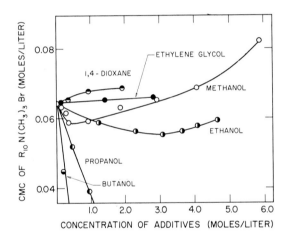

Fig. 1.27. The effect of added dioxane, glycol, methanol, etc. on the CMC of decyltrimethylammonium bromide.

long chain alcohols penetrate into the palisade layer of the micelle and depress the CMC. But in the case of dioxane, glycol, and methanol, these liquids are too soluble in water and only a few molecule may penetrate into the micelle due to the partition equilibrium. The effects of the addition of these soluble nonelectrolytes are accordingly very small. Only large amounts of these substances can change the properties associated with the environment of a micelle, e.g., the solvent property of the medium: in this regard, (i) the free energy required to bring the hydrocarbon chain of the micelle-forming ion into solution may decrease and the CMC tend to increase, and (ii) the dielectric constant of the medium may decrease slightly, which also tends to decrease the CMC. However, both these effects may be very small compared with the effects of higher alcohol or salt, which decrease the charge density or electrical potential on the micelle surface. Similar changes in nonelectrical free energy and electrical energy on aggregation, equivalent to a change of environment of the micelle, occur when the temperature of the solution is changed. The effect of temperature on the CMC (285), was summarized in Table 1.4.

VII. Surface Activity

One of the most fundamental and important physical constants for the elucidation of the various phenomena of surface active agents is the CMC because the following can all be estimated from the CMC values: (i) the change in thermodynamic functions at the micellization point; (ii) the surface tension vs. concentration curve; (iii) the partition equilibrium of surface active agent between the bulk and the surface; and (iv) the effect of additives on the surface activity of agents and additives. All of these properties are closely related to each other by a single concept, surface activity. Though differences between the lowest values of the surface tension or between the cross-sectional areas of the molecules affect the surface activity, this quantity is, to a first approximation, inversely proportional to the CMC.

TABLE 1.25

SELECTIVE ADSORPTIVITY[a] OF COMPOUND 1 AGAINST COMPOUND 2

	Compound 1					
	$R_{10}COOK$			$R_{13}COOK$		
Compound 2	(1)	(2)	(3)	(1)	(2)	(3)
R_7COOK	28	27	—	850	730	—
R_9COOK	3.1	3	—	80	81	—
$R_{11}COOK$	—	—	—	9	9	—
	$R_{15}COOK$			$R_{12}C_6H_4SO_3Na$		
	(1)	(2)	(3)	(1)	(2)	(3)
$R_{11}COOK$	55	50—60	50—70	—	140	180—280
$R_{13}COOK$	6	6—7	5—8	—	16	(5—6)
$R_{12}SO_4N_a$	—	8	8—9	—	25	35—50

[a] In columns (1) are listed relative adsorptivities obtained from measurements of the CMC of mixtures. In columns (2) are listed the selective adsorptivities calculated from CMC ratios. In columns (3) are listed selective adsorptivities determined directly. (See Section VII.)

For practical purposes, the determination of the relative activity (adsorptivity) is very important, in order to analyze the action of a mixture of surface active agents and to clarify the effect of highly surface active impurities. Recently, selective adsorptivity has been determined directly for several pairs of detergents by radiotracer technique (243) and is listed in the third column for each substance given in Table 1.25.

We can also estimate the selective adsorptivity of agents from the measurements of the CMC of detergent mixtures or from the effect of additives on the CMC.

The change of CMC' of one agent as a function of initial concentration of added agent is expressed as follows:

$$CMC' = CMC^\circ - KC'' \tag{1.89}$$

where CMC° is the CMC in the pure state, and C'' the concentration of added agent. Then, K is the relative micelle-forming ability of added agent against the initial agent. If $K = 1$, $CMC' + C'' = CMC_{mix} = CMC^\circ$. From measurements of the CMC of mixtures of surface active agents at a definite concentration of gegenions, we have obtained the relative adsorptivity listed in the first column for each substance in Table 1.25.

From the ratio of the CMC at the given concentration of gegenions, we have also estimated the selective adsorptivity (listed in the second column for each substance in Table 1.25). From the good agreement we can conclude that the selective adsorptivity can be estimated from the ratio of the CMC at the same concentration of gegenions.

Selective adsorptivity of surface active agents and paraffin chain alcohols can be similarly treated; that is, we can either estimate it from experiments on the effect of alcohol on the CMC or from the ratio of the CMC of the agent and the solubility of the alcohol. The direct determination of selective adsorptivity of alcohol against various agents and among gegenions of different valence by radiotracer technique (285a) is now being carried out.

VIII.   The Formation of Micelles in Nonaqueous Solution

In this section the author has attempted to discuss the formation of micelles in nonaqueous solution in comparison with that in aqueous solution. Reviews (286) and original papers should be consulted for a detailed description.

Nonaqueous solvents in this section mean hydrocarbons or solvents whose solvent properties are similar to those of hydrocarbons: the term does not include some solvents whose dielectric constants are large or whose solvent properties are mainly hydrophilic. Most of the nonaqueous solvents investigated have been hydrocarbons or chlorohydrocarbons. Although the formation of aggregates in nonaqueous solutions of surface active agents was early recognized (287–291), it is only within the past 15 years that much information has become available concerning the CMC and the size of micelles in nonaqueous solvents (50, 57, 60, 61, 292–295).

1. *Factors for Micelle Formation*

In the micelles formed in hydrocarbons the polar portions of the amphipathic molecule are buried in the central core. The orientation of the micelle-forming molecule is just reversed from that in water. As the dielectric constants of ordinary nonaqueous solvents are not large, ionic agents do not dissociate in the medium. Some molecules may be ionic but will not be dissociated. Moreover, the micelle does not carry ions comparable with those of micelles in aqueous solution. The driving force for the formation of an aggregate comes from the strong attraction of the polar groups, either as a generalized dipole attraction, by hydrogen bonds, or by the formation of specific coordination bonding, together with some segregation of the oleophilic portion of the molecule with solvents. The entropy of mixing will be the main factor which tends to disperse molecules. The forces governing the formation of micelles are quite different in nonaqueous solution from those in aqueous solution. The length of the hydrocarbon chain does not affect the CMC so much in hydrocarbon media (62). As the intermolecular forces of agents are in many cases larger than those of solvent molecules, surface activity is almost absent in hydrocarbon media. Only fluorocarbon compounds and some silicone compounds, whose intermolecular forces are smaller than those of hydrocarbons, show surface activity.

In aqueous solution the added hydrocarbon exerts only a small effect on the CMC because hydrocarbons solubilized in the interior of a micelle do not change the heat of micellization appreciably. But the strong interaction between ion pairs seems to be a driving force for the aggregation of molecules in nonaqueous solvents, and the water solubilized in the center core of the micelle will change the dielectric constant in the core and affect the CMC and the size of the micelle. Though the purity of the sample is always important, small amounts of higher homologs may not affect the results as much as in the case of aqueous solutions because impurities which were highly surface active in aqueous solution are no longer highly surface active in nonaqueous solvents. However, small amounts of water or free fatty acid sometimes affect considerably the size, shape, and CMC of agents in nonaqueous solution (295–297).

2. *The Size and Shape of Micelles*

The presence and size of micelles may be detected by a wide range

TABLE 1.26

SIZE OF MICELLES IN NONAQUEOUS SOLVENTS

Compound	Solvent	Aggregation number	Method	Temperature °C	Reference
Na dinonyl-naphthalene-sulfonate	Benzene	10	Fluorescence depolarization	25	(302)
Li dinonyl-naphthalene-sulfonate	Benzene	10	Fluorescence depolarization	25	(302)
Cs dinonyl-naphthalene-sulfonate	Benzene	6	Cryoscopic method	5.4	(302)
$\frac{1}{2}$Mg dinonyl-naphthalene-sulfonate	Benzene	11	Fluorescence depolarization	25	(302)
$\frac{1}{2}$Ca dinonyl-naphthalene-sulfonate	Benzene	10	Fluorescence depolarization	25	(302)
$\frac{1}{2}$Ba dinonyl-naphthalene-sulfonate	Benzene	14	Fluorescence depolarization	25	(302)
$\frac{1}{2}$Zn dinonyl-naphthalene-sulfonate	Benzene	7—10	Fluorescence depolarization	25	(302)
$\frac{1}{3}$Al dinonyl-naphthalene-sulfonate	Benzene	13	Fluorescence depolarization	25	(302)
NH_4 dinonyl-naphthalene-sulfonate	Benzene	9	Fluorescence depolarization	25	(302)
H dinonyl-naphthalene-sulfonate	Benzene	2	Cryoscopic method	5.4	(302)
$(iso\text{-}C_5H_{11})_4\text{-}NSCN$	Benzene	10—25	Cryoscopic method	5.4	(303)
$(n\text{-}C_{18}H_{37})(C_4H_9)_3\text{-}NOCOH$	Benzene	10—22	Cryoscopic method	5.4	(303)
$(n\text{-}C_5H_{11})C_4H_9)_3\text{-}NI$	Benzene	3—22	Cryoscopic method	5.4	(303)
$(n\text{-}C_4H_9)_4NClO_4$	Benzene	3—6	Cryoscopic method	5.4	(304)
Na 2-ethylhexyl sulfosuccinate	Dodecane	32	Ultracentrifuge	30	(301)
Na 2-ethylhexyl sulfosuccinate $H_2O(1:0.2wt)$	Dodecane	28	Ultracentrifuge	30	(301)
Na 2-ethylhexyl sulfosuccinate $H_2O(1:0.5wt)$	Dodecane	90	Ultracentrifuge	30	(301)
Na 2-ethylhexyl sulfosuccinate $H_2O(1:0.75wt)$	Dodecane	240	Ultracentrifuge	30	(301)

Compound	Solvent	Aggregation number	Method	Temperature °C	Reference
Na 2-ethylhexyl sulfosuccinate $H_2O(1:1wt)$	Dodecane	350	Ultracentrifuge	30	(301)
$C_{12}H_{25}NH_3$ oleate	Cyclohexane	5	Cryoscopic method	6.5	(305)
$C_{12}H_{25}NH_3$ propionate	Cyclohexane	10	Cryoscopic method	6.5	(305)
$C_{11}H_{23}COO$ $(CH_2CH_2O)_9H$	Cyclohexane +water	~4	Cryoscopic method	6.5	(306)
Hexanolamine oleate	Benzene	~3	Cryoscopic method	5.4	(306)
Hexanolamine caprylate	Benzene	~4	Cryoscopic method	5.4	(306)
$C_{12}H_{25}NH_2$-$HOCOC_7H_{15}$	CCl_4	3	V·p·depression	20	(133)
$C_{12}H_{25}NH_2$-$HOCOC_7H_{15}$	Cyclohexane	7	V·p·depression	20	(102)
$C_{12}H_{25}NH_2$-$HOCOC_7H_{15}$	Cyclohexane	4	V·p·depression	31	(102)
$C_{12}H_{25}NH_2$-$HOCOC_3H_7$	CCl_4	3	V·p·depression	20	(133)
$C_{12}H_{25}NH_2$-$HOCOC_3H_7$	Cyclohexane	9	V·p·depression	20	(102)
$C_{12}H_{25}NH_2$-$HOCOC_3H_7$	Cyclohexane	6	V·p·depression	31	(102)
$C_{12}H_{25}NH_2$-$HOCOC_6H_5$	Cyclohexane	10	V·p·depression	31	(102)
$C_{12}H_{25}NH_2$-$HOCOC_6H_5$	Cyclohexane	12	V·p·depression	20	(102)
Pb 2-ethylhexyl sebacate	Benzene	4	Fluorescence depolarization	26	(314)
$(R_7COO)_2Zn$	Toluene	~6.3	Ebullioscopic method	111	(308)
$(R_9COO)_2Zn$	Toluene	~5.4	Ebullioscopic method	111	(308)
$(R_{11}COO)_2Zn$	Toluene	~4.8	Ebullioscopic method	111	(308)
$(R_{11}COO)_2Mg$	Toluene	6—33	Ebullioscopic method	111	(308)
$(R_{11}COO)_2Cu$	Toluene	5—18	Ebullioscopic method	111	(308)
$(R_{11}COO)_3Fe$	Toluene	~2	Ebullioscopic method	111	(308)
$(R_{13}COO)_2Zn$	Toluene	~4.2	Ebullioscopic method	111	(308)
$(R_{17}COO)_2Zn$	Toluene	3.2,5.5	Ebullioscopic method	111	(308,299)
Li phenylstearate	Benzene	22—18	Fluorescence depolarization	25	(309)
Na phenylstearate	Benzene	58—260	Fluorescence depolarization	25	(309)

Compound	Solvent	Aggregation number	Method	Temperature °C	Reference
K phenylstearate	Benzene	24—21	Fluorescence depolarization	25	(309)
Cs phenylstearate	Benzene	11—9	Fluorescence depolarization	25	(309)
$\frac{1}{2}$Mg phenylstearate	Benzene	23—22	Fluorescence depolarization	25	(309)
$\frac{1}{2}$Ca phenylstearate	Benzene	43—39	Fluorescence depolarization	25	(309)
Na phenylstearate +0.2mole phenylstearic acid	Benzene	200	Viscosity	25	(296)
Na phenylstearate +trace of water	Benzene	(5000)	Viscosity	25	(296)
$\frac{1}{2}$Ca xenylstearate +2moles H_2O/ mole soap	Benzene	24	Fluorescence depolarization	25	(58)
$\frac{1}{2}$Ca xenylstearate +trace of water	Benzene	(1000)	Fluorescence depolarization	25	(57)
$(R_7COO)_2AlOH$	Benzene	(640—880)	Osmotic pressure, viscosity	30	(310)
$(R_{11}COO)_2AlOH$	Benzene	(840—1330)	Osmotic pressure, viscosity	30	(310)
$(R_{13}COO)_2AlOH$	Benzene	(520—980)	Osmotic pressure, viscosity	30	(310)
$(R_{15}COO)_2AlOH$	Benzene	(600—700)	Osmotic pressure, viscosity	30	(310)
$(R_{17}COO)_2AlOH$	Benzene	(670—970)	Osmotic pressure, viscosity	30	(310)
R_9COOCH_2 $CHOHCH_2OH$	Benzene	41	Light scattering	30—28	(295)
R_9COOCH_2 $CHOHCH_2OH$	Chlorobenzene	16	Light scattering	30—28	(295)
$R_{11}COOCH_2$ $CHOHCH_2OH$	Benzene	73	Light scattering	30—28	(295)
$R_{11}COOCH_2$ $CHOHCH_2OH$	Chlorobenzene	47	Light scattering	30—28	(295)
$R_{13}COOCH_2$ $CHOHCH_2OH$ (1.3% free fatty acid)	Benzene	192	Light scattering	30—28	(295)
$R_{13}COOCH_2$ $CHOHCH_2OH$ (1.3% free fatty acid)	Chlorobenzene	106	Light scattering	30—28	(295)
$R_{13}COOCH_2$ $CHOHCH_2OH$ (0.33% free fatty acid)	Benzene	93	Light scattering	30—28	(295)

Compound	Solvent	Aggregation number	Method	Temperature °C	Reference
$R_{13}COOCH_2$ CHOHCH$_2$OH (0.17% free fatty acid)	Benzene	86	Light scattering	30—28	(295)
$R_{15}COOCH_2$ CHOHCH$_2$OH	Benzene	15	Light scattering	30—28	(295)
$R_{15}COOCH_2$ CHOHCH$_2$OH	Chlorobenzene	9	Light scattering	30—28	(295)
$R_{17}COOCH_2$ CHOHCH$_2$OH	Benzene	11	Light scattering	30—28	(295)
$R_{17}COOCH_2$ CHOHCH$_2$OH	Chlorobenzene	3.3	Light scattering	30—28	(295)
Lecithin	Benzene	73	Osmotic pressure	25	(307)
Lecithin	Benzene	70	Diffusion, viscosity	25	(307)
Lecithin	Benzene	55	Diffusion, viscosity	40	(307)

of physical chemical properties. Colligative properties are a good way of detecting and determining the presence and size of micelle since there is no disturbance from dissociation (58, 102, 133, 298, 299). As the aggregation number is in many cases not large, the experimental accuracy can be good. If the refractive index of the solvent differs appreciably from that of the micelle-forming molecule, the size and shape of the micelle may be determined by the application of the light scattering techniques that have been developed in the past 15 years (300). In this respect, carbon tetrachloride or chlorohydrocarbons may be good solvents to use. A very few data obtained by this method are reported for solutions in nonaqueous solvents (295), based on the assumption of monodispersity of micelle (an assumption which seems less firmly established in nonaqueous solvents). The ultracentrifuge has been used to evaluate micelle size for Aerozol OT in benzene (301).

Kaufman and Singleterry et al. (60) have described a method for estimating micellar size in nonpolar solvents from measurements of the depolarization of the fluorescence of a dye which has been solubilized in the micelle. Micellar sizes estimated from fluorescence depolarization have been found to agree well with those obtained from measurements of the osmotic pressure of the solutions (58).

The sizes of micelles in nonaqueous solutions are summarized in Tabled 1.26. The solvents are different, but are mostly hydrocarbons, and the heat of solution due to the hydrocarbon portion of solute is probably always small. The solvent properties of carbon tetrachloride also resemble those of hydrocarbons. The aggregation numbers in the concentration range in which micelle formation is well established are usually 3–40 (286), far smaller than the aggregation numbers of micelles in aqueous solution. The addition of as little as 0.05% of water to benzene solution of the aryl stearate soaps converts the viscous fluid which is formed in the complete absence of water to a mobile liquid having a relative viscosity slightly larger than that predicted for the system by the Einstein equation for suspended spheres (57).

Kaufman and Singleterry have said (311), "The high viscosity of the dry arylstearate soap solution is considered to result from the aggregation of the soap molecules into polymer-like chains somewhat analogous to those proposed for the aluminum soaps in hydrocarbon

TABLE 1.27

CMC OF SURFACE ACTIVE AGENTS IN NONAQUEOUS SOLVENTS

Compound	Solvent	CMC (moles/liter)	Method	Temp. °C	Reference
Ca xenylstearate	C_6H_6	10^{-6}	Fluorescence depolarization	25	(60)
Na dinonylnaphthalenesulfonate	C_6H_6	10^{-6}–10^{-7}	Fluorescence depolarization	25	(311)
Ba dinonylnaphthalenesulfonate	C_6H_6	10^{-6}–10^{-7}	Fluorescence depolarization	25	(311)
$R_{12}NH_3$ propionate	C_6H_6	0.002,22,5	Solubilization	10,26,40	(62)
$R_{12}NH_3$ butyrate	C_6H_6	0.003,18,20	Solubilization	10,26,40	(62)
$R_{12}NH_3$ caproate	C_6H_6	0.018,20,25	Solubilization	10,26,40	(62)
$R_{12}NH_3$ coprylate	C_6H_6	0.020,25,25	Solubilization	10,26,40	(62)
$R_{12}NH_3$ caprate	C_6H_6	0.035,32	Solubilization	26,40	(62)
$R_{18}NH_3$ propionate	C_6H_6	0.008,10	Solubilization	26,40	(62)
$R_{18}NH_3$ butyrate	C_6H_6	0.005,27,28	Solubilization	10,26,40	(62)
$R_{12}NH_3$ butyrate	Cyclo-C_6H_{12}	0.002	Solubilization	26	(313)
$R_{12}NH_3$ butyrate	CCl_4	0.01	Vapor pressure depression	20	(133)
$R_{12}NH_3$ butyrate	CCl_4	0.016	Solubilization	26	(313)
$R_{12}NH_3$ butyrate	CCl_4	0.007	Infrared spectra	20	(133)
$R_{12}NH_3$ caprylate	Cyclo-C_6H_{12}	0.016	Solubilization	26	(313)
$R_{12}NH_3$ caprylate	CCl_4	0.013	V.p. depression	20	(133)
$R_{12}NH_3$ caprylate	CCl_4	0.072	Solubilization	26	(313)
$R_{13}NH_3$ caprylate	CCl_4	0.013	Infrared spectra	20	(133)
$R_{12}NH_3$ benzoate	Cyclo-C_6H_{12}	0.012	Ultraviolet spectra	30	(132)
$R_{12}NH_3$ benzoate	Cyclo-C_6H_{12}	0.015,12	Solubilization	25,30	(132)
$R_{18}NH_3$ benxoate	Cyclo-C_6H_{12}	0.014	Solubilization	30	(132)
$R_{18}NH_3$ benxoate	Cyclo-C_6H_{12}	0.018	Ultraviolet spectra	30	(132)
Pb 2-ethylhexyl sebacate	C_6H_6	10^{-3}	Fluorescence depolarization	26	(314)
Na 2-ethylhexyl sulfosuccinate	Cyclo-C_6H_{12}	0.0016	Light scattering	—	(314a)
Na 2-ethylhexyl sulfosuccinate	C_6H_6	0.003	Light scattering	—	(314a)

solvents (*310*, *312*). The reversion of the sodium phenylstearate to high and markedly non-Newtonian viscosity in the presence of larger amount of water or glycol results from a secondary reaggregation of small micelles into large, shear-sensitive structures. The water appears to hold the secondary aggregates together by a bridging action involving hydrogen bonding."

On the other hand, the micelles of dinonylnaphthalenesulfonates of ten cations (Li, Na, Cs, NH₄, Mg, Ca, Ba, Zn, Al, and H) in benzene, observed by fluorescence depolarization, contained 9–14 acid residues each (*302*). Their aggregation number was usually independent of concentration and almost independent of the water content of the system, although moisture moderately increased to aggregation of the zinc salt. Singleterry (*286*) has remarked in this context: "The relative insensitivity of the sulfonate micelle size to influences of the cation and moisture contrasts sharply with the behavior of the phenylstearate soaps. This indicates that the size of the dinonylnaphthalene sulfonate micelles depends primarily on the geometry of the acid residue. However, the apparent volume of the anion was inversely related to the coordinating tendency of the cation, suggesting that coordination forces are a factor in micelle stability. The acid is associated principally to the dimer, but in the presence of water some larger aggregates are formed."

3. Critical Micelle Concentration

The mass action theory in Section IV applies equally to the aggregation in nonaqueous solvents.

The CMC in nonaqueous solution can be determined by several methods described in Section II. There are several papers on CMC in nonaqueous solution. Some of the results are summarized in Table 1.27.

The effect of temperature on the CMC of dodecyl ammonium hexanoate, octanoate, and decanoate in benzene was studied cryoscopically and ebullioscopically. Micelle formation did not occur near the boiling point of benzene, but the van't Hoff factor decreased to 0.1 near the freezing point of benzene (*62*). At constant temperature the CMC increases and the solubilizing power decreases with increase in chain length. The trend agrees with the results obtained by Nelson and Pink (*308*). The CMC decreases by about one-third per one additional methylene group in aqueous solutions of nonionic agents, but the change is small in nonaqueous solution (*62*), because the energy required transferring a methylene group from the micelle to the bulk of the solution is rather small in hydrocarbon or carbon tetrachloride solution, where the intermolecular forces are close to those of the paraffin chain portion of amphipathic molecules.

References

1. Fowler, R., and Guggenheim, E.A. "Statistical Thermodynamics." Cambridge Univ. Press, London and New York, 1956.
2. Hartley, G. S. "Aqueous Solutions of Paraffin Chain Salts." Hermann, Paris, 1936.
3. Hildebrand, J. H. *Z. physik. Chem. (Frankfurt)* **16**, 245 (1958).
4. Shinoda, K., Yamaguchi, T., and Hori, R. *Bull. Chem. Soc. Japan* **34**, 237 (1961).
5. Hildebrand, J. H., and Scott, R. L. "The Solubility of Nonelectrolytes." Reinhold, New York, 1950.
6. Grindley, J., and Bury, C. R. *J. Chem. Soc.* **131**, 679 (1929).
7. Davies, M., and Griffiths, D. M. L. *Z. physik. Chem. (Frankfurt)* **6**, 143 (1956).
8. Harkins, W. D., Mattoon, R. W., and Mittelmann, R. *J. Chem. Phys.* **15**, 763 (1947).
9. Shinoda, K., and Hildebrand, J. H. *J. Phys. Chem.* **62**, 295 (1958).
10. Mizushima, S. "Structure of Molecules and Internal Rotation." Academic Press, New York, 1954.
11. McBain, M. E. L., Dye, W. B., and Johnston, S. A. *J. Am. Chem. Soc.* **61**, 3210 (1939).
12. Johnston, S. A., and McBain, J. W. *Proc. Roy. Soc.* **A181**, 119 (1942).
13. Mukerjee, P., Mysels, K. J., and Dulin, C. I. *J. Phys. Chem.* **62**, 1390 (1958).
14. Hutchinson, E., Inaba, A., and Bailey, L. G. *Z. physik. Chem (Frankfurt)* **5**, 344 (1955).
15. Nilsson, G. *J. Phys. Chem.* **61**, 1135 (1957)
16. Salley, D. J., Weith, A. J., Jr., Argyle, A. A., and Dixon, J. K. *Proc. Roy. Soc.* **A203**, 42 (1950).
17. Krafft, F., and Wiglow, H. *Ber.* **28**, 2566 (1895)
18. Murray, R. C., and Hartley, G. S. *Trans. Faraday Soc.* **31**, 183 (1935).
19. Hutchinson, E. *Z. physik. Chem. (Frankfurt)* **21**, 38 (1959).
20. Hutchinson, E., Manchester, K. E., Winslow, L. *J. Phys. Chem.* **58**, 1124 (1954).
21. Shinoda, K., Yamanaka, T., and Kinoshita, K. *J. Phys. Chem.* **63**, 648 (1959).
22. Ekwall, P. *J. Colloid Sci. Suppl.* **No. 1**, 66 (1954).
23. Preston, W. C. *J. Phys. & Colloid Chem.* **52**, 84 (1948).
24. McBain, M. E. L., and Hutchinson, E. "Solubilization and Related Phenomena." Academic Press, New York, 1955.
25. Schwartz, A. M., Perry, J. W., and Berch, J. "Surface Active Agents and Detergents," Vol. II. Interscience, New York, 1958.
26. Lottermoser, A., and Püschel, F. *Kolloid-Z.* **63**, 175 (1933).
27. Malsh, J., and Hartley, G. S. Z. physik. Chem. *(Leipzig)* **A170**, 321 (1934).
28. Wright, K. A., Abbott, A. D., Sivertz, V., and Tartar, H. V. *J. Am. Chem. Soc.* **61**, 549 (1939).
29. Ralston, A. W., and Hoerr, C. W. *J. Am. Chem. Soc.* **64**, 772 (1942).
30. Walton, H. F., Hiebert, E. N., and Sholtes, E. H. *J. Colloid Sci.* **1**, 385 (1946).
31. Williams, R. J., Phillips, J. N., and Mysels, K. J. *Trans. Faraday Soc.* **51**, 728 (1955).
32. Lin, W. *Bull. Chem. Soc. Japan* **28**, 227 (1955).
33. Hoerr, C. W., and Ralston, A. W., *J. Am. Chem. Soc.* **65**, 976 (1943).
34. Hartley, G. S., Callie, B., and Samis, C. S. *Trans. Faraday Soc.* **32**, 795 (1936).

35. Shirai, M. and Tamamushi, B. *Bull. Chem. Soc. Japan* **29**, 733 (1956).
36. Hartley, G. S. *Trans. Faraday Soc.* **30**, 444 (1934).
37. Sheppard, S. E., and Geddes, A. L. *J. Chem. Phys.* **13**, 63 (1945).
38. Corrin, M. L., and Harkins, W. D. *J. Am. Chem. Soc.* **69**, 679 (1947).
39. Kolthoff, I. M., and Stricks, W. *J. Phys. & Colloid Chem.* **52**, 915 (1948).
40. Tachibana, T., and Ofuka, T. *J. Chem. Soc. Japan* **72**, 586 (1951). (In Japanese.)
41. Colichman, E. L. *J. Am. Chem. Soc.* **73**, 3385 (1951).
42. Mukerjee, P., and Mysels, K. J. *J. Am. Chem. Soc.* **77**, 2937 (1955).
43. Winsor; P. A. *Trans. Faraday Soc.* **44**, 463 (1948).
44. Shinoda, K. *J. Phys. Chem.* **58**, 541 (1954)
45. Goto, R., Sugano, T., and Koizumi, N. *J. Chem. Soc. Japan* **75**, 73 (1954). (In Japanese.)
46. Nakagawa, T., Tori, K., and Kuriyama, K. *J. Chem. Soc. Japan* **77**, 1684 (1956). (In Japanese.)
47. Ross, S., and Olivier, J. P. *J. Phys. Chem.* **63**, 1671 (1959).
48. Becher, P. *J. Phys. Chem.* **63**, 1675 (1959).
49. Martin, J. T., and Standing, H. A. *J. Textile Inst., Trans.* **40**, 689 (1949).
50. Arkin, L., and Singleterry, C. R. *J. Am. Chem. Soc.* **70**, 3965 (1948).
51. Stearns, R. S., Oppenheimer, H., Simon, E., and Harkins, W. D. *J. Chem. Phys.* **15**, 496 (1947).
52. McBain, J. W., and Richards, P. H. *Ind. Eng. Chem.* **38**, 642 (1946).
53. Nakagawa, T., Kuriyama, K., Inaba, S., and Tori, K. *J. Chem. Soc. Japan* **77**, 1563 (1956). (In Japanese.)
54. McBain, J. W., Merrill, R. C., Jr., and Vinograd, J. R. *J. Am. Chem. Soc.* **62**, 2880 (1940).
55. Palit, S. R. *Nature* **153**, 317 (1944).
56. Pink, R. C. *J. Chem. Soc.* p. 53 (1939).
57. Arkin; L., and Singleterry, C. R. *J. Colloid Sci.* **4**, 537 (1949).
58. Singleterry, C. R., and Weinberger, L. A. *J. Am. Chem. Soc.* **73**, 4574 (1951).
59. Ross, S. *J. Colloid Sci.* **6**, 497 (1951).
60. Kaufman, S., and Singleterry, C. R. *J. Colloid Sci.* **7**, 453 (1952).
61. Kitahara, A. *Bull. Chem. Soc. Japan* **28**, 234 (1955).
62. Kitahara, A. *Bull. Chem. Soc. Japan* **29**, 15 (1956).
63. Powney, J. and Addison, C. C. *Trans. Faraday Soc.* **33**, 1243 (1937).
64. Addison, C. C., and Elliott, T. A. *J. Chem. Soc.* p. 3103 (1950).
65. Brown, A. S., Robinson, R. U., Sirois, E. H., Thibault, H. G., McNeill, W., and Tofias, A. *J. Phys. Chem.* **56**, 701 (1952).
66. Kushner, L. M., and Hubbard, W. D. *J. Phys. Chem.* **57**, 898 (1953).
67. Matuura, R., Kimizuka, H., Miyamoto, S., and Shimazawa, R. *Bull. Chem. Soc. Japan* **31**, 532 (1958).
68. Bury, C. R., and Browning, J. *Trans. Faraday Soc.* **49**, 209 (1953).
69. Miles, G. D., and Shedlovsky, *J. Phys. Chem.* **48**, 57 (1944).
70. Miles, G. D. *J. Phys. Chem.* **49**, 71 (1945).
71. Shedlovsky, L., Ross, J., and Jakob, C. W. *J. Colloid Sci.* **4**, 25 (1949).
72. Adam. N. K., and Shute, H. L. *Trans. Faraday Soc.* **34**, 758 (1938).
73. Nutting, G. C., Long, F. A., and Harkins, W. D. *J. Am. Chem. Soc.* **62**, 1496 (1940).

74. Bury, C, R., and Parry, *G*. A. *J. Chem. Soc.* p. 626 (1935).

75. Harkins, W. D., Mattoon, R. W., and Corrin, M. L. *J. Colloid Sci.* **1**, 105 (1946).

76. Ekwall, P., and Smeds, K. *Acta Chem. Scand.* **6**, 441 (1952).

77. Lal, H. *J. Colloid Sci.* **8**, 414 (1953).

78. Hutchinson, E., and Mosher, C. S. *J. Colloid Sci.* **11**, 352 (1956).

79. Shinoda, K., and Hildebrand, J. H. *J. Phys. Chem.* **61**, 789 (1957).

80. Hess, K., Philippoff, W., and Kiessig, H. *Kolloid-Z.* **88**, 40 (1939).

81. Klevens, H. B. *J. Phys. & Colloid Chem.* **52**, 130 (1948).

82. Thiele, H. *Kolloid-Z.* **113**, **155** (1949).

83. Debye, P. *J. Phys. & Colloid Chem.* **53**, 1 (1949).

84. Debye, P. *Ann. N. Y. Acad. Sci.* **51**, 575 (1949).

85. Debye, P., and Anacker, E. W. *J. Phys. & Colloid Chem.* **55**, 644 (1951).

86. Hutchinson, E. *J. Colloid Sci.* **9**, 191 (1954).

87. Mysels, K. J. *J. Phys. Chem.* **58**, 303 (1954).

88. Mysels, K. J. *J. Colloid Sci.* **10**, 507 (1955).

89. Phillips, J. N., and Mysels, K. J. *J. Phys. Chem.* **59**, 325 (1955).

90. Prins, W., and Hermans, J. J. *J. Phys. Chem.* **59**, 576 (1955).

91. Mysels, K. J., and Princen, L. H. *J. Phys. Chem.* **63**, 1696 (1959).

92. Zimm, B. H. *J. Chem. Phys.* **16**, 1093 (1948).

93. Princen, L. H. Ph. D. Dissertation, University of Utrecht, Netherlands, 1959.

94. Nakagawa, T., Kuriyama, K., Inoue, H., and Oyama, T. *J. Chem. Soc. Japan*
    79, 348 (1958). (In Japanese.)

95. Kuriyama, K., Inoue, H., and Nakagawa, T. *Ann. Rept. Shionogi Research Lab.*
    9, 1061 (1959). (In Japanese.)

96. Gonick, E., and McBain, J. W. *J. Am. Chem. Soc.* **69**, 334 (1947).

97. Hess, L., and Suranyi, L. A. *Z. physik. Chem. (Leipzig)* **A184**, 321 (1939).

98. McBain, J. W., and Salmon, C. S. *J. Am. Chem. Soc.* **43**. 426 (1920).

99. Brady, A. P., Huff, H., and McBain, J. W. *J. Phys. & Colloid Chem.* **55**, 304 (1951).

100. Huff, H., McBain, J. W., and Brady, A. P. *J. Phys. & Colloid Chem.* **55**, 311 (1951).

101. Müller, R. H., and Stolten, H. J. *Anal. Chem.* **25**, 1103 (1953).

102. Kitahara, A. *Bull. Chem. Soc. Japan* **31**, 288 (1958).

103. Krafft, F. *Ber.* **27**, 1747, 1755 (1894); **29**, 1328 (1896); **32**, 1584 (1899).

104. Tartar, H. V., and Wright, K. A. *J. Am. Chem. Soc.* **61**, 539 (1939).

105. Adam, N. K., and Pankhurst, K. G. A. *Trans. Faraday Soc.* **42**, 523 (1946).

106. Ralston, A. W., and Hoerr, C. W. *J. Am. Chem. Soc.* **68**, 851 (1946).

107. Miyamoto, S. *Bull. Chem. Soc. Japan* **33**, 371 (1960).

108a. Martin, E. P., and Pink, R. C. *J. Chem. Soc.* p. 1750 (1948).

108b. Kolthoff, I. M., and Johnson, W. F. *J. Phys. Chem.* **52**, 22 (1948).

109. Walton, H. F. *J. Am. Chem. Soc.* **68**, 1180 (1946).

110. Neff, L. L., Wheeler, O. L., Tartar, H. V., and Lingafelter, E. C. *J. Am. Chem.*
    Soc. **70**, 1989 (1948).

111. McBain, J. W., and Williams, R. C. *J. Am. Chem. Soc.* **55**, 2250 (1933).

112. Hutchinson, E., and Winslow, L. *Z. physik. Chem. (Frankfurt)* **11**, 165 (1957).

113. Weissler, A., Fitzgerald, J. W., and Resnick, I. *J. Appl. Phys.* **18**, 434 (1947),

114. Baccaredda, M., Baldacci, R., and Danusso, F. *Ann. chim. (Rome)* **40**, 411 (1950).

115. Sasaki, T., and Yasunaga, T. *Kagaku to Kôgyô* **7**, 138 (1954). (In Japanese.)

116. Colichman, E. L. *J. Am. Chem. Soc.* **72**, 4036 (1950).

117. Tamamushi, R., and Yamanaka, T. *Bull. Chem. Soc. Japan* **28**, 673 (1955).

118. Mysels, K. J., and Stigter, D. *J. Phys. Chem.* **57**, 104 (1953).

119. Stigter, D., Williams, R. J., and Mysels, K. J. *J. Phys. Chem.* **59**, 330 (1955).

120. Okuyama, H., and Tyuzyo, K. *Bull. Chem. Soc. Japan* **27**, 259 (1954).

121. Hess, K., Kiessig, H., and Philippoff, W. *Fette u. Seifen* **48**, 377 (1941).

122. Wright, K. A., and Tartar, H. V. *J. Am. Chem. Soc.* **61**, 544 (1939).

123. Vetter, R. J. *J. Phys. & Colloid Chem.* **51**, 262 (1947).

124. Kushner, L. M., Duncan, B. C., and Hoffman, J. I. *J. Research Natl. Bur. Standards* **49**, 85 (1952).

125. Flockhart, B. D., and Graham, H. *J. Colloid Sci.* **8**, 105 (1953).

126. Sata, N., and Tyuzyo, K. *Bull. Chem. Soc. Japan* **26**, 177 (1953).

127. Yang, J. T., and Foster, J. F. *J. Phys. Chem.* **57**, 628 (1953).

128. Harrap, B. S., and O'Donnell, I. J. *J. Phys. Chem.* **58**, 1097 (1954).

129. Stigter, D., and Mysels, K. J. *J. Phys. Chem.* **59**, 45 (1955).

130. Munro, L. A., and Sexsmith, F. H. *Can. J. Chem.* **31** 985 (1953).

131. Harkins, W. D., Krizek, H., and Corrin, M. L. *J. Colloid Sci.* **6**, 576 (1951).

132. Kitahara, A. *Bull. Chem. Soc. Japan* **30**, 586 (1957).

133. Kitahara, A. *Bull. Chem. Soc. Japan* **31**, 653 (1958).

134. Lovelock, J. E. *J. Chem. Soc.* p. 115 (1951).

135. Kolthoff, I. M., and Johnson, W. F. *J. Am. Chem. Soc.* **73**, 4563 (1951).

136. Exner, M. L. *Naturwissenschaften* **35**, 344 (1948).

137. Shirai, M., and Tamamushi, B. *Bull. Chem Soc. Japan* **28**, 545 (1955).

138. Shirai, M., and Tamamushi, B. *Bull. Chem. Soc. Japan* **30**, 542 (1957).

139. Carr, C. W., Johnson, W. F., and Kolthoff, I. M. *J. Phys. & Colloid Chem.* **51**, 636 (1947)

140. Chandler, R. C., and McBain, J. W. *J. Phys. & Colloid Chem.* **53**, 930 (1949).

141. Botre, C., Crescenzi, V. L., and Mele, A. *J. Phys. Chem.* **63**, 650 (1959).

142. Hartley, G. S. State of solution of colloidal electrolytes. *Quart. Rev. Chem. Soc.* **2**, 152 (1948)

143. Hartley, G. S. *Ann. Repts. Chem. Soc.* **43**, 33 (1949).

144. Moilliet, J. L., and Collie, B. "Surface Activity." Van Nostrand, New York, 1951.

145. McBain, J. W. "Colloid Science." Heath, Boston, 1950.

146. McBain, J. W. Solubilization and other factors in detergent action. In "Advances in Colloid Science" (E. O. Kraemer, ed.), Vol. I, p. 124. Interscience, New York, 1942.

147. Hess, K., and Gundermann, J. *Ber.* **70**, 1800 (1937).

148. Stauff, J. *Kolloid-Z.* **89**, 224 (1939), **96**, 244 (1942).

149. Hughes, E. W., Sawyer, W. M., and Vinograd, J.R. *J. Chem. Phys.* **13**, 131 (1945).

150. Harkins, W. D., Mattoon, R. W., and Corrin, M. L. *J. Am. Chem. Soc.* **68**, 220 (1946).

151. Hartley, G. S. *Kolloid-Z.* **88**, 22 (1939).

152. Harkins, W. D., and Mittelmann, R. *J. Colloid Sci.* **4**, 367 (1949).

153. Ancker, E. W. *J. Colloid Sci.* **8**, 402 (1953).

154. Laing, M. E., and McBain, J. W. *J. Chem. Soc.* **117**, 1506 (1920).

155. Laing, M. E. *J. Phys. Chem.* **28**, 673 (1924).

156. Kucher, R. V., and Yurzhenko, A. I. *Kolloid.Zhur.* **15**, 442 (1953).

157. Granath, K. *Acta. Chem. Scand.* **4**, 103 (1950).

158. Mankowich, A. M. *J. Phys. Chem.* **58**, 1027 (1954).

159. Yurzhenko, A. I., and Kucher, R. V. *Kolloid Zhur.* **14**, 219 (1952).

160. Hutchinson, E., and Melrose, J. C. *Z. physik. Chem. (Frankfurt)* **2**, 363 (1954).

161. Tartar, H. V., and Lelong, A. L. M. *J. Phys. Chem.* **59**, 1185 (1955).

162. Kushner, L. M., and Hubbard, W. D. *J. Colloid Sci.* **10**, 428 (1955).

163. Anacker, E. W. *J. Phys. Chem.* **62**, 41 (1958).

164. Lamm, O. *Kolloid-Z.* **98**, 45 (1942).

165. Andersen, D. E., and Carpenter, G. B. *J. Am. Chem. Soc.* **75**, 850 (1953).

166. Ludlum, D. B. *J. Phys. Chem.* **60**, 1240 (1956).

166a. Philippoff, W. *Discussione Faraday Soc* **11**, 96 (1951).

167. Shirai, M., and Tamamushi, B. *Bull. Chem. Soc. Japan* **30**, 411 (1957).

168. Vold, M. J. *J. Colloid Sci.* **5**, 506 (1950).

169. Brady, A. P., and Salley, D. J. *J. Am. Chem. Soc.* **70**, 914 (1948)

170. Shinoda, K., and Akamatu, H. *Bull. Chem. Soc. Japan* **31**, 497 (1958).

171. Cushman, A., Brady, A. P., and McBain, J. W. *J. Colloid Sci.* **3**, 425 (1948).

172. Samis, C. S., and Hartley, G. S. *Trans. Faraday Soc.* **34** 1288 (1938).

173. Philippoff, W. *J. Colloid Sci.* **5**, 169 (1950).

174. Warren, B. E. *Phys. Rev.* **44**, 969 (1933).

175. King, A. M., and Garner, W. E. *J. Chem. Soc.* p. 1449 (1934; p. 1368 (1936).

176. Garner, W. C., Madden, F. C., and Rushbrooke, J. E. *J. Chem. Soc.* p. 2491 (1926).

177. Hutchinson, E., and Bailey, L. G. *Z. physik. Chem. (Frankfurt)* **21**, 30 (1959).

178. Shinoda, K. *J. Phys. Chem.* **58**, 1136 (1954).

179. Davies, D. G., and Bury, C. R. *J. Chem. Soc.* p. 2263 (1930).

180. Ekwall, P. *Acta Acad. Aboensis Math. et Phys.* **4**, 6, 1–209 (1927)

181. Fowkes, F. M. Discussion in *J. Phys. Chem.* **63**, 1674 (1959).

182. Stainsby, G., and Alexander, A. E. *Trans. Faraday Soc.* **46**, 587 (1950).

183. Matijevic, E., and Pethica, B. A. *Trans. Faraday Soc.* **54**, 587 (1958).

184. Goddard, E. D., Hoeve, C. A. J., and Benson, G. C. *J. Phys. Chem.* **61**, 593 (1957).

185. White, P., and Benson, G. C. *J. Colloid Sci.* **13**, 584 (1958).

186. White, P., and Benson, G. C. *Trans. Faraday Soc.* **55**, 1025 (1959).

187. Flockhart, B. D., and Ubbelohde, A. R. *J. Colloid Sci.* **8**, 428 (1953).

188. Ginn, M. E., Kinney, F. B., and Harris, J. C. *J. Am. Oil Chemists' Soc.* **37**, 183 (1960).

189. Brady, A. P., and Huff, H. *J. Colloid Sci.* **3**, 511 (1948).

190. Nakagawa, T., Inoue, H., Tori, K., and Kuriyama, K. *J. Chem. Soc. Japan* **79**, 1194 (1958). (In Japanese.)

191. Shinoda, K., and Hildebrand, J. H. *J. Phys. Chem.* **62**, 481 (1958)

192. Frank, H. S., and Evans, M. W. *J. Chem. Phys.* **13**, 507 (1945).

193. Rushbrooke, G. S. "Introduction to Statistical Mechanics," Chapter 12. Oxford Univ. Press (Clarendon), London and New York, 1949.

194. Cassie, A. B. D., and Palmer, R. C. *Trans. Faraday Soc.* **37**, 156 (1941).

195. Corrin, M. L. *J. Colloid Sci.* **3**, 333 (1948).

196. Lange, H. *Kolloid-Z.* **117**, 48 (1950).

197. Hobbs, M. E. *J. Phys. & Colloid Chem.* **55**, 675 (1951).

198. Shishido, S. *Bull. Chem. Soc. Japan* **24**, 41 (1951).

199. Nakagaki, M. *J. Chem. Soc. Japan* **72**, 113, 115, 801 (1951). (In Japanese.)

200. Stauff, J. *Kolloid-Z.* **125**, 79 (1952).

201. Shinoda, K. *Bull. Chem. Soc. Japan* **26**, 101 (1953).

202. Ooshika, Y. *J. Colloid Sci.* **9**, 254 (1954).

203. Stigter, D. *Rec. trav. chim.* **73**, 593, 611 (1954).

204. Shinoda, K., and Kinoshita, K. *Bull. Chem. Soc. Japan* **27**, 73 (1954).

205. Phillips, J. N. *Trans. Faraday Soc.* **51**, 561 (1955).

206. Shinoda, K. *Bull. Chem. Soc. Japan* **28**, 340 (1955).

207. Overbeek, J. Th. G., and Stigter, D. *Rec. trav. chim.* **75**, 1263 (1956).

208. Ooshika, Y., and Ikeda, Y. *Kolloid-Z.* **145**, 3 (1956).

209. Reich, I. *J. Phys. Chem.* **60**, 257 (1956).

210. Hoeve, C. A. J., and Benson, G. C. *J. Phys. Chem.* **61**, 1149 (1957).

211. Stauff, J., and Rasper, J. *Kolloid-Z.* **151**, 148 (1957).

212. Nakagawa, T., Kuriyama, K., and Tori, K. *J. Chem. Soc. Japan* **78**, 1568, 1573 (1957). (In Japanese.)

213. Alexander, A. E. *Trans. Faraday Soc.* **38**, 54 (1942).

214. Alexander, A. E., and Johnson, P. "Colloid Science," p. 77. Oxford Univ. Press, London and New York, 1950.

215. Shinoda, K. *J. Phys. Chem.* **59**, 432 (1955).

216. Langmuir, I. *J. Am. Chem. Soc.* **39**, 1883 (1917).

217. Kruyt, H. R. "Colloid Science," Vol. I, p. 129–130 Elsevier, Amsterdam, 1952.

218. Verwey, E. J. W., and Overbeek, J. Th. G. "Theory of the Stability of Lyophobic Colloids." Elsevier Amsterdam, 1948.

219. Harris, J. C. *J. Am. Oil Chemists' Soc.* **35**, 670 (1958).

220. Stauff, J. *Z. physik Chem. (Leipzig)* **A183**, 55 (1938).

221. Howell, O. R., and Robinson, H. G. B. *Proc. Roy. Soc.* **A155**, 386 (1936),

222. Herzfeld, S. H. *J. Phys. Chem.* **56**, 953 (1952).

223. Klevens, H. B. *J. Am. Oil Chemists' Soc.* **30**, 74 (1953).

224. Corrin, M. L., Klevens, H. B. and Harkins, W. D. *J. Chem. Phys.* **14**, 480 (1946)

225. Wright, K. A., Abbott, A. D., Sivertz, V., and Tartar, H. V. *J. Am. Chem. Soc.* **61**, 549 (1939).

226. Ralston, A. W., Eggenberger, D. N., and Broome, F. K. *J. Am. Chem. Soc.* **71**, 2145 (1949).

227. Scott, A. B., and Tartar, H. V. *J. Am. Chem. Soc.* **66**, 292 (1943).

228. Shinoda, K. *J. Phys. Chem.* **60**, 1439 (1956).

229. Shick, M. J., and Fowkes, F. M. *J. Phys. Chem.* **61**, 1062 (1957).

230. Weil, J. K., Bistline, R. G., Jr., and Stirton, A. J. *J. Phys. Chem.* **62**, 1083 (1958).

231. Kinoshita, K., Ishikawa, H., and Shinoda, K .*Bull. Chem. Soc. Japan* **31**, 1081 (1958).

232. Lange, H. *Kolloid-Z.* **163**, 9 (1959).

233. Osipow, L., Snell, F. D., and Hickson, J. *In* "Surface Activity: Proceedings of the Second International Congress on Surface Activity, London, 1957" (J. H. Schulman, ed.), p. 50. Academic Press, New York, 1958.

234. Stirton, A. J., Weil, J. K. and Bistline, R. G., Jr. *J. Am. Oil Chemists' Soc.*

31, 13 (1954).

235. Weil, J. K., Bistline, R. G., Jr., and Stirton, A. J. *J. Am. Oil Chemists' Soc.* **32**, 370 (1955).

236. Weil, J. K., and Stirton, A. J. *J. Phys. Chem.* **60**, 899 (1956).

237. Williams, E. F., Woodberry, N. T., and Dixon, J. K. *J. Colloid Sci.* **12**, 452 (1957).

238. Evans, H. C. *J. Chem. Soc.* p. 579 (1956).

239. Ralston, A. W., Eggenberger, D. N., and Du Brow, P. L. *J. Am. Chem. Soc·* **70**, 977 (1948).

240. Ludlum, D. B. *J. Phys. Chem.* **60**, 1240 (1956).

241. Paquette, R. G., Lingafelter, E. C., and Tartar, H. V. *J. Am. Chem. Soc.* **65**, 686 (1943).

242. Gershman, J. W. *J. Phys. Chem.* **61**, 581 (1957).

242a. Griess, W. *Fette u. Seifen* **57**, 24 (1955).

243. Shinoda, K., and Mashio, K. *J. Phys. Chem.* **64**, 54 (1960).

243a. Gregory, N. W., and Tartar, H. V. *J. Am. Chem. Soc.* **70**, 1992 (1948).

244. Arrington, C. H., Jr., and Patterson, G. D. *J. Phys. Chem.* **57**, 247 (1953).

245. Klevens, H. B., and Raison, M. M. *Congr. mondial detergence et prod. tensio-actifs, 1er Congr., Paris* (1954).

245a. Klevens, H. B., and Raison, M. *J. chim. phys.* **51**, 1 (1954).

246. McBain, J. W., and McHan, H. *J. Am. Chem. Soc.* **70**, 3838 (1948).

246a. Klevens, H. B. *Kolloid-Z.* **158**, 53 (1958).

246b. Scholberg, H. M., Guenthner, R. A., and Coon, R. I. *J. Phys. Chem.* **57**, 923 (1953).

246c. Hendricks, J. O. *Ind. Eng. Chem.* **45**, 99 (1953).

246d. Bernett, M. K., and Zisman, W. A. *J. Phys. Chem.* **63**, 1911 (1959)

247. Ralston, A. W., Eggenberger, D. N., Harwood, H. J., and Du Brow, P. L. *J. Am. Chem. Soc.* **69**, 2095 (1947); **71**, 672 (1949).

248. Hartley, G. S. *J. Chem. Soc.* p. 1968 (1938).

249. Bolle, J., Ragon, P., and Bourgeois, L. *Mem. serv. chim. état (Paris)* **37**, 75 (1952).

250. Rossi, C., and Baldacci, R. *Ann. chem. (Rome)* **41**, 534 (1951).

251. Hsiao, L., Dunning, H. N., and Lorenz, P. B. *J. Phys. Chem.* **60**, 657 (1956).

252. Nakagawa, T., and Inoue, H. *J. Chem. Soc. Japan* **79**, 345 (1958). (In Japanese.)

253. Lange, H. *Kolloid-Z.* **121**, 66 (1951).

254. Lelong, A. L. M., Tartar, H. V., Lingafelter, E. C., O'Loane, J. K., and Cadle, R. D. *J. Am. Chem. Soc.* **73**, 5411 (1951).

254a. Nakagawa, T., Kuriyama, K., and Inoue, H. *J. Colloid Sci.* **15**, 268 (1960).

254b. Miyamoto, S. *Bull. Chem. Soc. Japan* **33**, 375 (1960).

255. Goddard, E. D., Harva, O., and Jones, T. G. *Trans. Faraday Soc.* **49**, 980 (1953).

256. Ralston, A. W., Hoerr, C. W., and Hoffman, E. J. *J. Am. Chem. Soc.* **64**, 97 (1942).

257. Grieger, P. F., and Kraus, C. A. *J. Am. Chem. Soc.* **70**, 3803 (1948).

258. Meguro, K., and Kondo, T. *J. Chem. Soc. Japan* **80**, 818 (1959). (In Japanese.)

259. Meguro, K., Kondo, T., Yoda, O., Ino, T., and Ooba, N. *J. Chem. Soc. Japan* **77**, 1236 (1956).

260. Kashiwagi, M., and Ezaki, H. *Bull. Chem. Soc. Japan* **32**, 624 (1959).

261. Ekwall, P. *Acta. Acad. Aboensis Math et. Phys.* **17**, 1 (1951).

262. Herzfeld, S. H. *J. Phys. Chem.* **56**, 959 (1952).

263. Lange, H. *Kolloid-Z.* **131**, 96 (1953); **132**, 45 (1953).

264. Corrin, M. L., and Harkins, W. D, *J. Colloid Sci.* **1**, 469 (1946).

265. Klevens, H. B. *J. Chem. Phys.* **14**, 742 (1946).

265a. Götte, E. *Fette u. Seifen* **56**, 670 (1954).

266. Nakagawa, T. *Ann. Repts. Shionogi Research Lab.* **8**, 835 (1958). (In Japanese).

267. Harva, O. *Rec. trav. chim.* **75**, 101 (1956).

268. Nakagaki, M., and Shinoda, K. *Bull. Chem. Soc. Japan* **27**, 367 (1954).

269. Klevens, H. B. *J. Am. Chem. Soc.* **72**, 3581 (1950).

270. Ward, A. F. H. *Proc. Roy. Soc.* **A176**, 412 (1940).

271. Corrin, M. L., and Harkins, W. D. *J. Chem. Phys.* **14**, 640 (1946).

272. Ralston, A. W., and Hoerr, C. W. *J. Am. Chem. Soc.* **68**, 2460 (1946).

273. Herzfeld, S. H., Corrin, M. L., and Harkins, W. D. *J. Phys. Chem.* **54**, 271 (1950)

274. Evers, E. C., and Kraus, C. A. *J. Am. Chem. Soc.* **70**, 3049 (1948).

275. Harva, O. *Rec. trav. chim.* **75**, 112 (1956).

276. Shinoda, K. *J. Chem. Soc. Japan* **75**, 1311 (1954). (In Japanese.)

277. Schulmann, J. H., and Riley, D. P. *J. Colloid Sci.* **3**, 383 (1948).

278. Mattoon, R. W., Sterns, R. S., and Harkins, W. D. *J. Chem. Phys.* **16**, 644 (1948).

279. Ekwall, P., Danielsson, I., and Henrikson, S. *Acta Chem. Scand.* **6**, 1297 (1952).

280. Klevens. H. B. *J. Phys. & Colloid Chem.* **54**, 1012 (1950).

281. Ralston, A. W., and Eggenberger, D. N. *J. Am. Chem. Soc.* **70**, 983 (1948).

282. Lottermoser, A., and Stoll, F. *Kolloid-Z.* **63**, 49 (1933).

283. Lottermoser, A., and Giese, E. *Kolloid-Z.* **73**, 155 (1935).

284. Harkins, W. D., Mittelemann, R., and Corrin, M. L. *J. Phys. & Colloid Chem.* **53**, 1350 (1949).

285. Flockhart, B. D. *J. Colloid Sci.* **12**, 557 (1957).

285a. Shinoda, K., and Ito, K. *J. Phys. Chem.* **65**, 1944 (1961).

286. Singleterry, C. R. *J. Am. Oil Chemists' Soc.* **32**, 446 (1955).

287. Kahlenberg, L. *J. Phys. Chem.* **6**, 1 (1902).

288. Soyenkoff, B. C. *J. Phys. Chem.* **34**, 2519 (1930).

289. Boner, C. J. *Ind. Eng. Chem.* **27**, 665 (1935).

290. Elliott, S. B. "The Alkaline Earth and Heavy Metal Soaps," p. 53. Reinhold, New York, 1946.

291. Baker, H. R., Jones, D. T., and Zisman, W. A. *Ind. Eng. Chem.* **41**, 137 (1949).

292. van der Waarden, M. *J. Colloid Sci.* **5**, 448 (1950).

293. Palit. S. R., and Venkateswarlu, V. *Proc. Roy. Soc.* **A208**, 542 (1951).

294. Inoue, T., and Iida, Y. *J. Chem. Soc. Japan* **74**, 145 (1953). (In Japanese.)

295. Debye, P., and Prins, W. *J. Colloid Sci.* **13**, 86 (1958).

296. Honig, J. G., and Singleterry, C. R. *J. Phys. Chem.* **58**, 201 (1954).

297. Honig, J. G., and Singleterry, C. R. *J. Phys. Chem.* **60**, 1108 (1956).

298. Batson, F. M., and Kraus, C. A. *J. Am. Chem. Soc.* **56**, 2017 (1934)

299. Martin, E, P., and Pink, R. C. *J. Chem. Soc.* p. 1750 (1948).

300. Oster, G. *Chem. Rev.* **43**, 319 (1948).

301. Mathews, M. B., and Hirschhorn, E. *J. Colloid Sci.* **8**, 86 (1953).

302. Kaufman, S., and Singleterry, C. R. *J. Colloid Sci.* **12**, 465 (1957).

303. Copenhafer, D. T., and Kraus, C. A. *J. Am. Chem. Soc.* **73**, 4557 (1951).

304. Rothrock, D. A., Jr., and Kraus, C. A. *J. Am. Chem. Soc.* **59**, 1699 (1937).

305. Palit, S. R., and Venkateswarlu, V. *J. Chem. Soc.* p. 2129 (1954).

306. Gonick, E. *J. Colloid Sci.* **1**, 393 (1946).

307. Elworthy, P. H. *J. Chem. Soc.* pp. 813, 1951 (1959).

308. Nelson, S. M., and Pink, R. C *J. Chem. Soc.* p. 1744 (1952).

309. Honig, J. G., and Singleterry, C. R. *J. Phys. Chem.* **60**, 1114 (1956).

310. Sheffer, H. *Can. J. Research* **26B**, 481 (1948).

311. Kaufman, S., and Singleterry, C. R. *J. Colloid Sci.* **10**, 139 (1955).

312. Gray, V. R., and Alexander, A. E. *J. Phys. Chem.* **53**, 9 (1949).

313. Kitahara, A. *J. Colloid Sci.* **12**, 342 (1957).

314. Kaufman, S., and Singleterry, C. R. *J. Phys. Chem.* **62**, 1257 (1958).

314a. Kitahara, A. To be published.

CHAPTER TWO

PHYSICOCHEMICAL STUDIES IN AQUEOUS SOLUTIONS OF NONIONIC SURFACE ACTIVE AGENTS

TOSHIO NAKAGAWA AND KŌZŌ SHINODA

I. Introduction

The production and application of nonionic surface active agents are rapidly increasing, owing to the decreasing costs of manufacture, increasing applications and appreciation in many fields, and the wide range of physical properties and performance characteristics covered by the various members of the nonionic agents.

The advantages of nonionic agents include the following: (i) the properties of each compound can be modified considerably by simply changing the length of the polyoxyethylene group, and (ii) nonionics are well suited for mixing and formulation with other materials, since they are chemically inert and stable toward pH change.

The physicochemical properties of nonionic agents are, however, not yet fully investigated. In reality, the physicochemical properties of nonionic surface active agents were discussed only by analogy with those of ionic agents until several years ago. Most of the published work was carried out using commercial or rather impure materials because the pure compounds are difficult to prepare; both the synthesis of pure nonionic agents and the purification of commercial nonionic agents are difficult and troublesome. But, at least in academic institutions, investigations using pure materials or mixtures of known amounts of pure materials are highly recommended. Recently, some systematic investigations have been undertaken with pure nonionic agents. It seems possible to give a general view of the physicochemical properties in aqueous solutions of nonionic agents at the present stage. More work using various types of nonionic agents seems very important.

Up to the critical concentration, it is considered that an ionic agent is a strong electrolyte, completely dissociated and unaggregated, except for the formation of a dimer. At the critical concentration, aggregation of the paraffin chain ions begins to produce a micelle, and the physicochemical properties of the solution show abrupt changes at this concentration (*1, 2, 3*) (CMC).

Similar phenomena are considered to occur also with the nonionics, as revealed in Sections II and III. The succeeding three sections are devoted to giving information with respect to the effects of temperature change and of interaction with other substances. The last two sections are concerned with purification and analysis. Their inclusion in this article is considered to be desirable because the purity of the examined material exerts a large influence on the behavior of its solutions, and the methods of purification and testing purity are not well known in the case of nonionic surface active agents. The sources and purification procedures of the materials cited in this chapter are summarized at the end of Section VIII. An asterisked superscript number indicates the key number to be referred to in Section VIII.

As for the theoretical aspects of micelle formation, it is still premature to draw any definite conclusions in detail. Therefore, only a brief discussion will be given here.

The possibility for the existence of a thermodynamically stable association colloid has been discussed qualitatively by Stauff (4). He concluded that the necessary condition for a stable micelle is the coexistence of two portions with different interaction properties in the molecule.

In the case of ionic surface active agents, micelle formation is considered to be controlled by two opposite factors, the strong intermolecular force between water, which repels hydrocarbon chains, and the electrical repulsion between ionized hydrophilic groups, as proposed by Debye (5) and succeeding theorists.

Reich (6) thought that the cross-sectional area of the hydrophilic group of a nonionic surface active agent is the dominant factor preventing the association of individual molecules and corresponds to electrical repulsion in the case of ionic agents, but his theory is too qualitative and leads to conclusions at variance with the experimental facts, as pointed out by Kushner et al. (7).

Hoeve and Benson (8) have published a theory which takes into account various factors that might play some part in the process of micelle formation. The usefulness of their theory beyond the point of qualitative predictions seems limited because there are too many numerically unknown factors involved (9).

Later, a theory was proposed by Nakagawa and Kuriyama (10) who considered that the main factors preventing the association are the heat of hydration and the configurational entropy terms of the flexible hydrophilic chain. It gives quantitative predictions for the CMC, micellar weight, and other properties of the solution, but cannot reasonably explain temperature effects and clouding phenomena.

II. Critical Micelle Concentration

Physical properties in an aqueous solution of an ionic surface active agent show abrupt changes in a certain narrow concentration range, and micelle formation occurs at this concentration. Conversely, these sudden changes in physicochemical properties have been used to determine the critical micelle concentration (CMC). As for nonionic surface active agents, there have been opposite opinions as to whether a clearly defined CMC does exist or not. Gonick and McBain (11) obtained CMC values of 6.3×10^{-4} and 9×10^{-4} moles/liter for nonaoxyethylene monododeca-noate[*1] and Triton X-100[*2] (polyoxyethylene isooctylphenyl ether, $\bar{M} = $ ca. 680), respectively, by means of freezing point depression measurements. Goto and his collaborators (12) attempted to synthesize pure hexaoxye-thylene dodecyl ether,[*3] finding a CMC which lay near 1×10^{-4} moles/liter (determined by specific molal volume, viscosity, spectral change, and solubilization measurements), but it turned out later that their material still contained impurities (13). Kushner et al. (14) measured the micellar weight of Triton X-100[*4] by the lightscattering method, but could not find a well-defined CMC. Hsiao et al. (15) have determined the CMC's of a series of Igepals[*5] (polyoxyethylene nonylphenyl ether) of varying hydrophilic chain length by means of surface tension meas-urements. It was found that the longer the hydrophilic group, the larger the CMC. In all these experiments, however, the materials were either commercial products or contained some impurities.

In order to clarify the phenomena, it seems instructive to determine the CMC's of carefully purified surface active agents by various methods and to compare them with results obtained from materials containing (known amounts of) impurities. The following experiments (16) were carried out along this line.

A commercial polyoxyethylene dodecyl ether $C_{12}H_{25}O(CH_2CH_2O)_nH$ was fractionated by moleculardistillation. A fraction[*6] having an average molecular weight of 440; a $3:10:7$ mixture[*7] of three fractions ($\bar{M} = 362$, 440, 473) whose over-all average molecular weight was 438; and the undistilled raw product[*8] (apparent $\bar{M} = 424$) were used. These will be called "fractionated," "mixed," and "raw" materials, repectively.

Surface tension measurements were carried out by the dropweight method. The results are plotted against the logarithm of the concentra-tion in Fig. 2.1. The curves thus obtained show a roughly constant slope at the beginning, followed by a flat portion.

This behavior is interpreted as follows (17): Applying the Gibbs adsorption isotherm, the surface excess is considered to be constant in the concentration range where the curve shows constant inclination, corresponding to the formation of a monomolecular layer. Above the

* Superscript numbers with asterisks refer to the sources and procedures listed in the "Purification Key" in Section VIII. See page 169.

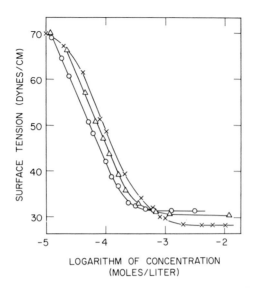

Fig. 2.1.   The surface tension vs. log concentration curves of the fractionated,[*6] mixed,[*7] and raw[*8] polyoxyethylene dodecyl ethers at 27°C: ○, fractionated; △, mixed; ×, raw.

CMC it is reasonable to suppose that the activity increases only slightly with an increase of concentration and thus the surface tension stays at a nearly constant value. From this standpoint, the departure from a straight line indicates the beginning of micelle formation, and the arrival at a horizontal line corresponds to its completion; this means that all of the amount added beyond this concentration dissolves in micellar state.

According to this view, the CMC's of the fractionated, mixed, and raw materials are 1.3–5×10^{-4}, 1.2–9×10^{-4}, and 2×10^{-4}–2×10^{-3} moles/ liter, respectively.   The purification narrows the range of micelle formation.   In the present case, the CMC values decreased with purification.

Solubilization of oil-soluble dye gives another confirmation.   Sudan III or aniline blue was added to an aqueous solution of each material, and the solubilization was examined by measuring absorbancy at the wavelength of maximum absorption.   The result with Sudan III is represented in Fig. 2.2.   The fractionated material gives a distinct break point, whereas that of the mixed material becomes somewhat ambiguous. The raw material does not show any recognizable break point.   A similar result was obtained for the addition of aniline blue.

The spectral change of water-soluble dyes has often been used to determine the CMC.   The molecular absorbancy at the wavelength of maximum absorption of the dye ε has been plotted against the con-

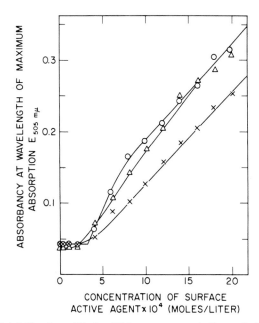

Fig. 2.2.   Solubilization of Sudan III by aqueous solutions of the fractionated,[*6] mixed,[*7] and raw[*8] polyoxyethylene dodecyl ethers: ◯, fractionated; △, mixed; ✕, raw.

centration of surface active agent in the case of ionic agents.   The break point on the ε vs. concentration curve is supposed to indicate the CMC.   Such a representation, however, does not afford a clear result in the case of nonionic agents.   Alternatively, the wavelength of maximum absorption λ_{max} vs. logarithm of the concentration showed a sigmoid curve.   The break point is the CMC, for the reason discussed in Section VI, 4.

The results obtained with pinacyanol chloride and erythrosin are illustrated in Figs. 2.3 and 2.4.   The former has two bands, α and β. Their successive shift with concentration change is shown in Fig. 2.5. The more impure the material, the more obscure is the break point, as indicated in Figs. 2.3 and 2.4.   Similar results were obtained using rhodamine 6G, eosin yellow, or tripan blue.

The electrocapillary maximum, half-wave potential or limiting diffusion current in polarography, shows a remarkable change at a certain concentration of surface active agent in the presence of supporting electrolytes, and this concentration is called the polarographic micelle point (PMP).   The minimum concentration of surface active agent necessary to suppress the maximum current is often called the maximum

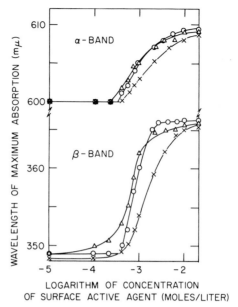

Fig. 2.3. Graph showing the shift of the wavelength of maximum absorption of pinacyanol chloride in aqueous solutions of the fractionated,*6 mixed,*7 and raw*8 polyoxyethylene dodecyl ethers at 27°C: ○, fractionated; △, mixed; ×, raw.

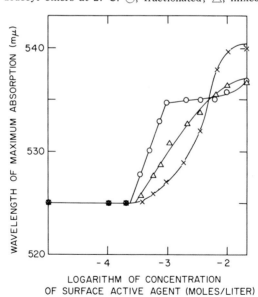

Fig. 2.4. Graph showing the shift of the wavelength of maximum absorption of erythrosin in aqueous solutions of the fractionated,*6 mixed,*7 and raw*8 polyoxyethylene dodecyl ethers at 27°C: ○, fractionated; △, mixed; ×, raw.

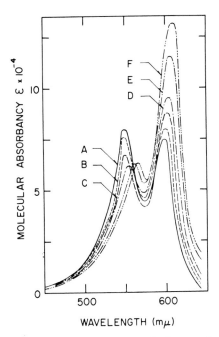

Fig. 2.5. Shift of the absorption spectrum of pinacyanol chloride as a function of concentration of the fractionated polyoxyethylene dodecyl ether.[*6] Concentration of surface active agent: (A) 0; (B) 1.01×10^{-4}; (C) 4.04×10^{-4}; (D) 8.08×10^{-4}; (E) 2.02×10^{-3}; (F) 1.01×10^{-2} moles/liter. Dye concentration: 1.42×10^{-5} moles/liter.

suppression point (MSP). It has been reported that the PMP and MSP are generally in accord with the CMC (18). The electrocapillary maximum vs. log concentration curves are compared for the fractionated and raw materials in Fig. 2.6. The ordinate represents the lifetime of a mercury drop that falls from the capillary at the cathode potential of maximum lifetime. The fractionated material shows the decay in a narrower range.

The half-wave potential of Zn^{2+} and diffusion current of Cd^{2+} are illustrated in Fig. 2.7. The concentration necessary to suppress the maximum current of nitrobenzene was examined. It was far lower than the CMC ($< 1 \times 10^{-5}$ mole/liter) determined by the other methods, supporting the finding of Tamamushi and Yamanaka (19) that the CMC and MSP are not identical.

CMC values of the fractionated material, estimated by various methods, are summarized in Table 2.1.

All of the above-mentioned experiments were carried out using surface active agents whose hydrophilic group is composed of polyoxyethylene

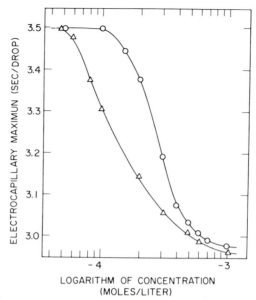

Fig. 2.6. Electrocapillary maximum (expressed as the lifetime of a falling mercury drop) vs. log concentration curves of the fractionated[*6] and raw[*8] polyoxyethylene dodecyl ethers at 27°C: ○, fractionated; △, raw. Supporting electrolyte, 0.1 N KCl.

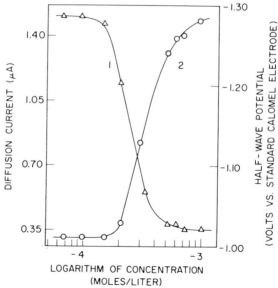

Fig. 2.7. Polarographic half-wave potential of Zn^{2+} and diffusion current of Cd^{2+} as a function of concentration of the fractionated polyoxyethylene dodecyl ether[*6] at 27°C: ○, half-wave potential; △, diffusion current. Curve (1) electrolyte $CdSO_4$ 0.5×10^{-4} moles/liter, KCl 0.1 moles/liter; curve (2) electrolyte $ZnSO_4$ 2×10^{-4} moles/liter, KCl 0.1 moles/liter.

TABLE 2.1

CRITICAL MICELLE CONCENTRATION OF FRACTIONATED POLYOXYETHYLENE
DODECYL ETHER[*6] (27°C)

A. Determined by Spectral Change of Dye		
Dye	Charge of dye ion	CMC (moles/liter)
Pinacyanol chloride	+	5×10^{-4}
Erythrosin	−	3×10^{-4}
Rhodamine 6G	+	6×10^{-4}
Eosin yellow	−	6×10^{-4}
Trypan blue	−	4×10^{-4}

B. Determined by Other Methods	
Method	CMC (moles/liter)
Surface tension	$1.3–5 \times 10^{-4}$
Solubilization of Sudan III	3.0×10^{-4}
Solubilization of aniline blue	5.5×10^{-4}
Electrocapillary maximum	5×10^{-4}
Half-wave potential	$1.5 \times 10^{-4}–1 \times 10^{-3}$
Diffusion current	$1.5–7 \times 10^{-4}$

chains. Even though a material is purified by molecular distillation, it may be composed of homologous compounds with different lengths of polyoxyethylene chain. On the other hand, polyol ethers of paraffin chain alcohols have an advantage for purification. Fractional distillation or recrystallization is applicable, and impurities of this type of compound may differ more in chemical properties.

Bury and Browning (17) have determined the CMC of octyl glucoside[*9] by surface tension measurements. The surface tension vs. log concentration curve exhibited a sharp inflection at 2.5×10^{-2} moles/liter.

More recently, Shinoda and collaborators (20) published data on octyl glycol ether,[*10] α-octyl glyceryl ether,[*11] and octyl β-D-glucoside.[*12] Their surface tension vs. log concentration curves are represented in Fig. 2.8. For the purpose of comparison, those of sodium dodecyl sulfate and (5, 8)-oxyethylene dodecyl ether (formerly named "the fractionated material")[*6] are also included. The inflections of these ethers are as sharp as, or even more sharp than, those of ionic surface active agents. Similar results were obtained recently for decyl glucoside[*12] and dodecyl glucoside[*12] (21). Applying the Gibbs adsorption isotherm equation, the surface excess was calculated from the inclination under the assumption that $\delta \ln a / \delta \ln c = 1$. The residual area per molecule is also calculated. These values, along with CMC's, are listed in Table 2.2. Osipow et al.

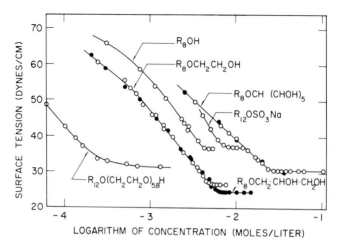

Fig. 2.8. The surface tension vs. log concentration curves of octanol, octyl glycol ether[*10], α-octyl glyceryl ether,[*11] and octyl glucoside.[*12]

TABLE 2.2

CRITICAL MICELLE CONCENTRATION, SURFACE EXCESS, AND RESIDUAL AREA PER MOLECULE OF SEVERAL PURIFIED NONIONIC SURFACE ACTIVE AGENTS

Surface active agent	CMC (moles/liter)	Surface excess $\times 10^{10}$ (moles)	Area/molecule ($\mathring{A}^2$)
R_8OH	—	5.6	30
$R_8OCH_2CH_2OH$[*10]	4.9×10^{-3}	5.2	32
$R_8OCH_2CHOHCH_2OH$[*11]	5.8×10^{-3}	5.2	32
$R_8OCH \angle (CHOH)_5$[*12]	2.5×10^{-2}	4.0	41
$R_8NC_5H_5Br$	2.3×10^{-1a}	4.9^a	34^a
$R_{10}OCH \angle (CHOH)_5$[*12]	2.2×10^{-3e}	3.5^e	47^e
$R_{12}OCH \angle (CHOH)_5$[*12]	1.9×10^{-4e}	4.6^e	36^e
$R_{12}OSO_3Na$	8.1×10^{-3b}	4.0^c	33^b, 40^c
$R_{12}O(CH_2CH_2O)_{5.8}H$[*6]	2.5×10^{-4d}	4.9^d	34^d

^{a} From reference (17), ^{d} From reference (16),
^{b} From reference (23), ^{e} From reference (21).
^{c} From reference (24),

(22) measured the surface tension of sucrose monododecanote[*13] and monooctadecanoate[*13] as a function of concentration; the CMC's were 34×10^{-5} and 64×10^{-7} moles/liter, respectively.

Putting together these results, we may conclude with fair confidence that if a nonionic surface active agent is pure it has a sharp, well-defined

CMC. On the contrary, if it is composed of a series of homologous compounds or contaminated with some impurities, it gives a more ambiguous CMC.

Now we return to the surface active agents belonging to the polyoxyethylene series. As already mentioned, Hsiao *et al* (*15*) have determined the CMC's of Igepals[*5] (polyoxyethylene nonylphenyl ether) of various hydrophilic chain lengths and found that the CMC becomes higher the longer the polyoxyethylene chain. Their results are reproduced in Table 2.3.

TABLE 2.3

CRITICAL MICELLE CONCENTRATION, SURFACE EXCESS, AND RESIDUAL AREA PER
MOLECULE OF VARIOUS IGEPALS[*5] (COMMERCIAL POLYOXYETHYLENB
NONYL (OCTYL) PHENYL ETHER)

Surface active agent	CMC (moles/liter)	Surface excess $\times 10^{10}$ (moles/cm^2)	Area/ molecule (Å^2)
$C_8H_{17}\text{-}C_6H_4O(CH_2CH_2O)_{8.5}H$	$1.8\text{-}2.3\times10^{-4}$	3.15	53
$C_9H_{19}\text{-}C_6H_4O(CH_2CH_2O)_{9.5}H$	$7.8\text{-}9.2\times10^{-5}$	3.05	55
$C_9H_{19}\text{-}C_6H_4O(CH_2CH_2O)_{10.5}H$	$7.5\text{-}9.0\times10^{-5}$	2.75	60
$C_9H_{19}\text{-}C_6H_4O(CH_2CH_2O)_{15}H$	$1.1\text{-}1.3\times10^{-4}$	2.30	72
$C_9H_{19}\text{-}C_6H_4O(CH_2CH_2O)_{20}H$	$1.35\text{-}1.75\times10^{-4}$	2.00	82
$C_9H_{19}\text{-}C_6H_4O(CH_2CH_2O)_{30}H$	$2.5\text{-}3.0\times10^{-4}$	1.65	101
$C_9H_{19}\text{-}C_6H_4O(CH_2CH_2O)_{100}H$	$1.0 \quad \times10^{-3}$	0.95	173

The materials examined by these authors, however, are commercial products and possibly contain nonylphenol and polyethylene glycol. Moreover, the numbers of oxyethylene groups shown in the molecular formulas in Table 2.3 are the average numbers of oxyethylene groups. According to the above-mentioned conclusion, the impurity and polydispersity of a material affect the CMC and introduce a certain degree of ambiguity in to the CMC determination. Therefore, experiments using pure materials or mixtures of known composition are highly desirable.

Nakagawa and collaborators (*25*) synthesized pure methoxypolyoxyethylene decanoates[*14] and methoxypolyoxyethylene dodecanoates[*14] of which the polyoxyethylene groups have different chain lengths. All of them except $C_9H_{19}COO(CH_2CH_2O)_{16}CH_3$ were synthesized from molecularly-distilled methoxypolyethylene glycols; $C_9H_{19}COO(CH_2CH_2O)_{16}CH_3$[*15] was synthesized from the undistilled glycol, and, therefore, it may be composed of widely distributed homologous compounds.

The CMC's of these nonionic agents were determined by the solubilization of Sudan III and by the spectral changes of pinacyanol chloride and/or erythrosin. Solubilization curves of $C_9H_{19}COO(CH_2CH_2O)_nCH_3$ are

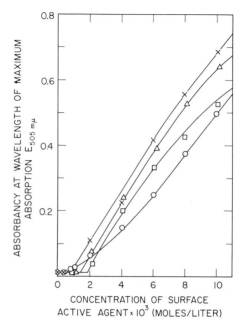

Fig. 2.9. Solubilization of Sudan III by methoxypolyoxyethylene decanoates[14],[15] whose polyoxyethylene groups have different chain lengths at 27°C.
$C_9H_{19}COO(CH_2CH_2O)_nCH_3$: $\times$, $n=7.0$; $\triangle$, $n=10.3$; $\square$, $n=11.9$; $\bigcirc$, $n=16.0$.

represented in Fig. 2.9. As $C_9H_{19}COO(CH_2CH_2O)_{16}CH_3$ was not purified, it did not show a clear break point. As an example, λ_{max} vs. log concentration curves of pinacyanol—$C_9H_{19}COO(CH_2CH_2O)_nCH_3$ systems are represented in Fig. 2.10. The results obtained are summarized in Table 2.4.

The CMC becomes higher with an increase of hydrophilic chain and with a decrease of hydrocarbon chain length, in agreement with the other results (15, 20, 21, 22). Two papers which contradict the above finding have been published. Lange (26) found that Traube's rule was invalid with polyoxyethylene ethers[16] of paraffin chain alcohols whose hydrocarbon chain is longer than dodecyl. The materials examined by him, however, were not pure materials. Therefore, a careful re-examination is desired. Becher (27) examined the CMC's of various commercial products[17] with different lengths of polyoxyethylene groups by the iodine solubilization technique (28). In many cases, the CMC (when expressed in moles/ liter) decreased with the length of hydrophilic chain. Purification of these materials is also desirable before any conclusions are drawn.

In connection with the above statement, it is interesting to compare

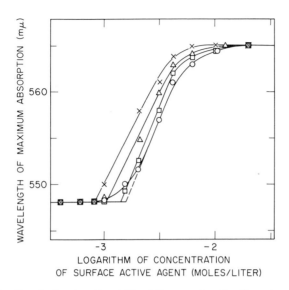

Fig. 2.10. Graph showing the shift of the wavelength of maximum absorption of pinacyanol chloride in aqueous solutions of methoxypolyoxyethylene decanoates[14],[15] whose polyoxyethylene groups have different chain lengths (27°C).
$C_9H_{19}COO(CH_2CH_2O)_nCH_3$: ×, $n=7.0$; △, $n=10.3$; □, $n=11.9$; ○, $n=16.0$.

TABLE 2.4

CRITICAL MICELLE CONCENTRATIONS OF METHOXYPOLYOXYETHYLENE
DECANOATES[14],[15] AND DODECANOATES[14] (27°C)

Surface active agent	Cloud point (1% soln) °C	CMC × 10⁴(moles/liter)		
		Solubilization of Sudan III	Spectral change of	
			pinacyanol chloride	erythrosin
$C_9H_{19}COO(CH_2CH_2O)_{7.0}CH_3$	44	10	8.0	9.5
$C_9H_{19}COO(CH_2CH_2O)_{10.3}CH_3$	65	14	10.5	11.5
$C_9H_{19}COO(CH_2CH_2O)_{11.9}CH_3$	74	18	14.0	14.5
$C_9H_{19}COO(CH_2CH_2O)_{16.0}CH_3$[a]	—		(16.0)	—
$C_{11}H_{23}COO(CH_2CH_2O)_{6.0}CH_3$	31	1.6	1.5	2.0
$C_{11}H_{23}COO(CH_2CH_2O)_{8.4}CH_3$	53	2.0	2.7	2.7
$C_{11}H_{23}COO(CH_2CH_2O)_{11.2}CH_3$	74	2.5	3.2	3.1
$C_{11}H_{23}COO(CH_2CH_2O)_{12.5}CH_3$	79	2.8	3.5	3.4

[a] The hydrophilic group of this compound was not fractionated by molecular distillation.

the CMC's of surface active agents which have an ionizable group at the (outer) end of the polyoxyethylene chain. Weil et al. (29) synthe-

TABLE 2.5

Critical Micelle Concentrations of Ether Alcohol Sulfates*[18] (25°C)

Surface active agent	CMC × 10⁴		
	Conductance method (moles/liter)	Surface tension method (moles/liter)	Dye titration method (moles/liter)
$C_{16}H_{33}OSO_3Na$[a]		4	
$C_{16}H_{33}OCH_2CH_2OSO_3Na$	2.34	2.1	2.2
$C_{16}H_{33}(OCH_2CH_2)_2OSO_3Na$	1.34	1.2	1.4
$C_{16}H_{33}(OCH_2CH_2)_3OSO_3Na$	1.23	0.7	1.0
$C_{16}H_{33}(OCH_2CH_2)_4OSO_3Na$		0.8	1.0
$C_{18}H_{37}OCH_2CH_2OSO_3Na$		1.9	1.1
$C_{18}H_{37}(OCH_2CH_2)_2OSO_3Na$		0.8	0.7
$C_{18}H_{37}(OCH_2CH_2)_3OSO_3Na$		0.5	0.5
$C_{18}H_{37}(OCH_2CH_2)_4OSO_3Na$		0.4	0.4

[a] Measurements at 30°C.

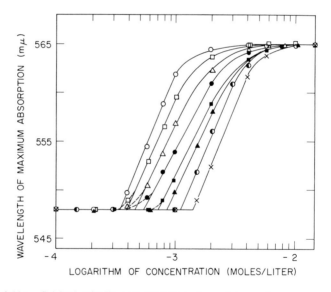

Fig. 2.11a. Critical micelle concentration of a mixture of
$C_9H_{19}COO(CH_2CH_2O)_{11.9}CH_3$*[14] and $C_{11}H_{23}COO(CH_2CH_2O)_{12.5}CH_3$*[14]
with varying ratio, determined by the spectral color change of pinacyanol chloride (27°C).
$C_9H_{19}COO(CH_2CH_2O)_{11.9}CH_3 : C_{11}H_{23}COO(CH_2CH_2O)_{12.5}CH_3$
(molar ratio): ×, 1.0 : 0; ◑, 0.9 : 0.1; ▲, 0.78 : 0.22; ■, 0.7 : 0.3; ●, 0.6 : 0.4;
△, 0.4 : 0.6; □, 0.3 : 0.7; ○, 0 : 1.0.

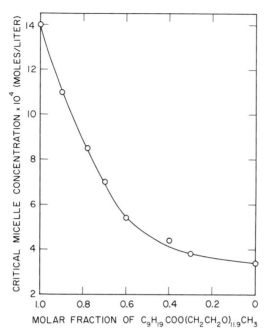

Fig. 2.11b. Critical micelle concentration of a mixture of
        $C_9H_{19}COO(CH_2CH_2O)_{11.9}CH_3$[14] and $C_{11}H_{23}COO(CH_2CH_2O)_{12.5}CH_3$[14]
with varying ratio, determined by the spectral color change of pinacyanol chloride
(27°C).

sized a series of ether alcohol sulfates[18] having a general formula $RO(CH_2CH_2O)_nSO_3Na$, and determined their CMC's by conductance, dye titration, and surface tension methods. The CMC decreased with an increase in the length of polyoxyethylene chain, as shown in Table 2.5. This tendency may be interpreted in terms of the electrical repulsion between ionizable groups.

In all examples hitherto reported, nonionic surface active agents show a much lower CMC value than that of ionic agents whose paraffin chain is the same. This small CMC results from the absence of dissociable groups. The reason was explained in detail in Chapter 1.

The CMC of a mixture of nonionic agents whose polyoxyethylene chain lengths are close, but whose paraffin chain lengths are different, was examined by the spectral color change of pinacyanol choride (30). The results obtained are illustrated in Fig. 2.11. The curve of the CMC vs. mole fraction resembles on the whole that of mixtures of ionic agents (31, 32) and was explained in Chapter 1. Some examples of the CMC's of mixtures of nonionics of the glucoside type (21) are shown in Table

1.20, along with data on other mixtures.

As revealed for octyl glucoside[*12] in Table 1.19 (21), added salts seem to decrease the CMC of nonionic agents, although in much lesser degree than is the case for ionic agents.

III. Micellar Weight

Nonionic surface active agents form micelles whose particle weights are ordinarily some tens of thousands in aqueous solution.   These micellar weights can in principle be determined by various methods, such as light scattering, diffusion, sedimentation velocity, sedimentation equilibrium, and their combinations, which can be applied in the determination of molecular weights of high polymers. Of these methods, light scattering and diffusion-viscosity techniques have been applied in the determination of micellar weights in aqueous solutions of purified nonionic surface active agents.

According to the theory of light scattering in dilute colloidal solutions, the following relation holds for scattering units whose dimensions are less than 1/20 of the wavelength of light:

$$\frac{KC}{R_{90}} = \frac{1}{M} + 2A_2C \tag{2.1}$$

$$K = \frac{2\pi^2 n_0^2 (dn/dc)^2}{N\lambda^4}$$

where R_{90} is the reduced intensity of scattered light at an angle of $90°$; n_0 is the refractive index of solvent; n is the refractive index of solution; C is the concentration in gm/cc; N is the Avogadro number; λ is the wavelength of radiation in a vacuum; M is the weight-average molecular weight of the colloidal particles; and A_2 is the second virial coefficient. The following equation, which is equivalent to Eq. (2.1), is also used frequently.

$$\frac{HC}{\tau} = \frac{1}{M} + 2A_2C \tag{2.2}$$

where $H = 32\pi^3 n_0^2 (dn/dc)^2 / 3\lambda^4 N$ and τ is the turbidity of the solution.

In the case of solutions of surface active agents, the scattering unit, namely, the micelle, forms above the critical micelle concentration.   The concentration of molecularly dispersed surface active agents is considered to be approximately constant above the CMC. Then, in the concentration range of interest the results may be represented by

$$\frac{H(C - C_0)}{\tau - \tau_0} = \frac{1}{M} + 2A_2(C - C_0) \tag{2.3}$$

where C_0 is the critical micelle concentration, and τ_0 is the turbidity of solution at the critical micelle concentration. From the intercept and slope of the plot of $K(C - C_0)/R_{90}$ or $[H(C - C_0)/(\tau - \tau_0)]$ against $(C - C_0)$, the micellar weight and second virial coefficient are determined; C_0 is obtained from the R_{90} vs. concentration curve, otherwise the CMC obtained by some other method is used. It should be remarked that the micellar weight and second virial coefficient thus obtained by the aid of Eq. (2.1) or (2.2) are derived on the assumption that the micellar weight does not vary as a function of the concentration of the solution. If the micellar weight changes as a function of the concentration of the solution, the slope of the line, i.e., the apparent value of A_2, changes considerably, but the micellar weight changes only a little.

Kushner et al. (7) have measured the micellar weight of fractionated[*19] and unfractionated[*4] Triton X-100 (polyoxyethylene isooctylphenyl ether) by the use of light scattering. The HC/τ vs. concentration relation was not linear below concentrations of 0.003–0.004 gm/cc. A plot of the results after subtraction of C_0, † the concentration below which the results deviate from a linear relation, showed a linear relation. The results are shown in Table 2.6.

TABLE 2.6

MICELLAR WEIGHTS OF FRACTIONATED[*19] AND UNFRACTIONATED[*4] TRITON X-100

$C_8H_{17}\text{-}C_6H_4O(CH_2CH_2O)_nH$	n^a	Micellar weight
Lowboiling fraction	8	208,000
Unfractionated	10	90.000
Highboiling fraction	12	53,500

[a] Estimated by freezing point depression of benzene solution.

Stauff and Rasper (33) have measured the micellar weight of fractionated polyoxyethylene dodecyl ether[*20] by the same technique. In this case, the HC/τ vs. concentration curves were plotted neglecting the correction of C_0, C_0 being usually negligibly small in nonionic surface active agents. The results are shown in Table 2.7.

TABLE 2.7

MICELLAR WEIGHTS OF TWO FRACTIONS OF POLYOXYETHYLENE
DODECYL ETHER[*20]

Fraction[a]	Micellar weight	Aggregation number
$C_{12}H_{25}O(CH_2CH_2O)_{9.5}H$	38,500	63
$C_{12}H_{25}O(CH_2CH_2O)_{12}H$	32,000	45

[a] The numbers of oxyethylene groups were estimated by OH-value test.

† This concentration seems about ten times higher than the CMC of Triton X-100.

Nakagawa and his collaborators (34) have measured the micellar weights of purified methoxypolyoxyethylene decanoates[*14] and methoxypolyoxyethylene dodecanoates.[*14] The CMC's of these compounds have already been given in Table 2.4. The relationship between $K(C - C_0)/R_{90}$ and $(C - C_0)$ of these nonionics is shown in Fig. 2.12. The micellar weights and second virial coefficients calculated from these results are summarized in Table 2.8. In our calculation, the CMC values (2–18 × 10^{-4}

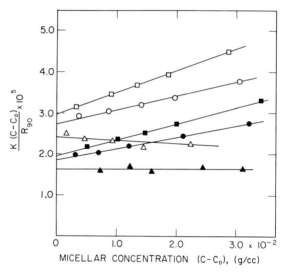

Fig. 2.12. $K(C - C_0)/R_{90}$ vs. micellar concentration $(C - C_0)$ curves of methoxy-polyoxyethylene decanoates[*14] and dodecanoates.[*14] $C_9H_{19}COO(CH_2CH_2O)_nCH_3$: $\square$, $n = 11.9$; $\bigcirc$, $n = 10.3$; $\triangle$, $n = 7.0$; $C_{11}H_{23}COO(CH_2CH_2O)_nCH_3$: $\blacksquare$, $n = 12.5$; $\bullet$, $n = 11.2$; $\blacktriangle$, $n = 8.4$.

TABLE 2.8

MICELLAR WEIGHTS AND SECOND VIRIAL COEFFICIENTS OF METHOXY-POLYOXYETHYLENE DECANOATES[*14] AND DODECANOATES[*14] (24–30°C)

Surface active agent	Micellar weight $(M \times 10^{-4})$	Partial specific volume, v (cc/gm)	Effective volume of 1 gm surfactant, V (cc/gm)	Second virial coeff., $A_2 \times 10^4$		
				Obs	Calc	
					Nonhydrated	Hydrated
$C_9H_{19}COO(CH_2CH_2O)_{7.0}CH_3$	4.15	0.9511	1.53	−0.75	+0.92	+1.47
$C_9H_{19}COO(CH_2CH_2O)_{10.3}CH_3$	3.68	0.9225	1.76	+1.75	1.00	1.91
$C_9H_{19}COO(CH_2CH_2O)_{11.9}CH_3$	3.37	0.9091	1.86	2.63	1.08	2.21
$C_{11}H_{23}COO(CH_2CH_2O)_{8.4}CH_3$	6.06	0.9511	1.60	0.00	0.63	1.06
$C_{11}H_{23}COO(CH_2CH_2O)_{11.2}CH_3$	5.40	0.9242	1.86	1.40	0.69	1.38
$C_{11}H_{23}COO(CH_2CH_2O)_{12.5}CH_3$	5.13	0.9191	1.97	2.00	0.72	1.54

moles/liter) determined by solubilization of Sudan III, were subtracted from the stoichiometric concentrations.

The turbidity of methoxyhexaoxyethylene dodecanote,

$$C_{11}H_{23}COO(CH_2CH_2O)_6CH_3,$$

changed remarkably with a small change in temperature, and accurate measurements were difficult to perform. The micellar weight of this solution obtained from exploratory measurements was about one million. This value seems far too large compared with the other compounds examined. Presumably, the micellar weight increases enormously when the temperature of the solution approaches the cloud point. The cloud point of $C_{11}H_{23}COO(CH_2CH_2O)_6CH_3$ was 31°C, whereas the cloud points of all the other compounds were 44–79°C.

To confirm the results obtained above, the micellar weights of the same nonionics were determined by diffusion-viscosity measurements (35), since two or more independent experiments are highly desirable for a determination of the particle size. If we assume that the micelle can be treated as a spherical particle, the frictional constant is given by Stokes' law as $f = 6\pi\eta r$, provided $\Delta\rho v r \ll \eta$, where η is the viscosity of the solvent, r is the radius of the particle, $\Delta\rho$ is the difference in density, and v is the velocity of the particle. Under these conditions, the important relation on diffusion known as the Sutherland-Einstein equation holds

$$D = \frac{kT}{6\pi\eta r} \tag{2.4}$$

where D is the diffusion coefficient.

From the measurement of the diffusion coefficient, the size of the hydrated micelle v can be determined. On the other hand, we can measure the volume fraction ϕ of dispersed spherical particles by the aid of the equation extended to concentrated solution by Guth and Simha, (36)

$$\eta r = 1 + 2.5\phi + 14.1\phi^2 \tag{2.5}$$

where ηr is the relative viscosity of the solution. If we express the effective volume of one gram of solute, i.e., the effective specific volume of surface active agent including hydrated water as V, then

$$V = \frac{\phi}{C}$$

where C is the concentration of solution in grams/cc.

Effective volumes of one gram of nonionic agent calculated from viscosity measurements by the aid of Eq. (2.5) are shown in Fig. 2.13.

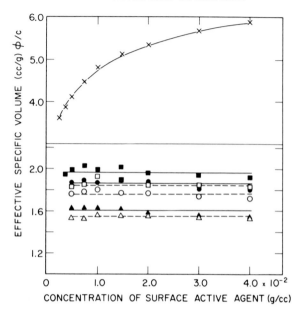

Fig. 2.13. Effective specific volumes of methoxypolyoxyethylene decanoates*[14] and dodecanoates,*[14] calculated assuming Guth and Simha equation:

$C_9H_{19}COO(CH_2CH_2O)_nCH_3$ (- - -): □, $n = 11.9$; ○, $n = 10.3$; △, $n = 7.0$.
$C_{11}H_{23}COO(CH_2CH_2O)_nCH_3$ (——): ■, $n = 12.5$; ●, $n = 11.2$; ▲, $n = 8.4$;
×, $n = 6.0$.

The effective volume of each nonionic agent stays constant over all the concentration ranges studied, except in the case of $C_{11}H_{23}COO(CH_2CH_2O)_6$ CH_3. The constancy of the effective specific volumes calculated at various concentrations supports the adequacy of the assumption of a spherical micelle. If the micelle were markedly deformed from a spherical shape, Eq. (2.5) would not hold, and therefore the ϕ-values calculated assuming Eq. (2.5) would lead to the unreasonable result that the volume fraction of the dispersed particles was not proportional to the concentration even in dilute solutions. The diffusion coefficients were measured using Neurath-type cells. The detergent concentrations in the upper and lower layers were 1 and 2%, respectively.

Expressing r in Eq. (2.4) in terms of the micellar weight and the effective specific volume V of nonionic surface active agent, including hydrated water, we obtain

$$MV = \frac{4}{3}\pi r^3 N = vN$$

$$M = \frac{(RT)^3}{162\pi^2\eta^3 N^2 D^3 V} \tag{2.6}$$

where N is the Avogadro number. As both v and V include hydrated water, and its effect cancels in the calculation, the micellar weight thus obtained does not include hydrated water.

The results for diffusion coefficient, micellar weight, micellar volume, and derived values are shown in Table 2.9a.

Comparing the effective volume and partial specific volume of surface active agent $\bar{v}$, the number of hydrated water molecules per nonionic molecule and the micellar weight including hydrated water, etc. were calculated, as shown in Table 2.9b.

TABLE 2.9a

DIFFUSION COEFFICIENTS, MICELLAR WEIGHTS, AND MICELLAR VOLUMES OF METHOXYPOLYOXYETHYLENE DECANOATES[*14] AND DODECANOATES[*14] (25°C)

Surface active agent	Diffusion coeff. $D \times 10^7$ (cm²/sec)	Radius of micelle $r \times 10^8$ (cm)	Effective volume of one micelle $v \times 10^{20}$ (cc)	Effective volume of 1 gm surfactant V (cc/gm)	Micellar weight ($M \times 10^{-4}$)	Association number (n)
$C_9H_{19}COO(CH_2CH_2O)_{7.0}CH_3$	8.29	29.5	10.8	1.53	4.25	86
$C_9H_{19}COO(CH_2CH_2O)_{10.3}CH_3$	8.29	29.5	10.8	1.76	3.70	58
$C_9H_{19}COO(CH_2CH_2O)_{11.9}CH_3$	8.36	29.2	10.4	1.86	3.37	48
$C_{11}H_{23}COO(CH_2CH_2O)_{8.4}CH_3$	7.29	33.5	15.8	1.60	5.93	102
$C_{11}H_{23}COO(CH_2CH_2O)_{11.2}CH_3$	7.47	32.7	14.6	1.86	4.74	67
$C_{11}H_{23}COO(CH_2CH_2O)_{12.5}CH_3$	7.38	33.1	15.2	1.97	4.64	60
$C_{11}H_{23}COO(CH_2CH_2O)_{6.0}CH_3$	2.8			$(1.40)^a$		

^{a} Extrapolated.

TABLE 2.9b

NUMBERS OF HYDRATED WATER MOLECULES PER NONIONIC MOLECULE (W_n),[a] NUMBERS OF HYDRATED WATER MOLECULES PER OXYGEN ATOM (W_o),[a] AND MICELLAR WEIGHTS INCLUDING HYDRATED WATER (M')[a] ESTIMATED FOR METHOXYPOLYOXYETHYLENE DECANOATES[*14] AND DODECANOATES[*14] (25°C)

Surface active agent	$W_n = m(V-\bar{v})d/18$	$W_o = m(V-\bar{v})d/18p$	$M' = M(V+1-\bar{v})d$ $M' \times 10^{-4}$
$C_9H_{19}COO(CH_2CH_2O)_{7.0}CH_3$	15.8	2.26	6.72
$C_9H_{19}COO(CH_2CH_2O)_{10.3}CH_3$	29.8	2.89	6.81
$C_9H_{19}COO(CH_2CH_2O)_{11.9}CH_3$	37.3	3.13	6.57
$C_{11}H_{23}COO(CH_2CH_2O)_{8.4}CH_3$	21.0	2.50	9.78
$C_{11}H_{23}COO(CH_2CH_2O)_{11.2}CH_3$	36.9	3.30	9.20
$C_{11}H_{23}COO(CH_2CH_2O)_{12.5}CH_3$	44.7	3.57	9.51

^{a} In the column headings, m denotes molecular weight of surface active agent; d, density of hydrated water ≈ 1; and p, number of oxyethylene groups.

The number of hydrated water molecules was about 2–3 per oxygen atom within experimental accuracy. This value seems reasonable. The number of hydrated water molecules assigned per oxygen atom increases for longer nonionic agents. Some of the water may simply be trapped among aggregated polyoxyethylene groups, and this amount evidently increases when the hydrophilic group becomes longer. The increase in hydrated water for longer polyoxyethylene nonionics agrees with the trend of rise in cloud point.

In the case of $C_{11}H_{23}COO(CH_2CH_2O)_6CH_3$, the assumption of a spherical micelle cannot apply because ϕ/C, calculated from Eq. (2.5), increases with the concentration and does not stay constant. The diffusion coefficient is also far smaller than for the other nonionic agents, and, moreover, the diffusion diagram is not symmetrical, depending on the concentration. Accordingly, we have assumed an ellipsoid as the shape of the micelle of $C_{11}H_{23}COO(CH_2CH_2O)_6CH_3$.

Onclay (37) has discussed the combined effects of hydration and axial ratio a/b in the contours (I) of $\eta_{sp}/\bar{v}C$, and those in the contours (II) of frictional ratio f/f_0 for dispersions of ellipsoids; η_{sp} is the specific viscosity, and $\bar{v}$ is the partial specific volume of solute. Effective volume per gram of $C_{11}H_{23}COO(CH_2CH_2O)_6CH_3$ was calculated from the extrapolation of effective volumes of $C_{11}H_{23}COO(CH_2CH_2O)_nCH_3$ for which $n = 8.4$, 11.2, and 12.5.

The amount of hydration per gram of surface active agent is then given as $(V - \bar{v})$. As Onclay's contours are drawn for protein of $\bar{v} = 0.75$, we should use $0.75(V - \bar{v})/\bar{v}$ instead of $(V - \bar{v})$ as the effective hydration value in the present system; $\eta_{sp}/\bar{v}C$ was obtained by extrapolating the experimental values to zero concentration. Using these values, the axial ratio was read on contour (I), and the frictional ratio was then obtained from contour (II). The results are summarized in Table 2.10. The

TABLE 2.10

MICELLAR DIMENSIONS ESTIMATED FOR $C_{11}H_{23}COO(CH_2CH_2O)_6CH_3$*[14] (25°C)

Assumption		Oblate	Prolate
Axial ratio (a/b)		0.17	4.7
Frictional ratio (f/f_0)		1.41	1.38
Micellar weight $(M \times 10^{-4})$		61.1	65.6
Association number (n)		1270	1360
Axis a (rotational axis) (Å)		21	200
Axis b (Å)		125	42
Rotational diffusion coeff.	$(\Theta_a \times 10^{-5}\ sec^{-1})$	1.82	5.78
	$(\Theta_b \times 10^{-5}\ sec^{-1})$	2.13	1.22

solution showed Newtonian flow in the concentration range investigated.*

According to Boltzmann's treatment (39), the differential diffusion coefficient can be calculated as a function of concentration by integrating the diffusion diagram. The differential diffusion coefficient at zero concentration $D(0)$ is estimated by extrapolation. From the equation $f/f_0 = D_0/D(0)$, D_0—the diffusion coefficient corresponding to $f = f_0$—is calculated; D_0 is the diffusion coefficient of an imaginary unsolvated spherical particle of the same molecular weight and density as that investigated. The micellar weight is then calculated by the aid of the equation

$$M = \frac{(RT)^3}{162\pi^2 \eta^3 N^2 D_0^3 \bar{v}} \qquad (2.7)$$

The shape of the micelle, assuming a hydrated ellipsoid, is shown in Table 2.10.

The micellar weight thus calculated is subject to the errors due to extrapolation in estimating the hydrated water, $\eta_{sp}/\bar{v}C$, and the diffusion coefficient. The short axes derived from the assumption of oblate and prolate ellipsoids are 21 Å and 42 Å, respectively. As the paraffin chain length and elongated length of the nonionic molecule are 16.6 Å and 38.2 Å, the prolate shape seems unreasonable for this micelle. The micellar weights obtained from lightscattering and diffusion-viscosity methods are compared in Table 2.11, where the data hitherto reported (available by the end of 1959) on the micellar weights of nonionic agents at moderate temperatures are collected. The agreement between the values obtained from the two methods is satisfactory except in the case of $C_{11}H_{23}COO(CH_2CH_2O)_6CH_3$.

It can be concluded from Tables 2.6, 2.7, 2.8, and 2.11 that (i) the longer the hydrophilic group for nonionic agents of the same hydrocarbon chain, the smaller the micellar weight, and (ii) the longer the oleophilic group, the larger the micellar weight. The micellar region seems to increase with increasing size of the hydrophilic group until the HLB** of the molecule approaches some optimum value.

From the light scattering experiments, the second virial coefficient A_2, can be calculated. If we express the exclusion volume of a micelle as u and assume that the micellar weight does not vary over the entire concentration range, and if the heat of solution is negligible, then from a well-known equation (40), we obtain

---

* A suspensoid of ellipsoidal particles should show non-Newtonian flow in principle as the result of prefered orientation of particles along the direction of flow. It is concluded, however, from the theory of Kuhn (38) that the solution will be practically Newtonian within the range of velocity gradient investigated in the viscometer used in these experiments.

** HLB stands for hydrophilic-lypophilic balance.

TABLE 2.11

MICELLAR WEIGHTS OF VARIOUS NONIONIC SURFACE ACTIVE AGENTS AT MODERATE TEMPERATURES (REPORTED BY THE END OF 1959)

Surface active agent	Temp. (°C)	Method[b]	Micellar weight ×10⁻⁴	Assoc- iation number	Ref.	Refer to Section	Refer to Table
$C_{12}H_{25}O(CH_2CH_2O)_{9.5}H$[*20]		LS	3.85	63	(33)	III	2.7
$C_{12}H_{25}O(CH_2CH_2O)_{12}H$[*20]		LS	3.20	45	(33)	III	2.7
$C_{12}H_{25}O(CH_2CH_2O)_{20.8}H$[*26] a	25	DV	6.17	56	(56)	VI, 1	2.16
$C_{12}H_{25}S(CH_2CH_2O)_9H$[*39]		LS	4.03	67	(42)	III	
		LS	5.16	86	(42)	III	
$C_8H_{17}\text{-}C_6H_4O(CH_2CH_2O)_8H$[*19]		LS	20.8	373	(7)	III	2.6
$C_8H_{17}\text{-}C_6H_4O(CH_2CH_2O)_9H$[*39]	25–26	LS	8.13	135	(42)	III	
		LS	6,67	111	(42)	III	
$C_8H_{17}\text{-}C_6H_4O(CH_2CH_2O)_{10}H$[*4]		LS	9.0	139	(7)	III	2.6
$C_8H_{17}\text{-}C_6H_4O(CH_2CH_2O)_{12}H$[*19]		LS	5.35	73	(7)	III	2.6
$C_7H_{15}COO(CH_2CH_2O)_{7.6}CH_3$[*22]	25	DV	2.55	52	(43)	IV	2.12
$C_9H_{19}COO(CH_2CH_2O)_{7.0}CH_3$[*14]		LS	4.15	84	(34)	III	2.8
	25	DV	4.25	86	(35)	III	2.9a
$C_9H_{19}COO(CH_2CH_2O)_{10.3}CH_3$[*14]		LS	3.68	58	(34)	III	2.8
	25	DV	3.70	58	(35)	III	2.9a
$C_9H_{19}COO(CH_2CH_2O)_{11.9}CH_3$[*14]		LS	3.37	48	(34)	III	2.8
	25	DV	3.37	48	(35)	III	2.9a
$C_{11}H_{23}COO(CH_2CH_2O)_{6.0}CH_3$[*14]		LS	(100.)	(2100)	(34)	III	
	25	DV	61.1	1270	(35)	III	2.10
$C_{11}H_{23}COO(CH_2CH_2O)_{8.4}CH_3$[*14]		LS	6.06	104	(34)	III	2.8
	25	DV	5.93	102	(35)	III	2.9a
$C_{11}H_{23}COO(CH_2CH_2O)_{11.2}CH_3$[*14]		LS	5.40	75	(34)	III	2.8
	25	DV	4.74	67	(35)	III	2.9a
$C_{11}H_{23}COO(CH_2CH_2O)_{12.5}CH_3$[*14]		LS	5.13	67	(34)	III	2.8
	25	DV	4.64	60	(35)	III	2.9a
$C_{10}H_{21}O(CH_2CH_2O)_8CH_3$[*23]	30	LS	4.31	83	(70)	VI, 2	2.17
$C_{10}H_{21}O(CH_2CH_2O)_{11}CH_3$[*23]	30	LS	4.29	65	(70)	VI, 2	2.17
$C_{10}H_{21}O(CH_2CH_2O)_{12}CH_3$[*23]	29	LS	3.71	53	(44)	IV	2.13

a In $0.4N$ NaCl solution.

b LS: light scattering, DV: diffusion-viscosity.

Numerical comparisons among these values should be made with care, especially among those obtained by different workers because method, apparatus, and analysis of data as well as purity of sample are different.

$$\frac{\pi}{C} = RT[A_1 + A_2C] \approx RT\left[\frac{1}{M} + \frac{Nu}{2M^2}C\right]$$

where π is the osmotic pressure, C is the concentration in gm/cc, M is the micellar weight, and N is the Avogadro number. As

$$M = \frac{4}{3}\pi r^3 \frac{N}{V} \quad \text{and} \quad u = \frac{4}{3}\pi(2r)^3$$

we obtain

$$A_2 = \frac{Nu}{2M^2} = \frac{4V}{M}$$

The A_2-values calculated from the values of V and M in Table 2.9 are shown in column 7 of Table 2.8. If there were no hydration of the micelle, we would obtain

$$\bar{A}_2 = 4\bar{v}/M$$

The values of $\bar{A}_2$, are shown in column 6 of Table 2.8. Both A_2 and $\bar{A}_2$ show an increase with the increase in hydrophilic group. The difference between the experimental slope and the calculated value can be attributed mostly to the increase in micellar weight with concentration. Okuyama and Tyuzyo (41) reported micellar weights of five commercial nonionic agents[*21] from their diffusion measurements; the values obtained are calculated on the unlikely assumption of a nonhydrated micelle.

The effect of added salts on the micellar weight of nonionic agents is not yet wholly clear, although some results on commercial products have been reported (42).

IV. Temperature Dependence of Critical Micelle Concentration and Micellar Weight

Aqueous solutions of nonionic surface active agents suddenly become turbid if the temperature of the solution is elevated to a certain temperature called the "cloud point," and, at a somewhat higher temperature, they separate into two phases. It is readily supposed from these phenomena that both CMC and micellar weight may change near the cloud point. In order to investigate the behavior of nonionic surface active agents near the cloud point, Nakagawa and his collaborators (43) have measured the change of CMC and micellar weight of methoxy-polyoxyethylene octanoate, $C_7H_{15}COO(CH_2CH_2O)_{7.6}CH_3$,[*22] as a function of temperature up to the cloud point.

The micellar weights obtained from the diffusion-viscosity measurements, assuming a hydrated spherical micelle, are shown in Table 2.12. Diffusion measurements were carried out with 2% solution as an upper layer and 3% solution as a lower layer. The effective volume $V = \phi/C$, calculated from Eq. (2.5), was approximately constant over a 0.6-4% concentration range.

The effective radius of the micelle a, the effective volume per gram of surface active agent V, and the aggregation number n are shown in

TABLE 2.12

EFFECT OF INCREASED TEMPERATURE ON MICELLAR WEIGHT AND EFFECTIVE
SPECIFIC VOLUME OF METHOXYPOLYOXYETHYLENE OCTANOATE
$C_7H_{15}COO(CH_2CH_2O)_{7.6}CH_3$*[22]

Temp. (°C)	Diffusion coeff. $D \times 10^8$ (cm²/sec)	Radius of micelle $a \times 10^8$ (cm)	Effective volume of one micelle $v \times 10^{20}$ (cc)	Effective volume of 1 gm surfactant, V (cc/gm)	Micellar weight $(M \times 10^{-4})$	Association number (n)
10	73.4	21.6	42.3	1.59	1.60	32
25	99.0	24.7	63.0	1.49	2.55	52
38	98.7	33.9	163.	1.38	7.10	144
43	79.3	47.1	436.	1.43	18.4	372

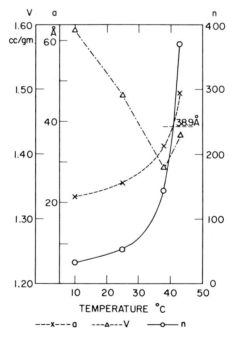

Fig. 2.14. Effective radius of the micelle a, effective specific volume V, and aggregation number n of methoxypolyoxyethylene octanoate
$C_7H_{15}COO(CH_2CH_2O)_{7.6}CH_3$*[22]
as a function of temperature.

Fig. 2.14 as a function of temperature.
    The calculated length of this molecule is 38.9 Å in its elongated state; the oleophilic portion is 11.5 Å and the hydrophilic portion is 27.4

Å. The micelle radius calculated from diffusion measurements at 43°C was considerably larger than this.   Therefore, the assumption of a spherical micelle encounters a contradiction with diffusion measurements at high temperature.   A calculation based on the assumption of an ellipsoidal micelle, such as is made in Section III, is impossible in the present stage because both the axial ratio and the amount of water of hydration are difficult to estimate.

The effective volume per gram of surface active agent decreases monotonically from 10° to 38°C.   This result may be explained as a progressive dehydration of the hydrophilic portion with rise of temperature.   The apparent increase in effective volume calculated from viscosity measurements at 43°C may be attributed to the assumptions involved in the use of Eq. (2.5).   In reality, dehydration may be still going on with a rise of temperature.

In order to confirm the results obtained above, the temperature dependence of the micellar weight was measured by light scattering (44) afterward.   Methoxydodecaoxyethylene decyl ether,

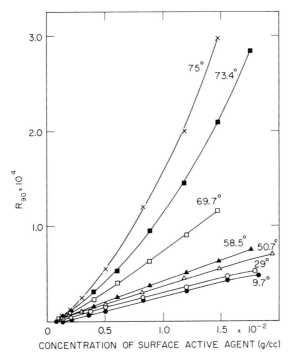

Fig. 2.15. R_{90} vs. concentration curves of methoxydodecaoxyethylene decyl ether $C_{10}H_{21}O(CH_2CH_2O)_{12}CH_3$[*23] at several temperatures.

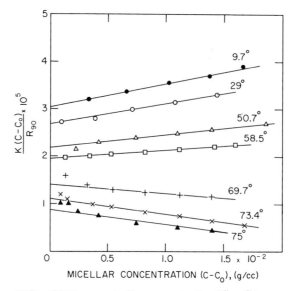

Fig. 2.16. $K(C - C_0)/R_{90}$ vs. micellar concentration $(C - C_0)$ curves of methoxy-dodecaoxyethylene decyl ether $C_{10}H_{21}O(CH_2CH_2O)_{12}CH_3$[*23] at several temperatures.

TABLE 2.13

Effect of Temperature on the Critical Micelle Concentrations, Micellar Weights, and Second Virial Coefficients of Methoxy-dodecaoxyethylene Decyl Ether $C_{10}H_{21}O(CH_2CH_2O)_{12}CH_3$[*23] and Sodium Dodecyl Sulfate

Surface active agent	Temp. (°C)	CMC×10³ (C_0) (gm/cc)	Micellar weight $(M×10^{-4})$	Association number (n)	2nd virial coefficient $(A_2×10^4)$
$C_{10}H_{21}O(CH_2CH_2O)_{12}CH_3$[a]	9.7	1.7	3.29	47	2.55
	29.0	1.1	3.71	53	2.06
	50.7	0.78	4.55	65	1.36
	58.5	0.70	5.15	73	1.01
	69.7	0.62	7.09	101	−0.85
	73.4	0.60	9.26	131	−1.50
	75.0	0.60	11.6	165	−1.51
$C_{12}H_{25}SO_4Na$ in 0.1 N NaCl[b]	17.0	0.40	3.04	106	5.40
	18.0	0.40	3.03	105	5.47
	20.0	0.41	2.92	101	5.90
	30.0	0.48	2.52	88	6.55
	50.2	0.72	2.24	78	9.85
	69.8	1.10	1.97	68	15.7

[a] Cloud point, 75.7°C (1% solution).
[b] Krafft point, slightly below 17°C.

$$C_{10}H_{21}O(CH_2CH_2O)_{12}CH_3, [*23]$$

with which we do not have to worry about hydrolysis, was chosen as the test material. The apparatus used for light scattering was maintained at the desired temperature within $\pm 0.1°C$ by circulating regulated water (45). Curves for R_{90} vs. concentration at several temperatures are shown in Fig. 2.15.

The concentrations above which the turbidity of the solution increased were taken as CMC $= C_0$ at the appropriate temperature. The values of $K(C - C_0)/R_{90}$ vs. $C - C_0$ are plotted in Fig. 2.16.

The CMC's, micellar weights, and second virial coefficients obtained from Figs. 2.15 and 2.16 are summarized in Table 2.13. Similar experiments carried out on an ionic surface active agent, sodium dodecyl sulfate, are also shown in Table 2.13 for comparison.

As will be seen in Fig. 2.14 and Tables 2.12 and 2.13, the micellar weights of $C_{10}H_{21}O(CH_2CH_2O)_{12}CH_3$ and $C_7H_{15}COO(CH_2CH_2O)_{7.6}CH_3$ increase acceleratively with temperature near the cloud point, and the second virial coefficients decrease. All tendencies are just opposite to the behavior of sodium dodecyl sulfate. The difference is clearly shown in

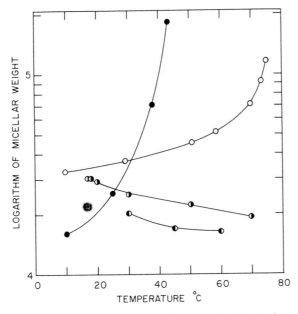

Fig. 2.17. Graph showing the difference between the effect of temperature on the micellar weight of ionic and nonionic surface active agents: ○, $C_{10}H_{21}O(CH_2CH_2O)_{12}CH_3$ in water; ●, $C_7H_{15}COO(CH_2CH_2O)_{7.6}CH_3$ in water; ◑, sodium dodecyl sulfate in 0.1 N NaCl; ◐, dodecyltrimethylammonium bromide in 0.034 N KBr (47).

Fig. 2.17.

Quite contrary to the behavior of the nonionic compound, the micellar weight of sodium dodecyl sulfate gradually increases with lowering of temperature, though the aggregation number does not markedly increase when the Krafft point is approached.

The temperature dependence of the CMC of $C_7H_{15}COO(CH_2CH_2O)_{7.6}$ CH_3[*22] was studied by the spectral color change of pinacyanol chloride and by solubilization measurements using Sudan III, over the temperature range from 10°C to the cloud point, 44°C. The procedures for these experiments are described in Section II. The results are shown in Figs. 2.18 and 2.19, and the CMC values obtained from these plots are summarized in Table 2.14.

The CMC's obtained by the two methods do not agree very well, but both show a trend of decrease in CMC with temperature rise. The same tendency is observed in the case of $C_{10}H_{21}O(CH_2CH_2O)_{12}CH_3$[*23] by lightscattering measurements. The difference between the CMC's determined by the color change of dye and by the solubilization of dye may be attributed to inaccuracy of these methods and possible hydrolysis of $C_7H_{15}COO$ $(CH_2CH_2O)_{7.6}CH_3$ at higher temperatures after long times for equilibration.

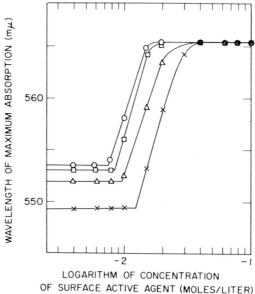

Fig. 2.18. Shift of the wavelength of maximum absorption of pinacyanol chloride in aqueous solutions of methoxypolyoxyethylene octanoate $C_7H_{15}COO(CH_2CH_2O)_{7.6}$ CH_3[*22] at several temperatures: ×, 11°; △, 25°; □, 40°; ○, 43°C. Dye concentration, 1.03×10^{-5} moles/liter;

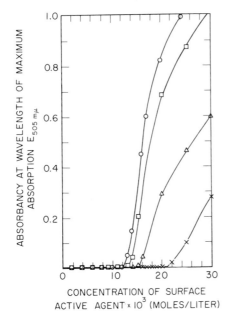

Fig. 2.19. Solubilization of Sudan III by aqueous solutions of methoxypolyoxyethylene octanoate $C_7H_{15}COO(CH_2CH_2O)_{7.6}CH_3$[*22] at several temperatures: ×, 10°: △, 25°; □, 40°; ○, 43°C.

TABLE 2.14

EFFECT OF INCREASED TEMPERATURE ON CRITICAL MICELLE CONCENTRATION OF METHOXYPOLYOXYETHYLENE OCTANOATE $C_7H_{15}COO(CH_2CH_2O)_{7.6}CH_3$[*22]

Temp. °C	$CMC \times 10^3$	
	Spectral change of pinacyanol chloride (moles/liter)	Solubilization of Sudan III (moles/liter)
10	12.5[a]	20.0
25	9.8	14.8
40	8.2	12.8
43	7.8	12.0

[a] Temperature, 11°C.

The heat of micelle formation has been conventionally calculated from the temperature dependence of the CMC. If we assume that a micelle can be treated as a phase and that the CMC is a saturation concentration of molecularly dispersed molecules, we obtain (46)

$$\frac{d \ln \text{CMC}}{dT} = -\frac{\Delta H_m}{RT^2} \qquad (2.8)$$

where ΔH_m is the conventional heat of micelle formation.

The temperature dependence of the logarithm of CMC of $C_7H_{15}COO$ $(CH_2CH_2O)_{7.6}CH_3$, determined by spectral change of pinacyanol chloride, and of $C_{10}H_{21}O(CH_2CH_2O)_{12}CH_3$, sodium dedecyl sulfate, and dodecyltrimethylammonium bromide (47) determined by light scattering are plotted in Fig. 2.20. The conventional heat of micelle formation calcu-

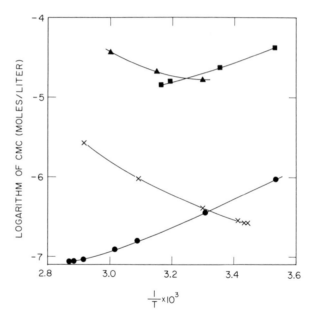

Fig. 2.20. Logarithm of critical micelle concentration vs. reciprocal of absolute temperature (ln CMC~$1/T$) curves of $C_7H_{15}COO(CH_2CH_2O)_{7.6}CH_3$,[*22] $C_{10}H_{21}O(CH_2CH_2O)_{12}CH_3$[*23], sodium dodecyl sulfate, and dodecyltrimethylammonium bromide: ●, $C_{10}H_{21}O(CH_2CH_2O)_{12}CH_3$ in water; ■, $C_7H_{15}COO(CH_2CH_2O)_{7.6}CH_3$ in water; ✕, sodium dodecyl sulfate in 0.1 N NaCl; ▲, dodecyltrimethylammonium bromide in 0.034 N KBr.

lated from the slope of the plot by the aid of Eq. (2.8) was $+2.4$ kcal/mole (at 27°C) for $C_7H_{15}COO(CH_2CH_2O)_{7.6}CH_3$, 3.3 kcal/mole for $C_{10}H_{21}O(CH_2CH_2O)_{12}CH_3$ at 27°C, -2.4 kcal/mole for dodecyltrimethylammonium bromide in 0.034 N KBr solution at 45°C, and -2.9 kcal/mole for sodium dodecyl sulfate in 0.1 N NaCl solution at 27°C. The heat of micelle formation is positive in the above two nonionic agents, but that of ionic agents is in many cases negative, although in some ionics it is positive around room temperature (*46, 48, 49*) as shown in Table 1.4.

The heat of micelle formation thus calculated is, however, not the true heat of micelle formation, since (i) the change in aggregation number with temperature has to be taken into account, and (ii) the change of activity with concentration at constant temperature and pressure must be multiplied for the left-hand side of Eq. (2.8).* Direct calorimetric determination of the heat of micelle formation in potassium octanoate did not agree with the value obtained from the temperature dependence of the CMC (*49*). More accurate experimental investigations are needed on the heat of micelle formation.

V. Clouding

When the temperature of a solution of a nonionic surface active agent is elevated to a certain temperature, it suddenly becomes turbid in a narrow temperature range. This temperature is called "cloud point." The solution begins to separate into two phases at a somewhat higher temperature. The cloud point is rather insensitive to the concentration examined, but it is not a unique temperature like the Krafft point. It is generally believed that the solubility of nonionic surface active agents in water increases by virtue of the power of the ether oxygens to hydrate (*50*). Hydration seems rather sensitive to the temperature, and elevated temperatures cause dehydration, as a result of which poly-oxyethylene-type surface active agents tend to become markedly less soluble at increased temperatures. Nonionic surface active agents whose polyoxyethylene group is short generally show a lower cloud point.

The cloud points of aqueous solutions of Triton X-100[*2] are sub-

TABLE 2.15

EFFECT OF VARYING CONCENTRATIONS ON THE CLOUD POINT OF TRITON X-100[*2]

Weight % Triton	Cloud point (°C)
0.25	64
0.50	64
2.0	64
4.0	64
7.0	65
10.0	66
13.0	67
16.0	68.5
20.0	70
33.0	76

* Refer to Chapter 1, Section IV for more rigorous and detailed discussion.

stantially constant over a wide concentration range, as shown in Table 2.15 (*51*).

The mechanism of the clouding phenomenon is not yet clear, but the following interpretation may be proposed as a possible model. The micellar weight of a nonionic surface active agent, as we already saw in Section IV, becomes acceleratively larger and larger with elevation of temperature. If this tendency persists in higher temperature ranges, it can easily be supposed that micelles grow so large at a certain temperature that the turbidity of the solution becomes perceptible even with the naked eye. This temperature may be called the cloud point. If the micelle still continues to grow, it will begin to float or sink because the buoyancy will predominate over Brownian motion. This phenomenon will result in a phase separation.

It has been found that a phase rich in surface active agent separates out of solution above the cloud point after equilibration. The concentration of nonionics in the coexisting water phase is very low (*51, 52*) and is approximately equal to the CMC. It seems that surface active agent is dissolved in molecular dispersion and that there exist few or no micelles in the water layer. As will be stated in Section VI, 3, there are a number of facts which support this view (*52*).

The solubility of ionic surface active agents shows a steady change (an increase) with rising temperature, but above a certain temperature there is an abrupt change in the slope of the solubility-temperature curve. The temperature at which this abrupt change occurs is known as the Krafft point, and the concentration at which it occurs is the CMC at that temperature. There is no micelle present in the bulk phase below the Krafft point (*2*).

The phase separation in a solution of nonionic agent and the phenomenon of the Krafft point in a solution of ionic agent resemble each other with respect to the disappearance of micellar regions beyond these temperatures. The difference is that the former occurs with increasing temperature, whereas the latter occurs with decreasing temperature. Once the micelles are formed, the activity of the solute increases very slowly with concentration, as expected, and the solubility increases enormously.

It can be seen from Fig. 2.17 that the micellar weight of a nonionic surface active agent acceleratively increases when the temperature of the solution approaches the cloud point. It seems, therefore, that the micelle becomes much larger with a rise in temperature and finally separates from the water phase. In other words, the clouding phenomenon and the succeeding phase separation occur as the result of the formation of giant aggregates. On the contrary, there is no striking change in the micellar weight of ionic surface active agents near the

Krafft point; rather, it converges to some definite value. The nonexistence of micelles below the Krafft point in the case of ionic agents, therefore, does not seem attributable to the separation of giant aggregate, but to the freezing of the micelle out of solution below the Krafft point.[*]

It should be noted that the above explanation is not a proven fact, but merely a possible interpretation.

The cloud point of dilute aqueous solutions of nonionic surface active agents is affected by the addition of coexisting substances. It would appear then that a coexisting substance may affect the cloud point (water solubility) of a nonionic surface active agent in either of two ways: (a) by changing the structure of the micelles by penetration; or (b) by dissolving in the water phase and thus changing the environment of the micelles. For materials which are insoluble in water, e.g., benzene, other hydrocarbons, and higher alcohols, mechanism (a) must apply. In the case of strong electrolytes and other water soluble additives, mechanism (b) applies (51). The effect of added water-insoluble substances (a) will be described later in Section VI, where the interaction between the micelle and other substances is discussed.

When inorganic salts are added to the Triton X-100[*2] solution, as shown in Fig. 2.21, the cloud point is depressed. In view of the nature

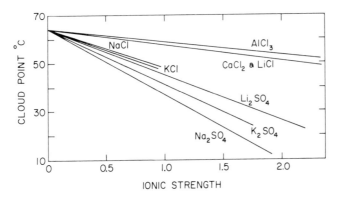

Fig. 2.21. Effect of added electrolytes on the cloud point of 2% Triton X-100[*2] solutions.

of this phenomenon, it would appear difficult to explain the effectiveness in cloud point lowering by the concepts of ionic radius, hydration, or lyotropic series.

It is interesting to compare these results with those of Doscher *et al.* (53) who measured the turbidities and viscosities of Triton X-100[*24]

---

[*] Refer to Fig. 1.1.

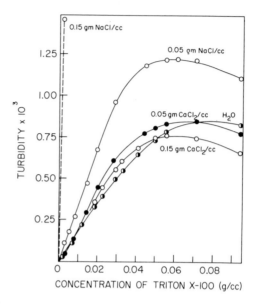

Fig. 2.22a.   Effects of added electrolytes on the turbidity of Triton X-100[24] solutions.

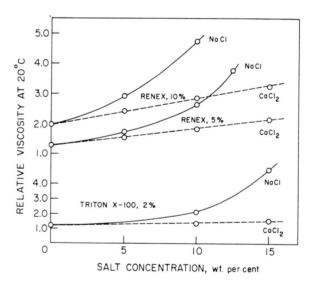

Fig. 2.22b.   Effects of added electrolytes on the viscosity of Triton X-100[24] solutions.   The effect on the viscosity of Renex[25] (polyoxyethylene esters of mixed fatty and resin acids) solutions is also illustrated.

solutions in the presence of added electrolyte. Some of the results are shown in Fig. 2.22. These workers report the order for cations of increasing effectiveness in raising turbidities and viscosities to be lithium, potassium, and sodium. Aluminum was somewhat lower than calcium. If it may be assumed that the order of increasing turbidity should correspond with the order of increasing effectiveness as a cloud point depressant, then these results are in agreement with each other, with the exception of the sodium and potassium chlorides. These two curves on Fig. 2.21 are almost coincident, however, so that any disagreement is mild. The above assumption of the parallelism of turbidity and cloud point depression can be explained at least qualitatively without contradiction. As the clouding is a phenomenon in which the micelle becomes very large, the greater the effect of inorganic salt in increasing turbidity (i.e., micellar weight), the larger is its effect in depressing the cloud point. The multivalent cations aluminum and calcium are less effective than the monovalent alkali metal ions in salting out the Triton X-100. Doscher attributes this behavior to interaction of the multivalent metal ions with the polyoxyethylene chains of the nonionic detergent which produces a salting-in rather than a salting-out effect. On this view, salts sometimes affect the cloud point not by changing the environment of the micelle, but rather by directly changing the association number due to the adsorption on or in the hydrophilic portion of the micelle.

The suggestion by Livingston (54) that the cloud point function may be pH sensitive has been examined, and it turned out that pH itself does not affect the cloud point (51). The influences of pH on the cloud point were determined (i) by measuring the cloud point of 2% Triton X-100[*2] in disodium phosphate and citric acid buffer mixtures, on the one hand, and (ii) by adding small amounts of hydrochloric acid to a 2% Triton solution so that the pH could be varied at extremely low electrolyte concentration, on the other. The results are shown in Fig.

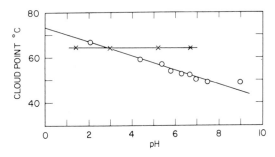

Fig. 2.23. Variation of cloud point with pH of buffered and unbuffered 2% Triton X-100[*2] solutions: ×, unbuffered (HCl); ○, buffered.

2.23 and indicate that the total electrolyte concentration is the important variable. The pH has been varied over a 5.5-unit range in the latter case, yet the cloud point was not influenced at all. Now the cloud point of an unbuffered 2% Triton solution is 64°C, and its pH is 6.7. At this pH the former experiment indicates a cloud point of 52°C. This clearly implies the existence of a salt effect on the cloud point. Figure 2.23 also reveals the linear relationship obtained over a pH range of 2–9 units in the former experiment. The cloud point is seen to change by 22°C over the indicated pH range. From the separate measurements of the effects of disodium phosphate or citric acid on the cloud point of Triton X-100 solution, it turns out that the effects of citric acid and disodium phosphate on the cloud point are additive.

Finally, we would like to draw attention to the discovery of double cloud points reported by Goto and Sugano (55). Aqueous solutions of commercial nonionic agents showed double cloud points, as seen in Fig. 2.24; namely, the solution becomes turbid at first and then becomes far less turbid, almost transparent, and then becomes turbid again and separates into two phases with increased temperature. In the temperature range at which the solution is semitransparent, no phase separation occurs and the solution exhibits small but definite elasticity and stream-

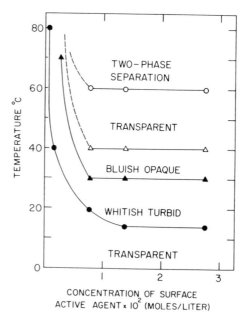

Fig. 2.24. Diagram illustrating the double cloud points observed in a commercial nonionic surface active agent.

ing birefringence. Goto and Sugano have observed similar phenomena in solutions of hexaoxyethylene dodecyl ether[*3] (which contained some impurities). This rather peculiar phenomenon disappeared when the sample was purified. The double cloud points again appeared on adding small amounts of higher alcohols to solutions of the purified solution which alone did not show such phenomena.

The presence of an anionic surface active agent also modifies the solubility behavior of the nonionic agent. Cloud point measurements were made by Maclay (51) on systems composed of mixtures of 2% solutions of Triton X-100[*2] and several anionic materials. It was found that, in the absence of a solubilizate, small amounts of an anionic agent raised the cloud point of the nonionic agent. The mixtures generally did not display sharp cloud points characteristic of the Triton X-100 alone, but rather cloud over a 10–20°C temperature range, so that it was often impossible to find a cloud point in the usual sense.

The cloud point in dilute solutions of a mixture of nonionic agents lies somewhere intermediate between the cloud points of the two components.

VI.   Interaction with Other Substances

1.   *Interaction with Ionic Surface Active Agents*

It has been confirmed from the following experiment that a mixed micelle is formed in aqueous solutions of a mixture of ionic and non-ionic surface active agents (56). Mixtures of polyoxyethylene dodecyl ether $C_{12}H_{25}O(CH_2CH_2O)_nH$ (Brij 35, Atlas Powder Co., average molecular weight 1100)[*26] and sodium dodecyl sulfate in various mixing ratios were used. The viscosity of solutions (0.3–3%) of these mixtures was determined in the presence of 0.4 N sodium chloride. The diffusion and electrophoresis measurements were performed using 0.3% and 1.5% solutions of these mixtures in the presence of 0.4 N sodium chloride as upper and lower layers, respectively.

Two "false'" nearly stationary boundaries, δ and ε, commonly appear in the ordinary electrophoresis experiment. At the descending side, the composition of the liquid in the space vacated by colloidal electrolyte is in some way altered to a value different from that of the original buffer, giving rise to a gradient (ε) of salt concentration near the original boundary, which moves slowly. In a similar way, the entry of colloidal electrolyte at the ascending side into buffer previously free from colloid gives rise in this liquid to an "adjustment" of both colloid and salt concentration, causing another gradient of both colloid and salt concentration (δ), which is also found to move very slowly (57, 58). As Longsworth (59) suggested, for the optimum concentrations of sodium chloride and

T. NAKAGAWA AND K. SHINODA

TABLE 2.16

Micellar Weight, Effective Charge, ζ-Potential, and Other Micellar Dimensions, Calculated for the Mixed Micelle of Sodium Dodecyl Sulfate and Polyoxyethylene Dodecyl Ether (Brij 35)[*26] in Varying Ratio (25°C) in 0.4 N NaCl

Mixing ratio[a] (wt/wt)	Mobility $-\mu \times 10^4$ (cm²/volt sec)	Effective volume of 1 gm surfactant V (cc/gm)	Diffusion coefficient $D \times 10^7$ (cm²/sec)	Radius of micelle $a \times 10^8$ (cm)	Effective charge (q/e)	ζ-Potential $-\zeta$ (mv)	Micellar weight ($M \times 10^{-4}$)	Association number of		Apparent electrolytic dissociation (α)
								ionics (n_i)	nonionics (n_n)	
L10/B 0	2.61	1.30	9.08	25.9	29	45.8	3.37	117	0	0.25
L 7/B 3	2.14	1.44	9.76	24.1	21	37.6	2.45	60	7	0.36
L 6/B 4	1.28	1.63	8.18	28.8	17	22.2	3.70	77	14	0.22
L 5/B 5	0.85	1.89	7.82	30.1	12	15.1	3.63	63	17	0.19
L 3/B 7	0.37	2.29	6.79	34.7	7	6.3	4.60	48	29	0.14
L 2/B 8	0.32	2.41	6.59	35.7	6	5.4	4.77	33	35	0.19
L 1/B 9	0.20	2.50	5.65	41.7	5	3.3	7.33	25	60	0.20
L 0/B10	0.02	2.52	5.96	39.5	0	0.4	6.17	0	56	—

[a] L: sodium dodecyl sulfate;   B: $C_{12}H_{25}O \cdot (CH_2 \cdot CH_2 \cdot O)_n H$, average molecular weight, 1100.

surface active agent these two peaks almost disappear.

As there was only one peak in the electrophoresis diagram on each side at any mixing ratio, it is concluded that the mixture of ionic and nonionic surface active agent forms only one kind of micelle. If we assume a hydrated micelle of spherical shape, the micellar weight and the effective radius of this micelle a can be determined from viscosity and diffusion measurements by the aid of Eq. (2.5) and (2.6), as shown in Table 2.16. It is deduced (60) that the electroviscous effect due to the electric charges on the micelle will be negligibly small.

In the ordinary electrophoresis experiment, where there are no colloidal particles in the upper layer, the mobility μ is given by the following equation:

$$\mu = V_d K; \qquad V_d = \frac{d_d S}{ti}$$

d_d/t is the rate of downward boundary migration; i, the current in amperes; S, the area of cross section of the cell, and K, the specific conductivity of the lower layer. In the present experiment, however, there exist micelles in both layers, and only their concentrations are different. According to the basic equation of the moving boundary proposed by Dole (61) and Svensson (58), the mobility is given by the following equation,

$$\mu = V_d K - \frac{V_a K_0 - V_d K}{n - 1}$$

$$V_a = \frac{d_a S}{ti}$$

(2.9)

d_a/t is the rate of upward boundary migration; K_0. the specific conductivity of the upper layer; and n, the ratio of the concentration of colloidal particle in the upper and lower layers.

In the present experiment, n may be taken as 5. As the second term in Eq. (2.9) is small compared with the first term, the ambiguity in the value of n does not introduce any significant difference in the result. According to Henry's (62) method, in which a distribution of ion atmosphere of the Debye-Hückel type and an ionic radius $r_i = 2.5$ Å for gegenions are assumed, the net charge of the micelle q was calculated from the mobility, the effective radius of the micelle, and viscosity measurements by means of the equation

$$q = \frac{4\pi \eta a(1 + \mathcal{K}a + \mathcal{K}r_i)}{f(\mathcal{K}a)(1 + \mathcal{K}r_i)} \mu$$

(2.10)

where a is the radius of particle; η, the viscosity of solvent; $f(\mathcal{K}a)$, the Henry factor; $1/\mathcal{K}$, the thickness of electrical double layer = $(1000 \, DkT/$

$8\pi e^2 NI)^{1/2}$; I, the ionic strength; e, the electrical charge quantum; and q/e, the number of effective charges per micelle. According to Henry's theory, the ζ-potential of the micelle is given as

$$\zeta = \frac{q}{\varepsilon a}\left(\frac{1 + \mathcal{K}r_i}{1 + \mathcal{K}a + \mathcal{K}r_i}\right) = \frac{4\pi\eta}{\varepsilon f(\mathcal{K}a)}\mu \qquad (2.11)$$

where ε is the dielectric constant of the solvent. The net charge of the micelle and the ζ-potential are also shown in Table 2.16.

Assuming that the mole ratio of ionic to nonionic agents in the micelle is equal to the stoichiometric mole ratio, the aggregation numbers of ionic and nonionic agents per micelle were calculated from the micellar weight. Dividing the effective charge by the aggregation number of the ionic agent, an apparent degree of dissociation was also calculated.

Though the mobility, the effective charge, the ζ-potential, etc are subject to some experimental errors and also to theoretical shortcomings, the trend of the change of these values as a function of the mole fraction agrees with our expectations.

The critical micelle concentration of mixtures of ionic and nonionic surface active agents has not yet been wholly investigated. Yoda et al. (63) measured the electrical conductivity vs. concentration of sodium dodecyl sulfate in the presence of definite amounts of polyoxyethylene dodecyl ether.[*27] The average numbers of oxyethylene groups per molecule were

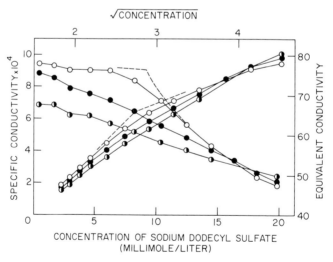

Fig. 2.25. Specific conductivity and equivalent conductivity of sodium dodecyl sulfate plotted as a function of concentration, in the presence of definite amounts of polyoxyethylene dodecyl ether, $C_{12}H_{25}O(CH_2CH_2O)_{\overline{20}}H$.[*27] Added $C_{12}H_{25}O(CH_2CH_2O)_{\overline{20}}H$: (- - -) 0: ○, 10^{-4}; ●, 10^{-3}; ◗, 10^{-2} moles/liter.

5, 10, 15, 20, and 25, respectively. Some of the results are plotted in Fig. 2.25. The break points in the specific conductivity and equivalent conductivity curves become more and more ambiguous with increase in the concentration of nonionic surface active agent. The results were similar for all the other nonionic compounds investigated.

The presence of an ionic surface active agent enhances the cloud point of a nonionic agent (51). Some examples are shown in Fig. 2.26. The mixture generally does not display sharp cloud points, but rather clouds over a wide temperature range. The above phenomenon also confirms the formation of mixed micelles between ionic and nonionic agents.

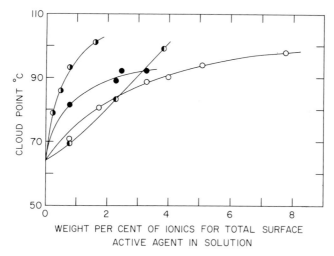

Fig. 2.26. Effect of anionic surface active agents on the cloud points of solutions of Triton X-100.*² (total concentration, 2%): ○, Santomerse D; ◑, Nacconol NRSF: sodium salt of alkyl benzenesulfonate; ●, Triton X-301: sodium salt of alkyl aryl polyether sulfate; ◐, Triton X-200: sodium salt of alkyl aryl polyether sulfonate.

The micellar weight of ionic agents decreases with an increase of temperature, as mentioned in Section IV. It can easily be supposed that the presence of an ionic agent obstructs the increase in micellar weight of nonionic agent with an increase of temperature* and enhances the cloud point.

2. Solubilization

The ability of detergent solutions to dissolve organic compounds

---

* This tendency was confirmed by a lightscattering experiment now in progress in the authors' laboratory.

insoluble or only slightly soluble in water is one of their rather striking properties, called solubilization. Little additional uptake is found until the CMC is reached, indicating that the compounds are taken up in some way by the micelles. Large numbers of experiments have been carried out on solubilization by ionic surface active agents and explained in detail in the book by McBain and Hutchinson (2).

It is generally believed that with nonpolar hydrocarbons uptake occurs by solution into the interior of the micelle and with partially miscible polar compounds, such as octanol, long chain amines, and phenols, by adsorption on the micelle surface, with the hydrocarbon part inside and the polar group in the aqueous phase. In addition, water-soluble polar substances, such as glycerol, sugar, and some kinds of dyes which are insoluble in hydrocarbons are thought to adsorb on the exterior of the micelles. The probable structures in the three cases are shown schematically in Fig. 2.27 (64, 65). The situation will be similar in case of nonionic agents.

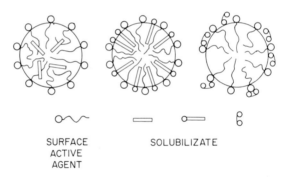

SURFACE   SOLUBILIZATE
ACTIVE
AGENT

Fig. 2.27. Schematic diagram to illustrate three probable modes of incorporation.

Riegelman et al. (66) have determined the ultraviolet absorption spectra of various kinds of solubilizates in aqueous solutions of potassium dodecanoate, dodecylamine hydrochloride, and polyoxyethylene dodecyl ether (Brij 35)[*28] and compared them with those in water or octane, etc. The absorption spectra of the various solubilizates were similar in solutions of these surface active agents, and no distinctive difference was observed between ionic and nonionic compounds, nor was any change due to the sign of the charges of surface active agents. Absorption spectra were compared on the basis of the positions of their maxima and the relative degree of fine structure. Solubilizates are classified according to the following four modes of incorporation: (a) inclusion into the hydrocarbon interior of the micelle; (b) deep penetration in the palisade layer; (c) short penetration in the palisade layer; and (d) adsorption on the surface of the micelle.

In the case of nonionic agents which possess polyoxyethylene groups, there is another possible mode of incorporation. Some molecules, such as pinacyanol chloride, may be incorporated into the polyoxyethylene group of the micelle (Fig. 2.28). It seems adequate to classify this type of solubilization as inclusion into the polyoxyethylene exterior of the micelle rather than to classify it as adsorption on the surface of the micelle. The solubilization of phenol and its analogs in solutions of nonionic agents belongs to this mode of incorporation. The phenolic hydroxy group is supposed to bind with the ether oxygen of the oxyethylene group (67) by hydrogen bonding.

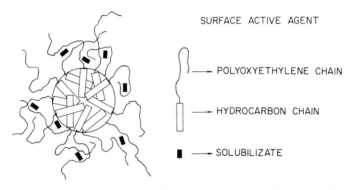

SURFACE ACTIVE AGENT

POLYOXYETHYLENE CHAIN

HYDROCARBON CHAIN

SOLUBILIZATE

Fig. 2.28. Schematic diagram to illustrate another possible mode of incorporation.

Higuchi et al. reported complex formation of phenolic substances with polyoxyethylene groups (68). It has been observed also that many phenolic substances are readily dissolved in concentrated solutions of polyethylene glycol and solubilized in aqueous solutions of polyoxyethylene-type nonionic agents (69).

It is supposed, as in case of ionic agents, that the micellar size will increase and the CMC decrease with the addition of water-insoluble substances. In order to confirm this view, the following experiments were carried out (70). The surface active agents employed in this experiment were methoxyoctaoxyethylene decyl ether, $C_{10}H_{21}O(CH_2CH_2O)_8$ CH_3.[*23] and methoxyundecaoxyethylene decyl ether, $C_{10}H_{21}O(CH_2CH_2O)_{11}$ CH_3.[*23] n-Decane, which may be incorporated in the hydrocarbon interior of the micelle, and n-decanol, which penetrates into the palisade layer of the micelle, were used as solubilizates. The intensity of scattered light was measured during the dilution of concentrated solutions of mixtures of nonionic agents and solubilizates of varying compositions at $30 \pm 1°C$.

Figure 2.29 illustrates the change in reduced intensity of scattered light R_{90} against the total solute concentration, for various mixing ratios of $C_{10}H_{21}O(CH_2CH_2O)_{11}CH_3$ and n-decanol.

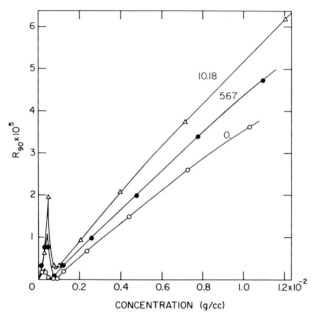

Fig. 2.29. R_{90} vs. concentration curves for methoxyundecaoxyethylene decyl ether $C_{10}H_{21}O(CH_2CH_2O)_{11}CH_3$*[23] in the presence of added n-decanol (30°C). Mixing ratio: 0, 5.67, 10.18 (gm decanol/100 gm surface active agent).

It can be seen from Fig. 2.29 that the reduced intensity of a nonionic solution with no solubilizate added has an almost zero value until a certain concentration, the CMC, is reached, whereas solutions of nonionic agents with added solubilizate show a sharp peak in reduced intensity at low concentrations. The larger the amount of solubilizate, the higher the peak. The height of this peak in reduced intensity is also affected by the time or process employed in the dilution. This phenomenon was found earlier by Phillips and Mysels in solutions of sodium dodecyl sulfate containing some dodecanol (71). The appearance of a peak is attributed to the formation of small droplets of excess solubilizate in the dilution process. This droplet may be composed of solubilizate alone or may be a molecular complex between solubilizate and nonionic agent.

In order to plot $K(C - C_0)/R_{90}$ against $(C - C_0)$, the monomer concentration, nonionic agent plus solubilizate, C_0, was obtained from the intercept of the R_{90} vs. concentration curve. The monomer concentration decreases monotonically with an increase in the concentration of solubilizate, as shown in Table 2.17. One example of $K(C-C_0)/R_{90}$ vs. $(C-C_0)$ curves is shown in Fig. 2.30. The curves obtained are linear except at the lower end. The micellar weights and the slopes of the lines, i.e.,

TABLE 2.17

EFFECT OF ADDED SOLUBILIZATE ON MICELLAR CONSTITUTION OF METHOXY-OCTAOXYETHYLENE DECYL ETHER[*23] AND METHOXYUNDECAOXYETHYLENE DECYL ETHER[*23] (30°C)

Solubilizate (H)	H/S wt%	Monomolecular conc. $C_0 \times 10^4$ (gm/cc)	Micellar weight $(M \times 10^{-4})$	No. of soap molecules per micelle	No. of solubilizate molecules per micelle	Second virial coefficient $(A_2 \times 10^4)$
Surface active agent (S): $C_{10}H_{21}O(CH_2CH_2O)_8CH_3$						
n-Decane	0.	6.0	4.31	83	0	1.69
	1.32	5.7	4.56	87	4	1.13
	2.33	5.4	4.78	90	8	0.98
	3.16	5.2	5.05	94	11	0.91
	3.78	5.1	5.20	96	13	0.68
	4.93	4.8	5.75	105	19	0.66
	(12.0)	4.0	8.85	158[a]	46[a]	0.50
	(150.)	4.0	9.07	162[a]	47[a]	0.48
n-Decanol	3.40	5.2	4.78	89	10	1.43
	6.19	4.5	5.13	93	19	0.92
	8.50	4.0	6.13	109	30	0.25
	11.42	3.3	9.09	157	59	0.00
	16.61	2.0	21.3	351	192	0.00
Surface active agent (S): $C_{10}H_{21}O(CH_2CH_2O)_{11}CH_3$						
n-decane	0.	9.5	4.29	65	0	1.99
	1.40	9.2	4.48	67	4	1.61
	2.58	9.0	5.15	76	9	1.43
	3.31	8.8	5.43	80	12	1.41
n-Decanol	5.67	8.4	5.26	75	18	1.90
	10.18	7.5	6.29	86	37	1.54
	17.12	6.3	12.2	158	113	0.71

[a] Each value is calculated assuming that the ratio of solubilizate/surface active agent in a micelle is 8.0 wt%, i.e., the composition at saturation solubilization (cf. Fig. 2.31).

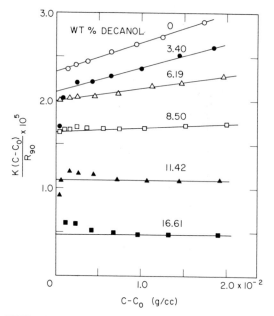

Fig. 2.30. $[K(C - C_0)/R_{90}]$ vs. micellar concentration $(C - C_0)$ curves for methoxyoctaoxyethylene decyl ether $C_{10}H_{21}O(CH_2CH_2O)_8CH_3$[*23] in the presence of added
n-decanol (30°C).

the apparent second virial coefficients, were calculated by means of the
equation

$$\frac{K(C - C_0)}{R_{90}} = \frac{1}{M} + 2A_2(C - C_0) \tag{2.12}$$

The micellar weight and mixing ratio of nonionic agent against
solubilizate permit us to calculate the number of molecules of the various
species per micelle. The values are summarized in Table 2.17. The
saturation value for the solubilization of n-decane in $C_{10}H_{21}O(CH_2CH_2O)_8$
CH_3 was 8%. The figures in lines 7 and 8 are obtained by diluting the
solution after the excess decane was separated. The change of micellar
weight with amount of solubilizate is shown in Fig. 2.31.

As can be seen from Table 2.17 and Fig. 2.31, the concentration of
molecularly dispersed species decreases and the micellar weight increases
with increasing amount of solubilizate in all cases. The increase in
micellar weight is accounted for not only by the incorporation of solubilizate molecules, but also by the increase of the aggregation number
of the nonionic agents themselves. In other words, solubilization proceeds with the reorganization of the micelle. The same conclusion was

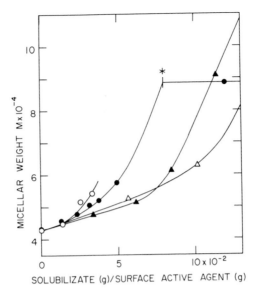

Fig. 2.31. Graph showing increase in micellar weight of methoxypolyoxyethylene decyl ether*[23] with increasing addition of n-decane or n-decanol (30°C): ●, $C_{10}H_{21}O$ $(CH_2CH_2O)_8CH_3$ + n-decane; ▲, $C_{10}H_{21}O(CH_2CH_2O)_8CH_3$ + n-decanol; ○, $C_{10}H_{21}O(CH_2$ $CH_2O)_{11}CH_3$ + n-decane; △, $C_{10}H_{21}O(CH_2CH_2O)_{11}CH_3$ + n-decanol; *, saturation solubilization.

arrived at in the case of ionic agent (72). The micellar weight of $C_{10}H_{21}O(CH_2CH_2O)_8CH_3$ did not change on the addition of excess n-decane over saturation.

In analyzing the light scattering measurements, the following two conditions are assumed: (i) the total monomer concentration C_0 is constant above the CMC for a given solution of constant mixing ratio; and (ii) the composition of the micelle does not change with the concentration of solution. The plausibility of the above assumptions is somewhat doubtful in systems where some solubilizate is present.

It seems irrational to assume a definite composition for the micelle, particularly in the low concentration region where the proportion of molecularly dispersed molecules is large compared with that of aggregated molecules. In fact, the $K(C - C_0)/R_{90}$ vs. $(C - C_0)$ curves deviate from linearity at low concentration, as shown in Fig. 2.30. In the higher concentration region, however, good linearity of all curves supports the assumption of micelles of nearly fixed composition in this concentration region. At the same time, it should be kept in mind that the linear relationship does not always support the plausibility of this assumption. The intercepts $1/M$ obtained by extrapolation of this linear relationship between $K(C - C_0)/R_{90}$ and $(C - C_0)$ are not markedly affected by a small change in the concentration of molecularly dispersed species. The uncertainty included in C_0, therefore, does not introduce any significant difference into the final results.

The results shown in Table 2.17 are subject to some uncertainty which is difficult to eliminate, but it gives us at least qualitatively clear information concerning the change in the properties of micelles accompanying solubilization.

The effect of added n-decane on the micellar weight of methoxydodecaoxyethylene decyl ether, $C_{10}H_{21}O(CH_2CH_2O)_{12}CH_3$,[*23] has also been investigated by light scattering techniques at a higher temperature, 50°C (73). Procedures for the light scattering measurements are the same. The results are shown in Table 2.18.

TABLE 2.18

EFFECT OF ADDED n-DECANE ON THE MICELLAR CONSTITUTION OF
METHOXYDODECAOXYETHYLENE DECYL ETHER[*23] (50°C)

Decane / Soap (wt%)	Monomolecular conc. $C_0 \times 10^4$ (gm/cc)	Micellar weight $(M \times 10^{-4})$	No. of soap molecules per micelle	No. of decane molecules per micelle	Second virial coefficient $(A_2 \times 10^4)$
0^a	7.8	4.55	65	0	1.36
1.86	7.8	5.10	71	6.5	1.36
2.23	7.6	5.14	71	8	1.33
3.53	7.5	5.37	74	13	1.24
5.58	7.3	5.99	80	22	0.81
7.52	7.1	6.27	83	30	0.78
8.7^b	7.0	7.41	97	41	0.65

^{a} 50.7°C.
^{b} Saturated.

It is observed again that the concentration of monodispersed molecules and the second virial coefficient decrease and that the micellar weight increases with the amount of solubilizate (n-decane) added.

3. *Effect of Temperature on Solubilization and Effect of Solubilizate on Clouding*

We have already stated in Section IV that the micellar weight increases and the CMC decreases with a rise of temperature in aqueous solutions of nonionic agents. Similar changes occur in solutions of nonionic agents containing solubilizate. The changes of micellar weight and CMC with temperature have been measured by light scattering techniques in solution of pure methoxydodecaoxyethylene decyl ether, $C_{10}H_{21}O(CH_2CH_2O)_{12}CH_3$[*23], containing a definite amount of n-decane or

TABLE 2.19

EFFECT OF TEMPERATURE ON THE MICELLAR CONSTITUTION OF METHOXY-
DODECAOXYETHYLENE DECYL ETHER $C_{10}H_{21}O(CH_2CH_2O)_{12}CH_3$[*23]
CONTAINING A DEFINITE AMOUNT OF n-DECANE OR n-DECANOL

Temp. °C	Monomolecular conc. $C_0 \times 10^4$ (gm/cc)	Micellar weight $M \times 10^{-4}$	No. of soap molecules per micelle	No. of solubilizate molecules per micelle	Second virial coeff. $A_2 \times 10^4$
n-Decane/$C_{10}H_{21}O(CH_2CH_2O)_{12}CH_3$: 1.86 wt%					
9.6	16.5	4.67	65	5.9	3.20
30.0	10.5	4.83	67	6.1	2.33
50.0	7.8	5.10	71	6.5	1.36
60.0	7.0	6.12	85	7.8	0.57
66.6	6.2	6.90	96	8.8	−1.10
69.0	6.2	7.87	110	10.1	−2.88
n-Decanol/$C_{10}H_{21}O(CH_2CH_2O)_{12}CH_3$: 9.17 wt%					
10.0	14.5	5.62	73	30	2.37
29.9	8.8	6.42	83	33	1.81
43.4	7.6	8.45	110	44	0.54
49.7	7.0	10.75	140	57	0.18
55.4	6.6	14.3	186	76	−0.36
61.4	6.2	31.1	404	163	−0.45

n-decanol (73). The amounts of n-decane and n-decanol added were 1.86 wt% and 9.17 wt% of nonionic agent, respectively. The procedures for analyzing the data are the same, and the results are summarized in Table 2.19. Similar experiments on $C_{10}H_{21}O(CH_2CH_2O)_{12}CH_3$[*23] saturated with n-decane were also carried out (73). The amount of n-decane solubilized increased with increasing temperature. The light scattering was measured during the dilution process of aqueous solutions of nonionic agents saturated with n-decane at various temperatures. Some of the n-decane solubilized at a higher concentration forms emulsion droplets in the dilution process, and the intensity of scattered light R_{90} sometimes increases with dilution. The Debye plot also shows some deviation from linearity. Accordingly, the experimental results are subject to errors of induced scattering and small changes in components. The micellar constitution deduced is shown in Table 2.20 in order to show the change of properties at least qualitatively.

As will be seen in Tables 2.19 and 2.20, the micellar weight increases with a rise of temperature, especially near the cloud point. The clouding phenomenon, followed by separation into two phases, may be explained as follows, at least tentatively. The micelle swollen with the solubilizate becomes so large at the cloud point that the solution shows

TABLE 2.20

EFFECT OF TEMPERATURE ON THE MICELLAR CONSTITUTION OF METHOXY-
DODECAOXYETHYLENE DECYL ETHER $C_{10}H_{21}O(CH_2CH_2O)_{12}CH_3$[*23]
SATURATED WITH n-DECANE.

Temp. (°C)	Decane / Soap (wt%)	Monomolecular conc. $C_0 \times 10^4$ (gm/cc)	Micellar weight ($M \times 10^{-4}$)	No. of soap molecules per micelle	No. of decane molecules per micelle	Second virial coeff. ($A_2 \times 10^4$)
10.0	2.6	16.3	5.67	78	10	4.00
30.0	4.4	10.2	6.27	85	18	2.20
50.0	8.7	7.0	7.41	97	41	0.65
60.0	13.5	6.8	10.2	127	84	0.00

strong turbidity, and further elevation of temperature results in separation into two phases. Maclay (51) and Goto and Sugano (55) have investigated the effect of added solubilizates on the cloud point. Their results are shown in Figs. 2.32. and 2.33.

The relation between the molecular structure of the solubilizate and the effect on the cloud point is not yet wholly clear. Hydrocarbons generally do not depress the cloud point very much and sometimes even enhance the cloud point, whereas aliphatic alcohols or fatty acids depress the cloud point remarkably. Aoki and Iwayama (74) investigated the

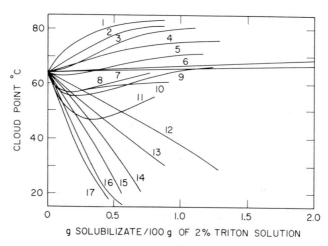

Fig. 2.32. Effect of added solubilizates on the cloud point of 2% Triton X-100[*2] solutions. Solubilizates: (1) cetane; (2) dodecane; (3) decane; (4) tetradecene-1; (5) n-tetradecyl mercaptan; (6) acetone; (7) citric acid; (8) n-octene; (9) hexane; (10) 2-ethylhexene; (11) cyclohexane: (12) aniline; (13) butyl acetate; (14) ethylene dichloride; (15) phenol and oleic acid; (16) n-dodecanol and nitrobenzene; (17) benzene.

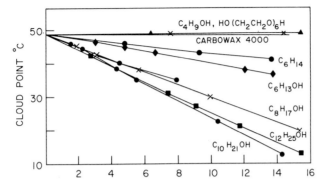

Fig. 2.33. Effect of added solubilizates on the cloud points of solutions of $C_{12}H_{25}O(CH_2CH_2O)_6H$.[*3]   The concentration of surface active agent is 4.22gm/100cc solution.

effect of various additives on the cloud point of polyoxyethylene isooctylphenyl ether[*29] and found marked depression on the addition of various phenols. The effect of a solubilizate on the cloud point may be related to its mode of incorporation and its effect on aggregation number and CMC.

Recently, Nakagawa and Tori (52) observed a change of state with temperature variation in solutions of methoxydecaoxyethylene decyl ether, $C_{10}H_{21}O(CH_2CH_2O)_{10}CH_3$[*30] containing various amounts of solubilizates. n-Octane, n-decane, n-dodecane, n-decyl chloride, n-octanol, n-decanol, n-dodecanol, n-decanoic acid, and n-decylamine were added as solubilizates. The effects of added n-decane, n-decanol, and n-decylamine are shown in Figs. 2.34, 2.35, and 2.36.

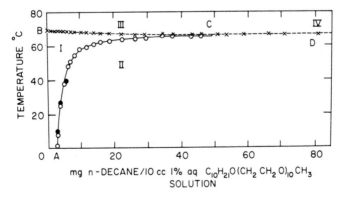

Fig. 2.34. Solubilization and cloud point curves of 1% $C_{10}H_{21}O(CH_2CH_2O)_{10}CH_3$[*30] solution in the presence of added n-decane.

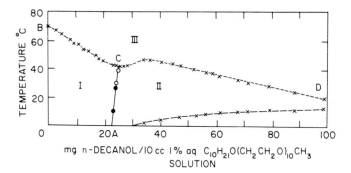

Fig. 2.35. Solubilization and cloud point curves of 1% $C_{10}H_{21}O(CH_2CH_2O)_{10}CH_3$[*30] solution in the presence of added n-decanol.

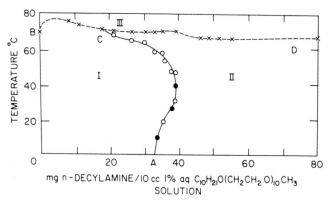

Fig. 2.36. Solubilization and cloud point curves of 1% $C_{10}H_{21}O(CH_2CH_2O)_{10}$ CH_3[*30] solution in the presence of added n-decylamine.

We will explain Fig. 2.34 as an example. Only one transparent phase exists in a solution of given composition and temperature described as realm I. Emulsion droplets of solubilizate appear in realm II, due to the addition of solubilizate to the solution described as realm I. These droplets are easily separated into another layer by the application of centrifugal force. We may designate the AC curve as a solubilization curve. If the temperature of a solution described either as realm I or II is elevated to a temperature expressed by the BCD curve, the solution suddenly becomes turbid and, at a somewhat higher temperature, begins to separate into two (realm III) or three (realm IV) layers. The boundary between realms III and IV cannot be accurately determined. As there exists some excess solubilizate in realm II, the solution is slightly turbid. The turbidity, however. suddenly increases above the CD curve and, at somewhat higher temperatures, another phase, rich in nonionic agent, separates. We may designate the *BCD* curve as a cloud point curve. The addition of *n*-octane, *n*-decane, *n*-dodecane, and *n*-decyl chloride produces analogous diagrams. The longer the hydrocarbon chain length, the smaller the amount of solubilization. Some features of the diagrams containing these solubilizates are: (i) a slight decrease in the *BC* curve; (ii) an almost horizontal *CD* curve; and (iii) a rapid increase in solubilization near the cloud point, shown by the *AC* curve. This peninsular-like region suggests an increase in the solubilization of hydrocarbon with an increase in micellar size. The addition of *n*-octanol, *n*-decanol, *n*-dodecanol, and *n*-decanoic acid to the solution produces diagrams similar to Fig. 2.35. The shorter the chain length of solubilizate, the larger the amount of solubilization. Features of the diagrams containing these solubilizates are: (i) a rather rapid decrease in the cloud point (curve *BC*); and (ii) the existence of a maximum, followed by a continuing decrease in the *CD* curve. The emulsion droplets in realm II are stable and do not separate into one layer without the addition of dye, etc. Realm IV was not observed in these experiments, probably because the alcohols and nonionic agents examined are miscible. Solutions containing *n*-decylamine show a somewhat different diagram. There is neither a remarkable decrease nor a clear minimum or maximum in the cloud point curve. It seems probable that *n*-decylamine acts as an ionic agent producing a small amount of carbonate owing to the absorption of carbon dioxide.

The heat of solution of a solubilizate into an aqueous solution of a surface active agent can be calculated from the solubilization curve. If we assume that any excess solubilizate separated from the aqueous phase is pure, the conventional heat of solution is given by the following equation (75).

$$\Delta H_{solub} = RT^2 \left(\frac{\delta \ln S_{solub}}{\delta T} \right)_p \tag{2.13}$$

S_{solub} is the saturation solubilization. In the case of hydrocarbons ΔH_{solub} is positive; it is nearly zero for alcohols.

As the amount of saturation solubilization is affected by the aggregation number of the nonionic agent and the separated solubilizate contains some amount of nonionic agent, particularly in the case of alcohol, the applicability of Eq. (2.13) is doubtful. The slope of the solubilization curve *AC* suggests in many cases whether the heat of solution is positive or negative.

Let us then discuss the composition and structure of realms I, II, III, and IV separated by curves *AC*, *BC*, and *CD*, on the basis of our present knowledge.

Realm I: The solution corresponding to this realm consists of only one phase and is composed of an aqueous solution of molecularly dispersed species and micelles swollen with solubilizate.

Realm II: The solution which corresponds to this realm is composed of aqueous solution, like the one we discussed above, and another phase rich in solubilizate.

Realm III: Two phases coexist.   One is an aqueous solution containing molecularly dispersed species, but may not contain micellar aggregates; the other is a phase rich in nonionic agent with a small amount of solubilizate and water dissolved in it.   The latter phase is considered to be separated from the water layer due to the formation of very large aggregates.

Realm IV: Three phases coexist.   Two of them are similar to the phases described in realm III, and the third one is a phase rich in so-

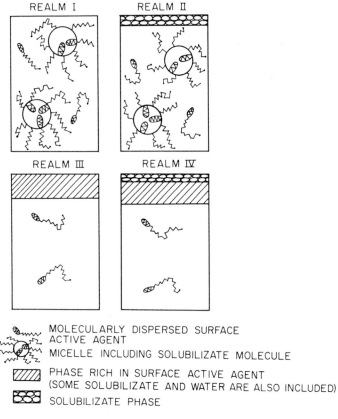

MOLECULARLY DISPERSED SURFACE ACTIVE AGENT

MICELLE INCLUDING SOLUBILIZATE MOLECULE

PHASE RICH IN SURFACE ACTIVE AGENT (SOME SOLUBILIZATE AND WATER ARE ALSO INCLUDED)

SOLUBILIZATE PHASE

Fig. 2.37.   Idealized model proposed for the phase separation of the surface active agent-solubilizate-water system.

lubilizate and similar to the separated phase in realm II.

The models of these solutions are shown in Fig. 2.37.

Several phenomena to support the above view were found from the observation of partition of added dyestuff in these solutions. A series of 1% solutions of $C_{10}H_{21}O(CH_2CH_2O)_{10}CH_3$[*30] containing various amounts of n-decane or n-decanol and small amounts of pinacyanol chloride or Sudan III were prepared. These solutions were then heated or cooled above or below cloud point and solubilization curve, and the color of each layer was observed.

Water-soluble pinacyanol chloride shows a blue color in aqueous solution above the CMC and a violet color in solution below the CMC. This dye is insoluble in hydrocarbons and soluble in alcohols. The results are shown in Table 2.21. It is evident from Table 2.21 that there exists a micelle in the water layer which corresponds to realm I or II and not in the solution which corresponds to realm III or IV. As we might expect, the phases rich in solubilizate are colorless in the case of decane and blue in the case of decanol.

Oil-soluble Sudan III is insoluble in aqueous solutions of nonionic agent below the CMC, but it is solubilized and shows an orange color above the CMC. This dye also dissolves in either hydrocarbons or long chain alcohols. The partitions of this dye shown in Table 2.21 again agree with our expectations. Emulsion droplets of decanol in the solution corresponding to realm II do not separate from water in the absence of coexisting dye, but separate from the water in the presence of dye.

TABLE 2.21

DISTRIBUTION OF ADDED DYE IN COEXISTING LAYERS[a] (COLOR OF LAYERS)

Realm	Layer	n-Decane		n-Decanol	
		Pinacyanol chloride	Sudan III	Pinacyanol chloride	Sudan III
I	Water	Blue	Orange	Blue	Orange
II	Solubilizate	Colorless	Deep orange	Blue	Deep orange
	Water	Blue	Orange	Blue	Orange
III	Surfactant	Dark blue	Red	Dark blue	Red
	Water	Faint violet	Colorless	Faint violet	Colorless
IV	Solubilizate	Colorless	Deep orange		
	Surfactant	Dark blue	Red		
	Water	Faint violet	Colorless		

[a] Each layer is named by its main constituent and arranged in order from the top to bottom layer.

The concentrations of nonionic agent in each layer can be determined by Siggia *et al.* (*76*) method. Though the reliability of the analysis is not very good, the concentrations of nonionic agent in the water layer in the solution corresponding to realms III and IV are close to the CMC, and the greater part of the agent exists in the oil layer. In the solution corresponding to realm II, most of the nonionic agent exists in the water layer, and the amount of nonionic agent in the decane phase was very small, 2.43 mg/cc.

The fact that the composition of the micelle and the concentration of the molecular dispersion in the aqueous phase stay practically constant (Table 2.17) and that the cloud point also stays constant (*CD* curve in Fig. 2.34) for further additions of *n*-decane above saturation solubilization is concordant with these findings. Thus, if excess decane separates as an almost pure phase, there will be no appreciable change in composition, concentration, or cloud point of the solution.

In the system containing *n*-decanol, emulsion droplets of excess *n*-decanol were difficult to separate.

Finally, the diagram of the $C_{10}H_{21}O(CH_2CH_2O)_{12}CH_3$[*23]—$n$-decane—water system which was most thoroughly studied is shown in Fig. 2.38a.

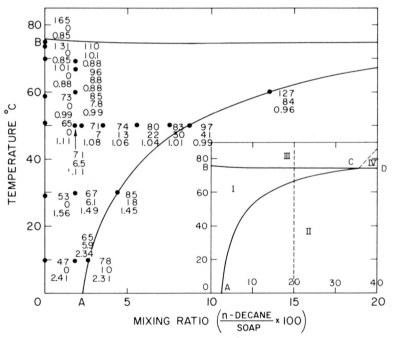

Fig. 2.38a. Diagram illustrating the composition and structure of the $C_{10}H_{21}O$ $(CH_2CH_2O)_{12}CH_3$[*23]–n-decane–water system.

The numbers in each point express the micellar compositon (aggregation numbers of nonionic agent and solubilizate) and the concentration of molecularly dispersed species in millimoles/liter. The values are quoted from Tables 2.13, 2.18, 2.19, and 2.20.

An analogous diagram was obtained recently[*] for the $C_{10}H_{21}O(CH_2CH_2O)_{12}CH_3$[*23]—$n$-decanol—water system (Fig. 2.38b).

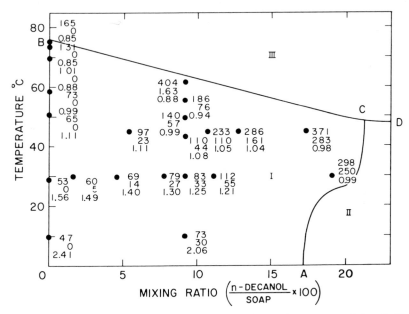

Fig. 2.38b. Diagram illustrating the composition and structure of the $C_{10}H_{21}O$ $(CH_2CH_2O)_{12}CH_3$[*23]-n-decanol-water system.

4. Water-Soluble Dye

It has often been observed that the spectral color of a water-soluble dye changes with the concentration of surface active agent in solution. This phenomenon has been used as a method of determining the CMC. In solutions of ionic agents the color change of dye occurs when the dye ion and ionic agent have opposite charges, and almost no interaction occurs when both ions have charges of the same sign. On the other hand, in solutions of nonionic agents a color change can occur when the charge of dye ions is either negative or positive, but to a lesser extent (Table 2.1).

The interaction between dyestuff and surface active agent is generally complicated, and not much research has been done in this field. Even

---

* Unpublished data.

the behavior of dye in water is not yet satisfactorily elucidated. Some kinds of dyes associate at fairly low concentration, and the aggregate is in equilibrium with monomer; for example, pinacyanol choride belongs to this type (77).

The absorption spectrum of a dye such as pinacyanol chloride or erythrosin in aqueous solution does not change very much until the concentration of the polyoxyethylene-type nonionic agent reaches a certain value, but the absorption spectrum changes rather abruptly above this concentration and then stays almost constant again for further additions of nonionic agent. The concentration at which the spectrum of the dye changes abruptly is roughly equal to the CMC determined by other methods. This change in the absorption spectrum of the dye can be explained as a partition equilibrium of dye between the micelle and the bulk of the solution. That the incorporation of the dye molecule into the hydrophilic portion of the micelle seems likely is supported by two experimental findings. One is that a solution of a nonionic agent containing pinacyanol chloride or erythrosin, etc. separates into two phases above the cloud point, showing very weak color in the water

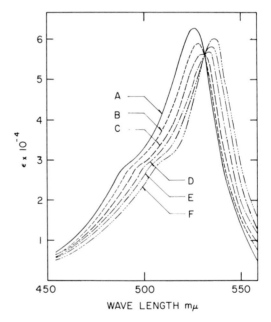

Fig. 2.39. Shift of the absorption spectrum of erythrosin as a function of concentration of the fractionated polyoxyethylene dodecyl ether.[*6] Concentration of surface active agent: (A) 0; (B) 4.08×10^{-4}; (C) 8.16×10^{-4}; (D) 1.02×10^{-3}; (E) 4.08×10^{-3}; (F) 5.10×10^{-2} moles/liter. Dye concentration 1.46×10^{-5} moles/liter.

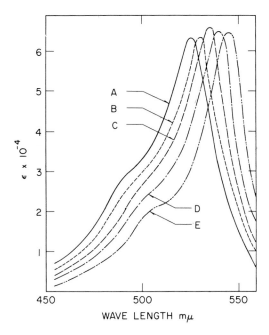

Fig. 2.40. Shift of the absorption spectrum of erythrosin as a function of concentration of polyethylene glycol (M = 439).*31 Polyethylene glycol/water (volume ratio): (A) 0 : 10; (B) 1 : 9; (C) 3 : 7; (D) 5 : 5; (E) 10 : 0. Dye concentration: 1.81×10^{-5} moles/liter.

phase and strong color in the detergent phase (cf. Table 2.21), and the other is that the absorption spectrum of dye in concentrated aqueous solutions of nonionic agent resembles that in concentrated aqueous solutions of polyethylene glycol. The change of absorption spectra of erythrosin in various concentrations of nonionic agent[*6] and in polyethylene glycol[*31] solutions is compared in Fgs. 2.39 and 2.40 as an example. The absorption spectrum of pinacyanol chloride in solutions has already been shown in Fig. 2.5. If we recall the fact that these dyes are insoluble in hydrocarbons, the mode of incorporation of the dye into the micelle seems to be solubilization into the hydrophilic polyoxyethylene portion of micelle, as shown in Fig. 2.28.

In order to confirm the above view, the spectral color change of erythrosin in aqueous solutions of methoxyundecaoxyethylene decyl ether, $C_{10}H_{21}O(CH_2CH_2O)_{11}CH_3$[*23] was investigated extensively, changing the concentrations of nonionic agent and dye (78). The absorption spectrum of erythrosin in aqueous solution is convenient for quantitative investigation because it has only one absorption band resembling a Gaussian

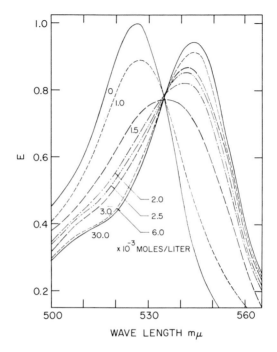

Fig. 2.41. Shift of the absorption spectrum of erythrosin as a function of concentration of methoxyundecaoxyethylene decyl ether $C_{10}H_{21}O(CH_2CH_2O)_{11}CH_3$.[*23]

distribution curve and does not show the complicated behavior pinacyanol chloride. The change in the absorption spectrum of erythrosin with concentration of $C_{10}H_{21}O(CH_2CH_2O)_{11}CH_3$ is shown in Fig. 2.41. Figure 2.41. shows a clear isosbestic point, suggesting the partition of dye between micelles and the bulk of the solution. Nakagawa (78) calculated the partition coefficient of the dye and found that the partition is very favorable to incorporation into micelle. If we add more and more surface active agent to a solution containing a definite amount of dye, micelles will begin to form at certain concentration, the CMC, and some of the dye molecules will then be incorporated in the micelles. At the same time, the wavelength of maximum absorption of the solution begins to shift abruptly, provided the partition coefficient is fairly large. This phenomenon was used to determine the CMC of nonionic agent in Section II.

5. *Miscellaneous*

In addition to the various substances described in Section VI, 1–4, starch shows marked interaction with surface active agents. It is well known that paraffinchain-type surface active agents inhibit the iodine-starch reaction, and it has been applied to the detection (79) or quantitative analysis (80) of surface active agents.

The addition of sucrose monooctadecanoate (stearate)[*32] to 0.1% NaCl solution of starch amylose or amylopectin results in precipitation (81), as shown in Tables 2.22 and 2.23. Amylopectin alone does not readily pre-

TABLE 2.22

PRECIPITATION OF STARCHES BY SUCROSE MONOOCTADECANOATE (STEARATE)[*32]

Type of starch	Polysaccharide concentration (%)	Sucrose mono-octadecanoate concentration (%)	Precipitate (per cent of polysaccharide)
"AnalaR"	1.0	0.1	21.6
Potato	1.0	0.1	70.9
Wheat	1.0	0.1	92.4
Waxy maize	1.0	0.1	13.0

TABLE 2.23

PRECIPITATION OF STARCH FRACTIONS BY SUCROSE MONOOCTADECANOATE (STEARATE)[*32]

Type of starch fraction	Polysaccharide concentration (%)	Sucrose mono-octadecanoate concentration (%)	Precipitate (per cent of polysaccharide)
Potato starch	0.4	0.04	72.7
Potato amylose	0.4	0.04	79.9
Potato amylopectin	0.4	0.04	11.1
Amylose 20% Amylopectin 80%	0.4	0.04	43.9

cipitate, but it precipitates more efficiently if amylose is also present in the solution. As sucrose octadecanoate is firmly bound by starch, it seems likely that it would interfere with the starch-iodine reaction. This was shown to be the case; iodine and sucrose octadecanoate compete for the amylose fraction. No evidence for any marked interaction between sucrose octadecanoate and amylopectin was discovered by this technique. It is possible that the paraffin chain of the sucrose octadecanoate molecule occupies a position down the center of an amylose helix, in the same way that iodine does.

Ionic surface active agents also precipitate similarly with amylose. It is confirmed that an inclusion compound is formed in which the hydrocarbon chain penetrates into the amylose helix (82). There are

other substances which precipitate with polyoxyethylene-type non-
agents or show color change in the presence of the agent. The
application of these substances in analysis or detection of a nonionic
agent will be described in Sections VIII and IX.

VII. Other Physicochemical Properties

Traube's Rule: In a homologous series of fatty acid soaps, the surface activity in aqueous solution regularly increases with hydrocarbon
chain length. The concentration of fatty acid soaps required for the
same depression of surface tension decreases by one-third for each additional methylene group, and this behavior has been termed Traube's
rule.

Shinoda *et al.* (*21*) have measured the surface tension of dodecyl,
decyl, and octyl glucoside.[*12] Similar results were obtained within this
range of hydrocarbon chain, and the surface activity increased about
3.2 times per methylene group. The change of the CMC of nonionic
agents with hydrocarbon chain length is similar to that of ionic agents
under the condition of a definite concentration of gegenions, where the
change in CMC was 3.0 for each methylene group (*83*). For more

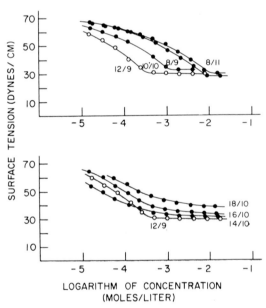

Fig. 2.42. Surface tension of aqueous solutions of polyoxyethylene alkyl ethers
$C_nH_{2n+1}O(CH_2CH_2O)_mH$.[*16] The number before the oblique line indicates n, and the
number after the line, m.

detailed discussion refer to Chapter 1, Section V.

Lange (26) has measured the surface tension of a series of polyo-xyethylene alkyl ethers, $C_nH_{2n+1}O(CH_2CH_2O)_mH$ (not purified),[*16] where the number of carbon atoms in the alkyl group ranged from 8 to 18, as a function of the concentration. The results are plotted in Fig. 2.42. Surface tension vs. log concentration curves shift towards the dilute concentration region from octyl to dodecyl ether, whereas the curves for tetradecyl ether and higher homologs do not shift towards the dilute concentration, and the lowest surface tension increases. A similar relation was observed also for a series of nonionics whose ratio of m against n is roughly constant. The surface tension vs. log concentration curves show sharp inflections for purified nonionic agents whose alkyl chains are not longer than 12 carbon atoms. In Lange's experiment, the surface tension vs. log concentration curves did not show sharp inflections for nonionic agents whose hydrocarbon chains are longer than 12. It should be remarked that the latter experiments were performed with unpurified materials.

X-Ray Scattering: Kehren and Rösch (84) have measured the X-ray diffraction patterns of a series of polyoxyethylene alkyl ethers $C_nH_{2n+1}O$ $(CH_2CH_2O)_mH$[*16] and of $C_{14}H_{29}O(CH_2CH_2O)_{10}H$[*16] in aqueous solution. The d_I spacings calculated from diffraction patterns by means of the Bragg equation are plotted in Fig. 2.43. The physical meaning of so-called d_I spacing in concentrated solution is not yet wholly understood.

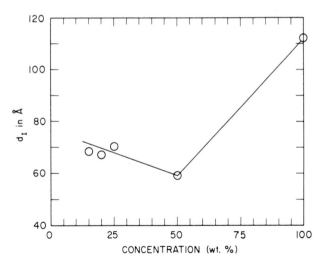

Fig. 2.43. The d_I-spacing of polyoxyethylene tetradecyl ether
$C_{14}H_{29}O(CH_2CH_2O)_{\overline{10}}H$[*16]
plotted as a function of concentration.

HLB System: Surface active agents have been widely applied in various fields of industry. It is difficult for customers, however, to find suitable surface active agents because manufacturers emphasize the versatile applicability of only their own products, and there is no good parameter for comparing agents from different producers. The hydrophilic-oleophilic balance (HLB) system has appeared in order to fulfill this requirement in emulsifying applications. Thus, each emulsifier could be assigned a number representing the extent to which it would behave as an oil-soluble vs. a water-soluble type of emulsifier. There are several ways of estimating the HLB value. The most reasonable way of determining the HLB value seems to be given not by the weight per cent of hydrophilic group, but by an actual emulsifying test using a standard emulsifier of known HLB. Griffin (85) defined the HLB number of nonionic surface active agent as the weight per cent of hydrophilic group in the molecule divided by 5. A true HLB number, however, should change with the kind of hydrophilic group. The crude HLB number also neglects the size of the hydrophilic and oleophilic groups. It seems a tentative, incomplete, yet useful parameter in emulsification at the present stage.

Apart from the HLB number in emulsion technology, the hydrophilic-oleophilic balance of the molecule seems a useful concept for understanding the properties of nonionic agents. If the molecules are too oleophilic, phase separation occurs immediately after the concentration exceeds the CMC; i.e., the micellar region is very narrow like that of octanol or octyl glycol ether. But this region gradually increases, for example, from octanol to octyl glucoside, as shown in Fig. 2.8. The importance of having a large hydrophilic group in a nonionic agent molecule is not primarily to increase the CMC, but to increase the micellar region. Thus, the solubility increases enormously. In other words, the addition of long hydrophilic groups is important not to decrease the activity, but to increase solubility while the activity of the nonionic agent stays almost constant.

Nonionic Polysoap: Recently two nonionic polysoaps, poly [methoxypolyoxyethylene 10-(*p*-styryl) undecanoate][*33] (I) and poly [methoxypolyoxyethylene 10-(*p*-acrylylphenyl) undecanoate][*33] (II) were synthesized by Medalia *et al.* (86). Molecular weights of these polysoaps, as determined by lightscattering measurements of their aqueous solutions, were 159,000 and 33,000, respectively. The structural formulas are shown here together with the abbreviations used.

Solubilization studies were carried out with *p*-dimethylaminoazobenzene (DMAB), following the conventional technique (87). As found with anionic polysoaps (87), the CMC is zero for the two nonionic polysoaps, and the concentration of DMAB solubilized is exactly proportional to

$$\left[\begin{array}{c} -CH-CH_2- \\ \\ \bigcirc \\ \\ CH_3CH \\ (CH_2)_8 \\ O=C \\ O(CH_2CH_2O)_{15-20}CH_3 \end{array}\right]_n \qquad \left[\begin{array}{c} -CH-CH_2- \\ O=C \\ \\ \bigcirc \\ \\ CH_3CH \\ (CH_2)_8 \\ O=C \\ O(CH_2CH_2O)_{15-20}CH_3 \end{array}\right]_n$$

(I)   (II)

Poly [methoxypolyoxyethylene   Poly [methoxypolyoxyethylene
10-(*p*-styryl) undecanoate]   10-(*p*-acrylylphenyl) undecanoate]
(Poly-NI-SUA)   (Poly-NI-UPK)

the concentration of polysoap in the solution. Thus, at 38°C, 1 gm of poly-NI-SUA solubilizes 13.6 mg of DMAB, and 1 gm of poly-NI-UPK solubilizes 20.1 mg of DMAB; in comparison, 12.4 mg of DMAB is solubilized by 1 gm of potassium tetradecanoate (corrected for the CMC).

The amounts of cholesterol solubilized at 38°C by the polysoaps were 18±3 mg/gm poly-NI-SUA and 40±20 mg/gm poly-NI-UPK. However, the analytical procedure was accurate only for poly-NI-SUA.

VIII. Purification and Chromatography

The impurity or heterogeneity of a nonionic surface active agent introduces many complications in its physicochemical properties. Convenient methods for purifying the sample and detecting impurities are therefore highly desirable. The molecular distillation technique is a powerful method, but it is applicable only to the heat-resistant agents having lower molecular weights. Chromatography has proved to be a useful means for purification and detection. Paper partition chromatography of polyethylene glycols (*88*), $HO(CH_2CH_2O)_nH$, will be mentioned first because nonionic surface active agents of the polyoxyethylene series are ordinarily contaminated by their presence.

If we spot 50μg of polyethylene glycols of different molecular weights on filter paper, develop with *n*-butanol saturated with water, and, after drying, spray with modified Dragendorff reagent, a pink spot will appear on the yellow background. The modified Dragendorff reagent is prepared by mixing the four liquids (bismuth subnitrate 0.85 gm, acetic acid 100cc, water 40 cc), (KI 8 gm, water 20 cc), (acetic acid), and (water) in the ratio 1 : 1 : 4 : 10. immediately before spraying.

Another method of dyeing follows. After developing and drying, the paper strip is sprayed with 10% HCl, 10% BaCl₂, and 10% phosphomolybdic acid solutions, successively. Polyethylene glycol and its derivatives form a yellow water-insoluble complex using this procedure. After washingout the sprayed reagents with pure water, a yellow spot remains at the position where the glycol was. This color is, in general, too faint to be recognized distinctly. In such a case, the paper strip may be dipped into a mixture of one part of phenylhydrazine and two parts of acetic acid containing a small amount of water; the yellow spot then turns dark blue, which is easily detectable.

Both of the above two methods show less sensitivity for polyethylene glycols of lower molecular weight. Spotting of a larger amount of material is recommended in this case, but glycols of too low molecular weight give no colorreaction.

Some of the results obtained with various polyethylene glycols[34] of different molecular weight and mixtures of equal amounts of two of

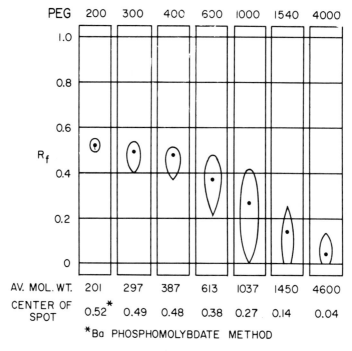

Fig. 2.44a. Chromatograms of several polyethylene glycols.[34]

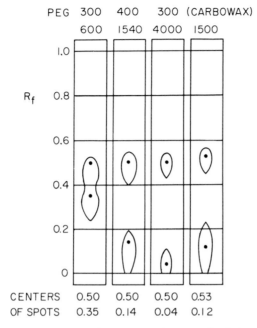

Fig. 2.44b. Chromatograms of mixtures of two polyethylene glycols*[34] with different molecular weights.

them are shown in Fig. 2.44. The black point indicates the position of the strongest color. Average molecular weights were determined by the phthalic anhydride method (89). Figure 2.44 tells us that the higher the molecular weight, the lower the R_f value.*

Polyethylene glycol coexisting as an impurity in commercial nonionic surface active agents can be detected in the same way. The results obtained with representative commercial nonionics*[35] are illustrated in Fig. 2.45.

In these cases, the spots of surface active agents were easily distinguished from those of glycols because the former have much higher R_f values than the latter and show an orange-tinted color.

However, the surface active agent and polyethylene glycol generally give spots of similar color. In order to distinguish the difference, the following procedure is recommended. The sample is developed in the same manner as above and then sprayed with I_2-amylose reagent. Surface active agents containing long chain paraffin groups hinder the iodine-starch color reaction (79, 81), while polyethylene glycol does not.

---

* The R_f value indicates, as usual, the migration distance of the examined material divided by that of the developing solvent.

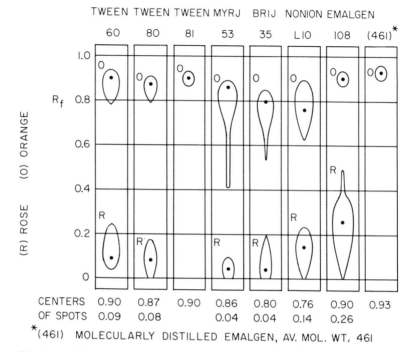

Fig. 2.45. Chromatograms of several commercial nonionic surface active agents.[*35]

The actual process is as follows. Spray 0.2% solution of potato amylose extracted by Schoch's method, (90), and then spray $N/350$ I_2 solution after 10 min (35-fold dilution of $N/10$ I_2 solution, U. S. Pharmacopoeia). A yellow or reddish yellow spot of surface active agent will then appear on the bluish violet background at the position where the surface active agent is. On the other hand, glycol retains the same color as the background. By comparing the chromatogram thus obtained with that dyed with Dragendorff's reagent, we can distinguish the spots of nonionic agents from those of polyethylene glycols.

If we apply silica gel chromatography instead of filter paper chromatography, it is possible to remove any polyethylene glycol included in a nonionic surface active agent (91). A glass U-tube, one limb of which is much wider than the other, serves as the developing vessel. The wider limb is filled with granular silica gel, which is soaked beforehand in water saturated with n-butanol, the sample dissolved in n-butanol (saturated with water) is then added through the narrower tube. The sample is developed slowly by the dropwise addition of butanol (saturated with water) through the narrower tube. The liquid which first overflows on silica gel column is collected, and the butanol is evaporated off under reduced pressure. The residue which remains contains no detectable polyethylene glycol.

The following phase separation method is, in many cases, more convenient and equally effective. An aqueous solution of nonionic agent (generally ca. 20%) is poured into a separatory funnel, heated above the cloud point, settled quietly to cause phase separation, and the water phase is discarded. The phase rich in surface active agent is redissolved in water, and the heat-separation process is repeated several times.

The selection of the developing solvent and regulation of temperature are most important to obtain a clear and reproducible chromatogram of the surface active agent itself. The solvent recommended by Nakagawa and Nakata (79) is the supernatant liquid which is formed when n-butanol, pyridine, and water (in the volume ratio 5 : 2 : 5) are mixed and shaken at 0°C. These authors chromatographed 26 kinds of commercial nonionics at 0°C in an icebox. The spots of nonionic agent and coexisting poly-ethylene glycol were made visible by the modified Dragendorff and I_2-amylose reagents. If we plot the HLB value of each agent as abscissa, and R_f as ordinates, we get Fig. 2.46. The surface active agent with

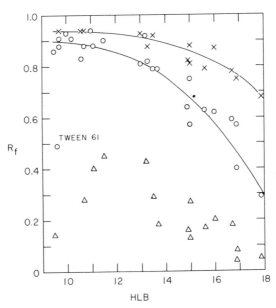

Fig. 2.46. Empirical relationship between Rf and HLB of nonionic surface active agents of polyoxyethylene series: ○, mainconstituent; ×, by-constituent; △, PEG.

the larger HLB shows, in general, the lower R_f value.

n-Aliphatic alcohols up to 14 carbon atoms and mono- to tetraethylene glycols can be detected by gas-liquid chromatography. For example, the chromatogram of a commercial polyoxyethylene dodecyl ether[*36] showed a peak having the same retention volume as that of dodecanol (92). This peak disappeared when the sample was allowed to flow down in a thin film through a molecular distillation apparatus under evacuation and became larger when dodecanol was added deliberately. Thus, the peak may be ascribable to the coexisting dodecanol as an impurity.

Quantitative analysis is also possible. Suppose that b grams of dodecanol is added to a grams of the sample, and w grams of this mixture is chromatographed. When we plot the area under the peak divided by w against $b/(a + b)$, a linear relation is obtained. Extrapolating the straight line, the intercept on abscissa gives $a/(1 - \alpha)$, where α is the dodecanol content per gram of the original sample.

When a suitable developing solvent is available, the fractionation of surface active agents is possible. Kelly and Greenwald (93) have fractionated p-2, 2, 4, 4-tetramethylbutylphenoxypolyoxyethyleneethanol[*37]

$$CH_3-\underset{\underset{CH_3}{|}}{\overset{\overset{CH_3}{|}}{C}}-CH_2-\underset{\underset{CH_3}{|}}{\overset{\overset{CH_3}{|}}{C}}-\left\langle\bigcirc\right\rangle-O-(CH_2CH_2O)_nH \qquad (n=9.7)$$

(III)

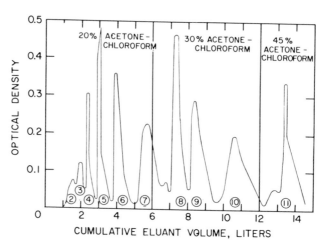

Fig. 2.47. Fractionation of p-2,2,4,4-tetramethylbutylphenoxypolyoxyethylene-ethanol[*37] by liquid chromatography.

(III) into its constituents by silica gel chromatography, using mixtures with varying ratios of chloroform and acetone. Their results are reproduced in Fig. 2.47. The number of oxyethylene groups of each fraction was calculated from the absorbancy of the chloroform solution at 277 $m\mu$ and encircled in Fig. 2.47. The fractionation seems quite satisfactory, Regrettably, colloid-chemical experiments using material thus fractionated have not so far been reported.

1. *Purification Procedures for Nonionics Cited*

The sources and purification procedures of the nonionics cited in this chapter will be described below.

PURIFICATION KEY

(*1) Glyco Products Co.; without any purification.

(*2) Rohm & Haas Co.; without any purification.

(*3) Synthesized from dodecyl bromide and sodium alcoholate of hexaethylene glycol which was prepared by the following reaction:

$$2HOCH_2CH_2OCH_2CH_2ONa + ClCH_2CH_2OCH_2CH_2Cl \longrightarrow$$
$$HO(CH_2CH_2O)_6H + 2NaCl$$

(*4) Rohm & Haas Co.; evacuated to remove volatile impurities.

(*5) General Aniline & Film Corp.; without any purification.

(*6) Emalgen 108 (Kao Soap Co.) was molecularly distilled at intervals of 10°C. The fraction distilled at 200°C had an average molecular weight of 440 determined by the phthalic anhydride method (*89*). The absence of free polyethylene glycol was verified by paper partition chromatography. The analytical value was in accord with the formula $C_{12}H_{25}O(CH_2CH_2O)_{5.8}H$.

(*7) A 3 : 10 : 7 mixture of three fractions (160°C, $\bar{M} = 362$; 200°C, $\bar{M} = 440$; 240°C, $\bar{M} = 473$); contained no detectable polyethylene glycol.

(*8) Emalgen 108 (Kao Soap Co.); without purification. The existence of polyethylene glycol was detected by paper chromatography.

(*9) Prepared by the following route: glucose → glucose pentaacetate → tetraacetyl octyl glucoside → octyl glucoside; m. p. 65°C.

(*10) Synthesized from octyl bromide and ethylene glycol; purified by fractional distillation; b. p. 132°C/21 mm Hg.

(*11) Prepared from glycerol α-monochlorohydrin and sodium octylate; purified by distillation; b. p. 132–133°C/0.5 mm Hg.

(*12) Octyl, decyl, and dodecyl glucosides were synthesized by a procedure similar to (*9). Their melting points and specific rotations were 63.8–65°C, $[\alpha]_D^{20}$ −33.8° (H_2O); 135°C, $[\alpha]_D^{25}$ −27.8°(H_2O); 143.5°C, $[\alpha]_D^{25}$ −24.7°(H_2O), respectively. They were purified by recrystallization from acetone + petroleum ether or methanol. Solutions were further purified by foam fractionation at concentrations slightly below their CMC's. There was no appreciable change in surface tension of octyl and decyl glucoside before and after foam fractionation.

(*13) Prepared by an alcoholysis reaction between the methyl ester of the desired fatty acid and the sugar.

(*14) Synthesized by esterification from molecularly distilled methoxypolyethylene glycols and the appropriate acid chlorides. The unreacted acid was removed by ionexchange resin, and methoxypolyethylene glycol by silica gel chromatography. The absence of acid and glycol was verified by the acid-value test and by paper chromatography. Analytical values were in fair agreement with the theoretical ones.

(*15) Synthesized and purified like (*14), but using an undistilled glycol ($\bar{M} = 750$).

(*16) Prepared by the addition of ethylene oxide to the desired alcohol; no purification.

(*17) Commercial polyoxyethylene dodecyl, octadecyl, octadecenyl (oleyl), and tridecyl ethers, and commercial polyoxyethylene sorbitan mono-dodecanoate; no purification.

(*18) Pure ether alcohols, which had been synthesized from the alkyl bromide and a glycol, were sulfated by chlorosulfonic acid. The product was recrystallized from absolute alcohol. Analytical values were in fair agreement with the theoretical ones.

(*19) A commercial product (Rohm & Hass Co.) was split into two fractions, one distilling below 200° and the other between 200° and 220°C, by molecular distillation. Each of these fractions was split into a higher and a lower boiling subfraction. In each case, the low boiling subfraction was insoluble in water, but the high boiling subfraction dissolved to give a clear solution. The two soluble subfractions were used for the measurements.

(*20) A product of Badischen Anilin- und Sodafabrik was fractionated by molecular distillation.

(*21) Commercial polyoxyethylene sorbitan fatty acid esters and a polyoxyethylene fatty alcohol ether (Kao Soap Co.); without any purification.

(*22) Synthesized by esterification from molecularly distilled methoxypolyethylene glycol and octanoic acid chloride. The unreacted acid was removed by ion exchange resin, and methoxypolyethylene glycol by silica gel chromatography. Their absence was verified by the acid-value test and paper chromatography. Average molecular weight 494 (by saponifying value); cloud point 44°C (1% solution).

(*23) Methoxypolyethylene glycol which had been fractionated by molecular distillation was converted into sodium alcoholate and reacted with decyl chloride. Water-soluble impurities were removed by the phase separation technique. The material was then allowed to flow down a molecular distillation apparatus as a thin film under high evacuation. After this treatment, the absence of decyl chloride, decanol, and methoxypolyethylene glycol was verified by chlorine analysis, gas-liquid chromatograpy, and paper chromatography. The elementary analysis was in fair coincidence with expectation.

(*24) Rohm & Haas Co. Electrolytes were removed by electrodialysis of 10% solution.

(*25) Atlas Powder Co. Electrolytes were removed by electrodialysis of 10% solution.

(*26) Atlas Powder Co.; purified by silica gel chromatography. The absence of polyethylene glycol was verified by paper chromatography. Average molecular weight 1100 [by OH-value test (89)].

(*27) Prepared by the addition of ethylene oxide to dodecanol. Inorganic salts were eliminated by passing through ion exchange resin.

(*28) Atlas Powder Co.; without purification.

(*29) Japan surfactant Co.; prepared by the addition of ethylene oxide to isooctyl phenol; without purification.

(*30) Synthesized by the same procedure as (*23). The absence of decyl chloride and methoxypolyethylene glycol was verified by chlorine analysis and paper chromatography. Average molecular weight 610 (by depression of freezing point of benzene solution); cloud point 69.5°C (1% solution).

(*31) PEG 400 (Carbide & Carbon Corp.) was molecularly distilled. The fraction distilled at 190°C had an average molecular weight of 439 determined by the phthalic anhydride method (89).

(*32) F. D. Snell, Inc.; commercial product.

(*33) Poly [methyl 10-(p-styryl) undecanoate] was prepared from the corresponding monomer by bulk polymerization at 60°C with an azo initiator. Similarly, poly [methyl 10-(p-acrylylphenyl) undecanoate] was prepared by bulk polymerization at 60°C with benzoyl peroxide. Both of these polyesters were transesterified with methoxypolyethylene glycol in diphenyl ether.

(*34) Carbide & Carbon Corp.; without purification.

(*35) Tween, Myrj, and Brij manufactured by Atlas Powder Co., Nonion, by Nihon Yushi Co.; Emalgen, by Kao soap Co.; without purification.

(*36) Brij 30 (Atlas Powder Co.); without purification.

(*37) Prepared by adding ethylene oxide to recrystallized p-2, 2, 4, 4-

TABLE 2.24

PRECIPITATION REACTIONS BETWEEN VARIOUS PRECIPITANTS AND POLYOXYETHYLENE DODECYL ETHERS,*[38] AND INFLUENCE OF ADDITION OF COMPLEX-FORMING AGENTS[a]

Precipitant	Complex-forming agent	$C_{12}H_{25}O(CH_2-CH_2-O)_nH$ (0.1%)	
		$\bar{n} = 3$	$\bar{n} = 15$
$Bi(NO_3)_3{}^b$		−	−
	NH_4I^b	−	−
	NH_4SCN^b	−	−
	KI^b	+ Reddish orange	+ Reddish orange
	$KSCN^b$	Orange (t)	+ Orange
	KCN^b	−	−
	$KI^b + BaCl_2$	+ Orange	+ Orange
	$KSCN^b + BaCl_2$	+ Yellowish orange	+ Yellowish orange
	$NH_4I^b + BaCl_2$	−	−
	$NH_4SCN^b + BaCl_2$	−	−
$HgCl_2{}^b$		−	+ White
	KI^b	+ Whitish pink	+ Whitish pink
	$KSCN^b$	+ White (t)	+ White
	NH_4I^b	−	−
$CdSO_4{}^b$		−	−
	KI^b	−	− Slightly white t
$Co(NO_3)_2{}^b$	KI^b	− Without change	− Bluish violet s
	$KSCN^b$	− Without change	− Blue s
	NH_4I^b	− Without change	− Bluish violet s
	NH_4SCN^b	− Without change	− Blue s
$MnSO_4{}^b$	$KSCN^b$	−	−
$FeCl_3{}^b$	$KSCN^b$	−	−
$ZnSO_4{}^b$	$KSCN^b$	−	−
$K_3Fe(CN)_6$		−	−
$K_4Fe(CN)_6$		White t	+ White
Iodine[b]	KI^b	+ Brown	+ Brown
Phenol		White t	White t
Resorcin		White t	White t
Tannin	(acid)	+ White	+ White
	(neutral)	−	−
RGC		+ Reddish brown (t)	+ Reddish brown
PTA		White t	+ White
	$CaCl_2$	+ White	+ White
	$BaCl_2$	+ White	+ White
STA		White t	+ White
	$CaCl_2$	+ White	+ White
	$BaCl_2$	+ White	+ White
PMA		Yellow t	+ Yellow
	$CaCl_2$	+ Yellow	+ Yellow
	$BaCl_2$	+ Yellow	+ Yellow

Precipitant	Complex-forming agent	$C_{12}H_{25}O(CH_2-CH_2-O)_nH$ (0.1%)	
		$\bar{n} = 3$	$\bar{n} = 15$
Na–TPB	—		Slightly white t
	CaCl$_2$	+ White	+ White
	BaCl$_2$	+ White	+ White

^{a} Test solution 1 cc + precipitant 1 cc + complex-forming agent 1 cc.

^{b} Solution is 0.1 M. Other solutions are 1%. Abbreviations used are t = turbid, s = solution, RGC = resorcin-glucose condensate, PTA = Phosphotungstic acid, STA = silicotungstic acid, PMA = phosphomolybdic acid, Na − TPB = sodium tetraphenyl borate.

tetramethylbutylphenol, in the mole ratio 9.7 : 1, in the presence of NaOH. The NaOH was neutralized with H_2SO_4, and sodium sulfate was filtered off in the presence of Celite 545. The sulfate ash remaining in the sample was 0.07%.

(*38) Prepared by the addition of ethylene oxide to dodecanol.

(*39) Commercial product; no purification.

IX. Analysis

Analytical methods for nonionic surface active agents, especially for the polyoxyethylene series, will be discussed briefly. The subject can be divided into two items: (i) characterization methods to determine the composition and structure of the nonionic agent; and (ii) quantitative methods to determine the nonionic agent in various formulations.

As for the first item, Siggia's review (*94*) and the references cited therein are highly recommended. Several important works which were either overlooked or published later are collected in reference number (*95*).

Many substances are known to precipitate with nonionics. Harada and Kimura (*96*) have examined some of these precipitation reactions. Some of their results are shown in Table 2.24. Some of these reactions have been applied to quantitative analysis (*97*, *98*). More recently, these authors have established two methods which are applicable to most of the polyoxyethylene derivatives (*99*).

When bismuth nitrate and potassium iodide are added to an aqueous solution of a nonionic agent, a precipitate is formed. Under certain conditions, the reaction proceeds quantitatively. The precipitate does not have a definite stoichiometric composition, but the inorganic components included in it have a constant composition given by $KBiI_4$. The chemical constitution may be represented by (IV).

$$[RO(CH_2CH_2O)_x(CH_2CH_2O)_yH][BiI_4]_x$$
$$|$$
$$K$$
$$(IV)$$

The weight of $KBiI_4$ included in the precipitate can be calculated from the concentration of bismuth in the supernatant liquid. The difference between this value and the total weight of precipitate gives the weight of active agent. Similarly, when phosphotungstic acid and barium chloride are added to the test solution, a precipitate having the composition (V) is formed.

$$[RO(CH_2CH_2O)_x(CH_2CH_2O)_y]_3[PO_4 \cdot 12WO_3]_x$$
$$\underset{\tfrac{1}{2}Ba}{|}$$

$$(V)$$

On ignition it is converted to $3BaO \cdot P_2O_5 \cdot 24WO_3$. The weight difference gives the amount of nonionic agent.

It should be noted here that a cationic surface active agent such as dodecyl pyridinium chloride reacts with these reagents, as well as, or even more easily than, nonionic agents do. In order to remove interfering substances, the extraction of nonionic agents by a suitable organic solvent is recommended (100). Another separation technique is the use of ion exchangers (98).

The length of the polyoxyethylene chain can be determined by Morgan's method (101). The ether linkages are split by hydriodic acid, yielding ethyl iodide and ethylene from the polyoxyethylene chain. These fragments are collected and measured.

$$-(CH_2CH_2O)_n + 2nHI \longrightarrow nICH_2CH_2I + nH_2O$$

$$ICH_2CH_2I - \left|\begin{array}{l} \xrightarrow{\text{decomp}} CH_2 = CH_2 + I_2 \\ \xrightarrow[\text{HI}]{} CH_3CH_2I + I_2 \end{array}\right.$$

Siggia *et al.* (76) have simplified this method so that only the iodine liberated by the hydriodic acid reaction need be titrated with thiosulfate. This reaction can also be applied to determine the nonionic agent in various formulations.

As mentioned in Section VI, 5, the iodine-starch color reaction is inhibited in the presence of a nonionic agent having a long hydrocarbon chain. This phenomenon has been utilized to determine the concentration of nonionics by the use of a calibration curve (80).

When nonionic surface active agents of the polyoxyethylene series are mixed with urea, the mixture sometimes solidifies (102). Mima (103) found that the straight chain alkyl ethers and esters of polyoxyethylene formed inclusion compounds, while sorbitan alkylate and alkyl aryl ethers of polyoxyethylene did not. The latter effect may be due to the fact that the size of the sorbitan or benzene ring is larger than the channel diameter (5 Å) postulated for the formation of the urea adduct. Possible applications for the separation or fractionation of surface active agents have been suggested.

References

1. McBain, J. W. "Colloid Science," pp. 240, Heath, Boston, 1950.
2. McBain, M. E. L., and Hutchinson, E. "Solubilization and Related Phenomena." Academic Press, New York, 1955.
3. Klevens, H. B. *Chem. Revs.* **47**, 1 (1950).
4. Stauff, J. *Kolloid-Z.* **125**, 79 (1952).
5. Debye, P. *J. Phys. Chem.* **53**, 1 (1949).
6. Reich, I. *J. Phys. Chem.* **60**, 257 (1955).
7. Kushner, L. M., Hubbard, W. D., and Doan, A. S. *J. Phys. Chem.* **61**, 371 (1957).
8. Hoeve, C. A. J., and Benson, G. C. *J. Phys. Chem.* **61**, 1149 (1957).
9. Debye, P., and Prins, W. *J. Colloid Sci.* **13**, 86 (1958).
10. Nakagawa, T., and Kuriyama, K. *J. Chem. Soc. Japan, Pure Chem. Sect.* **78**, 1568 (1957). (In Japanese.)
    Nakagawa, T. *Ann. Rept. Shionogi Research Lab.* **8**, 805 (1958). (In Japanese.)
11. Gonick, E., and McBain, J. W. *J. Am. Chem. Soc.* **69**, 334 (1947).
12. Goto, R., Sugano, T., and Koizumi, N. *J. Chem. Soc. Japan, Pure Chem. Sect.* **75**, 73 (1954). (In Japanese.)
13. Goto, R. *Symposium on Colloid Chem. (Chem. Soc. Japan), 8th Symposium* (1955).
14. Kushner, L. M., and Hubbard, W. D. *J. Phys. Chem.* **58**, 1163 (1954).
15. Hsiao, L., Dunning, H. N., and Lorenz, P. B. *J. Phys. Chem.* **60**, 657 (1956).
16. Nakagawa, T., Kuriyama, K., Inaba, M., and Tori, K. *J. Chem. Soc. Japan, Pure Chem. Sect.* **77**, 1563 (1956); Nakagawa, T., Tori, K., and Kuriyama, K. *ibid.* **77**, 1684 (1956). (In Japanese.)
17. Bury, C. R., and Browning, J. *Trans. Faraday Soc.* **49**, 209 (1953).
18. Colichman, E. L. *J. Am. Chem. Soc.* **72**, 4036 (1950).
    Meites, L., and Meites, T. *J. Am. Chem. Soc.* **73**, 177 (1951).
    Hubbard, H. M., and Reynolds, C. A. *J. Am. Chem. Soc.* **76**, 4300 (1954).
19. Tamamushi, R., and Yamanaka, T. *Bull. Chem. Soc. Japan* **28**, 673 (1955).
20. Shinoda, K,, Yamanaka, T., and Kinoshita, K. *J. Phys. Chem.* **63**, 648 (1959).
21. Shinoda, K., Yamaguchi, T., and Hori, R. *Bull. Chem. Soc. Japan* **34**, 237 (1961).
22. Osipow, L., Snell, F. D., and Nickson, J. *In* "Surface Activity: Proceedings of the Second International Congress on Surface Activity (J. H. Schulman, ed.), p. 50, Academic Press, New York, 1958.
23. Nilsson, G. *J. Phys. Chem.* **61**, 1135 (1957).
24. Wilson, A., Epstein, M. B., and Ross, J. *J. Colloid Sci.* **12**, 345 (1957).
25. Nakagawa, T., Kuriyama, K., and Tori, K. *J. Chem. Soc. Japan, Pure Chem. Sect.* **78**, 1573 (1957). (In Japanese.)
26. Lange, H. *Kolloid-Z.* **163**, 9 (1959).
27. Becher, P. *J. Phys. Chem.* **63**, 1675 (1959).
28. Ross, S., and Olivier, J. P. *J. Phys. Chem.* **63**, 1671 (1959).

29. Weil, J. K., Bistline, R. G., Jr. and Stirton, A. J. *J. Phys. Chem.* **62**, 1083 (1958).
30. Nakagawa, T. *Ann. Rept. Shionogi Research Lab.* **8**, 835 (1958). (In Japanese.)
31. Shinoda, K. *J. Phys. Chem.* **58**, 541 (1954).
32. Lange, H. *Kolloid-Z.* **131**, 96 (1953).
33. Stauff, J., and Rasper, J. *Kolloid-Z.* **151**, 148 (1957).
34. Nakagawa, T., Kuriyama, K., Inoue, H., and Oyama, T. *J. Chem. Soc. Japan, Pure Chem. Sect.* **79**, 348 (1958). (In Japanese.)
35. Nakagawa, T., and Inoue, H. *J. Chem. Soc. Japan, Pure Chem. Sect.* **79**, 345 (1958). (In Japanese.)
36. Guth, E., and Simha, R. *Kolloid-Z.* **74**, 266 (1936).
37. Onclay, J. L. *Ann. N. Y. Acad. Sci.* **41**, 121 (1941).
38. Kuhn, W., and Kuhn, H. *Helv. Chim. Acta* **28**, 97 (1945).
39. Boltzmann, L. *Ann. Phys. Lps.* **53**, 959 (1894); cf. Alexander, A. E., and Johnson, P. "Colloid Science," Vol. I, pp. 238, Oxford Univ. Press, London and New York, 1949.
40. Flory, P. J. "Principles of Polymer Chemistry," pp. 531, Cornell Univ. Press, Ithaca, New York, 1953.
41. Okuyama, H., and Tyuzyo, K. *Bull. Chem. Soc. Japan* **27**, 259 (1954).
42. Mankowich, A. M. *Ind. Eng. Chem.* **47**, 2175 (1955); Mankowich, A. M. *J. Phys. Chem.* **58**, 1027 (1954).
43. Nakagawa, T., Inoue, H., Tori, K., and Kuriyama, K. *J. Chem. Soc. Japan, Pure Chem. Sect.* **79**, 1194 (1958). (In Japanese.)
44. Nakagawa, T., Kuriyama, K., and Inoue, H. *Symposium on Colloid Chem. (Chem. Soc. Japan), 12th Symposium* pp. 29 (1959).
45. Kuriyama, K., Inoue, H., and Nakagawa, T. *Ann. Rept. Shionogi Research Lab.* **9**, 1061 (1959).
46. Stainsby, G., and Alexander, A. E. *Trans. Faraday Soc.* **46**, 587 (1950); Flockhart, B. D., and Ubbelohde, A. R. *J. Colloid Sci.* **8**, 428 (1953).
47. Debye, P. *Ann. N. Y. Acad. Sci.* **51**, 575 (1949).
48. Brady, A. P., and Huff, H. *J. Colloid Sci.* **3**, 511 (1948).
49. White, P., and Benson, G. C. *Trans. Faraday Soc.* **55**, 1025 (1959).
50. Ferguson, L. N. *J. Am. Chem. Soc.* **77**, 5288 (1955); Greenwald, H. L., and Brown, G. L. *J. Phys. Chem.* **58**, 825 (1954).
51. Maclay, W. N. *J. Colloid Sci.* **11**, 272 (1956).
52. Nakagawa, T., and Tori, K. *Kolloid-Z.* **168**, 132 (1960).
53. Doscher, T. M., Myers, G. E., and Atkins, D. C., Jr, *J. Colloid Sci.* **6**, 223 (1951).
54. Livingston, H. K. *J. Colloid Sci.* **9**, 365 (1954).
55. Goto, R., and Sugano, T. "Jikken Kagaku Koza" Vol. 7 ("Surface Chemistry"), 125 pp. Maruzen, Tokyo, 1956. (In Japanese.)
56. Nakagawa, T., and Inoue, H. *J. Chem. Soc. Japan, Pure Chem. Sect.* **78**, 636 (1957). (In Japanese.)
57. Alexander, A. E., and Johnson, P. "Colloid Science," Vol. I, 328 pp. Oxford Univ. Press, London and New York, 1949.
58. Svensson, H. *Arkiv Kemi Mineral. Geol.* **22A**, 156 (1946).
59. Longsworth, L. G. *J. Phys. Chem.* **51**, 171 (1947).

60. Alexander, A. E., and Johnson, P. "Colloid Science," Vol. I, 378 pp. Oxford Univ. Press, London and New York, 1949.
61. Dole, V. P. *J. Am. Chem. Soc.* **67**, 1119 (1945).
62. Henry, D. C. *Proc. Roy. Soc.* **A133**, 106 (1931).
63. Yoda, O., Meguro, K., Kondo, T., and Ino, K. *J. Chem. Soc. Japan, Pure Chem. Sect.* **77**, 905 (1956). (In Japanese.) Cf. also Biswas, A. K., and Mukherji, B. K. *J. Phys. Chem.* **64**, 1 (1960).
64. Alexander, A. E., and Johnson, P. "Colloid Science," Vol. II, 686 pp. Oxford Univ. Press, London and New York, 1949.
65. Harkins, W. D., Mittelmann, R., and Corrin, M. L. *J. Phys. & Colloid Chem.* **53**, 1350 (1949).
66. Riegelman, S., Allawala, N. A., Hrenoff, M. K., and Strait, L. A. *J. Colloid Sci.* **13**, 208 (1958).
67. Mulley, B. A., and Metcalf, A. D. *J. Pharm. and Pharmacol.* **8**, 774 (1956).
68. Higuchi, T., and Lach, J. L. *J. Am. Pharm. Assoc., Sci. Ed.*, **43**, 465 (1954); Guttman, D., and Higuchi, T. *ibid.* **45**, 659 (1956).
69. Nakagawa, T. *J. Pharm. Soc. Japan* **74**, 1116 (1954); **76**, 1113 (1956). (In Japanese.)
70. Nakagawa, T., Kuriyama, K., and Inoue, H. *J. Colloid Sci.* **15**, 268 (1960).
71. Phillips, J. N., and Mysels, K. J. *J. Phys. Chem.* **59**, 325 (1955).
72. Mattoon, R. W., Stearns, R. S., and Harkins, W. D. *J. Chem. Phys.* **16**, 644 (1948).
73. Nakagawa, T., Kuriyama, K., and Inoue, H. *Symposium on Colloid Chem. (Chem. Soc. Japan), 12th Symposium* pp. 32 (1959).
74. Aoki, M., and Iwayama, Y. *J. Pharm. Soc. Japan* **79**, 516 (1959). (In Japanese.)
75. Hutchinson, E., Inaba, A., and Baley, L. G. *Z. physik. Chem. (Frankfurt)* **5** 344 (1955).
76. Siggia, S., Starke, A. C., Garis, J. J., Jr., and Stahl, C. R., *Anal. Chem.* **30**, 115 (1958).
77. Sheppard, S. E., and Geddes, A. L. *J. Chem. Phys.* **13**, 63 (1945).
78. Nakagawa, T. *Ann. Rept. Shionogi Research Lab.* **8**, 886 (1958). (In Japanese.)
79. Nakagawa, T., and Nakata, I. *J. Chem. Soc. Japan, Ind. Chem. Sect.* **59**, 1154 (1956). (In Japanese.)
80. MacAllister, R. V., and Lisk, R. J. *Anal. Chem.* **23**, 609 (1951). Takayama, Y., and Kaneki, N. *J. Chem. Soc. Japan, Ind. Chem. Sect.* **59**, 661 (1956). (In Japanese.)
81. Bourne, E. J., Tiffin, A. I., and Weigel, H. *Nature* **184**, 110 (1959).
82. Takagi, T., and Isemura, T. *Bull. Chem. Soc. Japan* **33**, 437 (1960).
83. Shinoda, K. *J. Phys. Chem.* **59**, 432 (1955).
84. Kehren, M., and Rösch, M. *Fette, Seifen, Anstrichmittel* **59**, 1, 80 (1957).
85. Griffin, W. C. *J. Soc. Cosmetic Chemists* **1**, 311 (1949). Griffin, W. C. *Am. Perfumer Essent. Oil Rev.* **65**, No. 5, 26 (1955).
86. Medalia, A. I., Freedman, H. H. and Sinha, S. *J. Polymer Sci.* **40**, 15 (1959).
87. Sinha, S. K., and Medalia, A. I. *J. Am. Chem. Soc.* **79**, 281 (1957).
88. Nakagawa, T., and Nakata, I. *J. Chem. Soc. Japan, Ind. Chem. Sect.* **59**, 710 (1956). (In Japanese.)

89. *Drug Standards* **21**, 116 (1953). Originally devised for molecular weight determinations of polyethylene glycols, but applicable for nonionic surface active agents of polyoxyethylene series.
90. Schoch, T. J. *Advances in Carbohydrate Chem.* **1**, 259 (1945).
91. Nakagawa, T., and Muneyuki, R. *Ann. Rept. Shionogi Research Lab.* **7**, 509 (1957). (In Japanese.)
92. Nakagawa, T., Inoue, H., and Kuriyama, K. *Anal. Chem.* **33**, 1524 (1961).
93. Kelly, J., and Greenwald, H. L. *J. Phys. Chem.* **62**, 1096 (1958).
94. Siggia, S. *Soap Chem. Specialties* **34**, No. 3, 51 (1958).
95. van der Hoeve, J. A. *Rec. trav. chim.* **67**, 649 (1948).
    van der Hoeve, J. A. *J. Soc. Dyers Colourists* **70**, 145 (1954).
    Wurzschmitt, B. *Z. Anal. Chem.* **130**, 105 (1950); Karabinos, J. V., Kapella, G. E., and Bartels, G. E. *Soap Chem. Specialties* **30**, No. 6, 41 (1954); Rosen, M. J. *Anal. Chem.* **27**, 787 (1955); Nakagawa, T., and Nakata, I. *J. Chem. Soc. Japan, Ind. Chem. Sect.* **60**, 554 (1957). (In Japanese.)
96. Harada, T., and Kimura, W. *Abura Kagaku* **8**, 523 (1959). (In Japanese.)
97. Shaffer, C. B., and Critchfield, F. H. *Anal. Chem.* **19**, 32 (1947).
    Oliver, J., and Preston, C. *Nature* **164**, 242 (1949); Schönfeldt, N. *ibid.* **172**, 820 (1953); *J. Am. Oil Chemists' Soc.* **32**, 77 (1955); Stevenson, D. G. *Analyst* **79**, 504 (1954); Brown, E. G., and Hayes, T. J. *Analyst* **80**, 755 (1955); Kurata, M. *J. Japan Oil Chemists' Soc.* **4**, 293 (1955). (In Japanese.)
    Tate, J. R. *Chem. & Ind.* (*London*) 1324 (1957).
98. Barber, A., Chinnick, C. C. T., and Lincoln, P. A. *Analyst* **81**, 18 (1956).
99. Kimura, W., and Harada, T. *Ann. Rept. Nihon Gakujutsu Sinkokai, 120th Committee on Dyeing* p. 255 (1958). (In Japanese.)
    Kimura, W., and Harada, T. *Fette, Seifen, Anstrichmittel* **61**, 930 (1959).
100. Kortland, C., and Dammers, H. F. *J. Am. Oil Chemists' Soc.* **32**, 58 (1955).
101. Morgan, P. W. *Ind. Eng. Chem. Anal. Ed.* **18**, 500 (1946).
102. Barker, G. E., and Ranauto, H. J. *J. Am. Oil Chemists' Soc.* **32**, 249 (1955).
103. Mima, H. *J. Pharm. Soc. Japan* **79**, 857 (1959). (In Japanese.)

CHAPTER THREE

ADSORPTION

BUN-ICHI TAMAMUSHI

I. Introduction

Colloidal surfactants are characterized by their property of being adsorbed from solution at the interface between two phases, i.e., liquid-gas, liquid-liquid, or liquid-solid. The nature of the interface is profoundly altered by this adsorption, the most general effect being displayed by the lowering of the interfacial tension. In the case of the liquid-gas or liquid-liquid system, the interfacial tension is measurable, and the amount of adsorption or, more accurately, the surface excess may be calculated from the lowering of the interfacial tension by means of the well-known Gibbs adsorption equation, which expresses the thermodynamic relation between these two quantities. It should, however, be remarked that this fundamental equation will take different forms according to the nature of the surfactants, namely, whether they are electrolytes or nonelectrolytes. The derivation of the different forms of the Gibbs equation and their applicability will be treated in Section II of this chapter.

The interfacial tension and, accordingly, the adsorption may be influenced by the presence of small amounts of impurities contained in the samples of surfactants or in the medium. Therefore, very pure materials are required for obtaining exact knowledge of the phenomena. The reason why research on the adsorption and related phenomena of colloidal surfactants has developed rapidly in recent years is mainly due to the improvement of the purification procedures of technical surfactant products. Nevertheless, the effect of any minute third components (impurities) on the interfacial phenomena of colloidal surfactants still bears a meaning of paramount importance in the discussion of experimental results.

The amount of adsorption can be determined by the method of direct analysis of colloidal surfactants, which has also been improved in recent years. This provides another reason for the recent development of research on the subject under consideration. The adsorption at the solution-solid interface is determined only by the direct analysis of surfactants in solution before and after adsorption.

From the standpoint of the well-established purification procedure as well as the method of analysis, ionic surfactants, i.e., the compounds having surface active anions or cations in their molecules, are particularly suitable for investigation. The experimental data referred to in this chapter are chiefly concerned with compounds that have paraffin chain anions or cations as ionic parts of their molecules.

These paraffin chain electrolytes have in general a tendency to be strongly adsorbed at the interfaces owing to their property of *amphipathy** — the occurrence in a single molecule or ion of one or more groups which have an affinity for the phase in which this molecule or ion is dissolved, together with one or more groups which are antipathetic to the solvent medium or, rather, sympathetic to the other phase. It is usual to refer to these two types of groups as *lyophilic* and *lyophobic*, respectively. In the case under consideration, the solvent medium is water and the antipathetic groups are mainly paraffin chains, so that we may call the former groups *hydrophilic* and the latter *oleophilic*. As a result of these two opposing properties, the ions or molecules of the surfactants tend to become concentrated at the interface between the aqueous phase and the other phase, provided that the latter phase is sufficiently sympathetic to the paraffin chain groups in the surfactant molecules or ions. In other words, in the absence of special forces acting in the opposite direction, the ions or molecules of the surfactants will be adsorbed and oriented at the interface in such a manner that they turn their paraffin chain groups away from the aqueous phase. This causes a reduction in the interfacial free energy because the dissymmetry in the forces on the molecules or ions near the interface is now diminished.

Such a type of adsorption is likely to take place at the solution-air or solution-oil interface, as there may be no special forces acting in the opposite sense. In such cases, the adsorption layer may generally be formed as a monolayer and the state of that monolayer may be either gaseous or condensed according to variations in the structure of adsorbed molecules or ions, the nature of the external phase (air or oil), the surfactant concentration in the bulk phase, temperature, etc. It should also be noted that in the case of ionic surfactants the state of the adsorption layers may be a function of the electric double layer potential due to the oriented molecules or ions.

At the solution-solid interface, on the other hand, there is a possibility that the surfactant molecules or ions display another type of adsorption, i.e., the hydrophilic groups are attached to the solid surface, while the hydrocarbon parts are directed towards the aqueous phase. Such a type of adsorption will be realized when the solid surface possesses polar sites to which the hydrophilic groups are specifically bound, which is a type of *chemisorption*. In recent studies on the adsorption of paraffin chain electrolytes at the solution-solid interface, it has been found that in some cases the adsorption occurs in two steps: (i) the paraffin chain

---

* The term *amphipathy* was coined by G. S. Hartley in "Aqueous Solutions of the Paraffin-Chain Salts." Hermann, Paris, 1936.

ions are specifically adsorbed at the solid surface in the manner just described; and (ii) with the increase of the surfactant concentration, they are adsorbed onto the first monolayer by directing the hydrocarbon parts to this layer and the polar ionic groups towards the aqueous medium. In this way "two-layer" adsorption takes place, the mechanism of which will be discussed in Sections IV and V of this chapter.

The adsorption of colloidal surfactants at the solution-mercury interface treated in Section III is a subject of special interest. At this type of interface, the adsorption of surfactants is especially related to the electrical capacity of the double layer at the interface. Applying the dropping mercury electrode and the differential capacity determination method, we obtain curves for the differential capacity versus the applied potential, from which the Gibbs surface excess can be calculated. It has been found that the adsorption is characteristically influenced by the applied potential difference as well as by the presence of simple supporting electrolytes. From the characteristic features of the curves, information on the mechanism and structure of the adsorbed layers can be obtained. The adsorption of paraffin chain electrolytes at the solution-mercury interface may be either specific or nonspecific, according to variations in the applied potential difference and other factors.

The interaction between colloidal surfactants and other colloidal substances has been a subject of wide interest. Section V is concerned chiefly with the experimental results on the interaction of paraffin chain electrolytes with inorganic oleophilic colloids, such as silver iodide sol.

The flocculation and deflocculation phenomena of these colloids that are caused by surfactant electrolytes are in the main explained by the assumption of a "two-layer" adsorption mechanism. Concerning the interaction of colloidal surfactants with hydrophilic colloids, only a few experimental data are treated in Section V from viewpoint of the same adsorption mechanism. A rapidly increasing knowledge of the interaction between colloidal surfactants and proteins or other high molecular substances is beyond the scope of the present treatise.

II.   Adsorption at the Solution-Air and Solution-Oil Interfaces

1.   Interfacial Tension Results

The lowering of the interfacial tension at the solution-air or solution-oil interface is a general, characteristic property of colloidal surfactants. This property is sometimes complicated by phenomena such as the following: (i) the interfacial tension does not attain equilibrium over a long period of time (phenomenon of slow aging); or (ii) the interfacial tension vs. concentration curve passes through a minimum at a certain concentration fairly close to the CMC of a colloidal surfactant. Since the time when the first phenomenon was noticed by Adam and Shute (1) and the second phenomenon by McBain and Mills (2), critical work on these phenomena has been carried out by many investigators (3–6).

There has been some discussion as to the reason why the time required to reach final equilibrium may be a million times greater than that needed for diffusion to bring surfactant molecules or ions onto the surface. The idea that adsorbed molecules or ions will be oriented in a definite sense and that the final process of adsorption may be one requiring a large activation energy, suggested by Ward and Tordai (7), may present an explanation for the phenomenon. There may also be a possibility that in surfactant solutions there exists a certain third component having a different rate of diffusion and a different surface activity from those of the surfactant, so that time is required until final equilibrium is attained.

The minimum of the interfacial tension vs. concentration curve has been variously explained as due to metal ions in water, impurities in chemical compounds under examination, or the time effect. The most likely explanation is probably based on the presence of a third component, since it is possible to remove the minimum by successive purification processes and to produce it by adding that component.

The phenomena of slow aging and of the appearance of a minimum in the interfacial tension (γ) vs. concentration (C) curve seem to be related insofar as they can be attributed to the existence of impurities contained in water or surfactant. Generally, however, there may be different reasons for these two phenomena. In this section, some recent work on these phenomena will be referred to.

According to the results obtained by Pethica (8), the interfacial tension of sodium dodecyl sulfate at the solution-air interface does not exhibit a minimum in the γ vs. log C curves, provided the sample of the surfactant is a highly purified one. Two experimental methods, i.e., the drop-volume method and the Wilhelmy plate method, gave identical results for the interfacial tension, the equilibrium being attained in 2 to 3 minutes in both cases. A minimum appeared in the γ vs. log C curves when the surfactant sample was impure.

The experimental results obtained by Kling and Lange (9), who measured the interfacial tensions of a series of sodium alkyl ($C_8 - C_{20}$) sulfates at the solution-hexane interface by the drop-volume method, also demonstrate that no minimum in the γ vs. log C curves appears with carefully purified surfactant materials.

Harold (10), who measured the interfacial tensions of sodium dodecyl sulfate, sodium p-nonylbenzenesulfonate, and sodium tetrapropylenebenzenesulfonate at the solution-air interface, showed that the minimum in the γ vs. log C curves is removed by the addition of an excess salt having a common ion (0.2 M sodium chloride in this case), and this author discussed the result from the viewpoint of the Gibbs adsorption equation. The minimum which initially appeared was attributed to the small amount of impurities (probably dodecanol, etc.) in the compounds applied. The presence of excess salt lowers the CMC of the surfactant and, consequently, the bulk concentration at which the surface excess approaches saturation. This will increase the proportion of the surfactant in the surface at the expense of the third component (impurity), the contribution of this component being thereby reduced.

It was pointed out by Haydon and Phillips (11), who measured the interfacial tensions of sodium dodecyl sulfate and dodecyltrimethylammonium bromide at the petroleum ether-water interface, that the aging phenomenon is dependent on the purity of the water used. When ordinary distilled water of specific conductivity $\sim 4 \times 10^{-6} \text{ohm}^{-1} \text{cm}^{-1}$ was used, aging effects extending over hours were observed with sodium dodecyl sulfate at all concentrations studied ($\sim 10^{-2}$–$10^{-4} M$) and with dodecyltrimethylammonium bromide at concentrations $\sim 10^{-3} M$, whereas, if the water was very carefully purified and its specific conductivity was reduced to $0.9 \times 10^{-6} \text{ohm}^{-1} \text{cm}^{-1}$, little aging was observed except in very dilute solutions, and the γ vs. log C curves obtained were found to be displaced from the original curves towards higher interfacial tensions at comparable concentrations.

However, according to Clayfield and Matthews (12), interfacial tensions of surfactant solutions are generally time-dependent even when highly purified materials are used. They observed the change of the interfacial tension of sodium dodecyl sulfate at the solution-air interface at various molar concentrations and at various time intervals up to one and one-half hours. There appeared a minimum in the γ vs. log C curves at time intervals of about 10 minutes, while there was no trace of a minimum in the curves when true equilibrium was attained after 60–90 minutes. They pointed out that the existing controversial views concerning the minimum in the γ vs. log C curves in the literature may be due partly to the fact that very rarely have such slow changes of surface tension with time been observed carefully from beginning to end. They further remarked that a minimum is also produced by the addition of a minute amount of calcium chloride ($2.4 \times 10^{-5} M$), but this minimum was considered to be of a different character from that of a time-dependent one, as this minimum appeared at the stage of true equilibrium.

Sutherland (13) observed the interfacial tension lowering at the air-water interface with solutions of sodium hexadecyl sulfate (5×10^{-5}–$10^{-3} M$) over a period of 200 minutes by using a vertical film balance. From a comparison of interfacial tensions with and without added hexadecanol in the solution, the amount of hexadecanol diffusing from solution to the interface was shown to be related to a mechanism of convection plus diffusion near the interface.   In the presence of a large excess of sodium chloride, the rate of fall of the interfacial tension became independent of trace impurities, and this rate was considered to be approximately governed by the diffusion of hexadecyl sulfate into to the interface.

Eda and Fukuda (14) carried out the determination of the solution-air interfacial tensions of sodium decyl sulfate and sodium dodecyl sulfate by means of the sessile bubble method over a very long period, up to 24 hours, in the presence or absence of a third component.   Figure 3.1 indicates the γ vs. log C curves obtained with sodium decyl sulfate

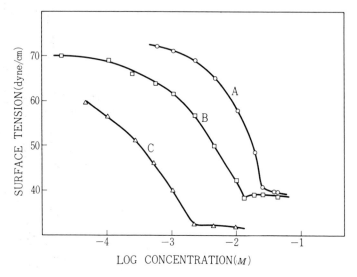

Fig.   3.1.   Surface tension vs. logarithm concentration curve for sodium decyl sulfate. (A) Distilled water; (B) 0.1 N sodium sulfate solution; (C) 1N sodium sulfate solution.

of very high purity, in the absence as well as in the presence of excess sodium sulfate at $30° \pm 0.05°$C.   The interfacial tension measurement was made at initial and final stages in 24 hours, neither aging nor the appearance of a minimum being observed.   However, when a small amount of decanol (in a molar ratio of 5.8×10^{-3}) was added to the original surfactant solution, a minimum appeared in the γ vs. log C curves, as shown in Fig. 3.2.

In this figure, the upper broken curve represents the initially (time, ~1 min) obtained curve, while the full curve, which has a distinct minimum, refers to the equilibrium state after 24 hours.   The slope of this equilibrium curve is found to be almost equal to that of the curve for

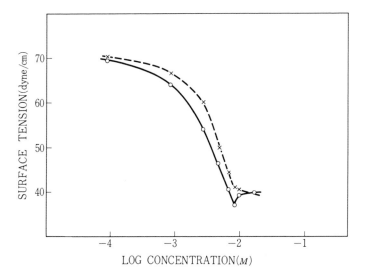

Fig. 3.2. Surface tension vs. logarithm concentration curves for sodium decyl sulfate in the presence of decanol. Broken curve, initial value; full curve, final value.

decanol, which suggests that the slow aging phenomenon may be due to the competitive adsorption of decanol, which is more surface active than sodium decyl sulfate.

The same kind of measurement over a very long period of time was applied by Eda (*15*) to a solution of polyoxyethylene dodecyl ether, a typical nonionic surfactant. It was found that there is a slow aging phenomenon and that the γ vs. $\log C$ curve initially obtained (in $\sim$1 min) goes downward after 1–2 hours when equilibrium is attained. The author considered that this experimental fact can also be attributed to the existence of a third component in the surfactant examined.

Besides the phenomenon of slow aging, the phenomenon of rapid aging has been observed with solutions of colloidal surfactants by means of the contracting-jet method, which permits recording of the change of interfacial tensions in less than a second. This latter phenomenon was systematically studied by Addison and Elliott (*16*). According to their observations on the interfacial tension of sodium dodecyl sulfate at the solution-air interface, the interfacial tension initially decreases with time and then increases to a constant value, as shown in Fig. 3.3. At this stationary state the rate of adsorption due to diffusion is supposed to balance the rate of increase of surface area at the interface.

Developing the contracting-jet method of Addison and co-workers for

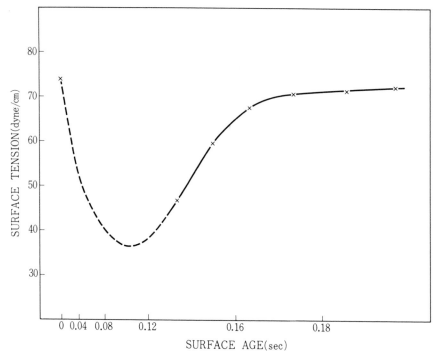

Fig. 3.3.   Graph showing the rapid aging of a solution of sodium dodecyl sulfate.

the study of the interfacial aging in liquid-liquid systems, Garner and
Mina (17) recently studied the effect of the chain length and other structural factors on the rapid interfacial aging of some homologous organic
compounds, including normal alcohols, normal carboxylic acids, and normal amines at the solution-paraffin interface.   According to this work,
the migration velocity of the adsorbable molecules or ions is a function
of the number of carbon atoms, the migration velocity being increased
as the number of carbon atoms is increased.   From the migration velocity
the surface diffusion coefficient is calculated; this coefficient rapidly increases with an increase in the number of carbon atoms.   It was also
shown that in solutions of nonionic surfactants the time required to attain surface tension equilibrium is due not to ordinary diffusion but to
a barrier of adsorption which exists at the interface and whose magnitude
decreases with increase in the hydrophobic chain length.   The over-all
adsorption rate is a function only of the chain length, while the nature
or the position of the hydrophilic endgroup has no direct effect.   The
velocity of migration V of the solute molecules increases with the hydrophobic chain length according to the following empirical relation:

$$V = \exp(0.6n - 1.4) + 2.5$$

where n is the number of carbon atoms.

The change of interfacial tensions in a time range of a half-second to a half-minute, which is most frequently the range of the contact time of a bubble with bulk of solution during the formation of foams, can be studied by means of the hanging-drop weight method. This method can be applied to the study of the interfacial aging of surfactants such as decanol whose rate of adsorption is comparatively slow. Brady and Brown (18) applied this method to the study of the aging of sodium dodecyl sulfate contaminated with decanol at the solution-air interface and confirmed that at a dropping time of about one second the surface tension is roughly independent of the decanol content and the dropping time.

2. Gibbs Adsorption Equation

The interfacial tension results are usually discussed from the standpoint of the fundamental Gibbs equation of adsorption. The general form of this equation applied to an aqueous solution is expressed, according to Guggenheim (19), as follows:

$$-d\gamma = RT\sum(\Gamma_i - \gamma_i\Gamma_{H_2O})d\ln a_i \qquad (3.1)$$

where γ is the interfacial tension; Γ_{H_2O}, the surface excess of water; Γ_i, γ_i, and a_i are the surface excess, the molar fraction, and the activity of the ith solute component, respectively.

Practically, for dilute solutions of surfactants of high surface activity, the term Γ_{H_2O} may be omitted, and therefore the equation becomes in approximation

$$-d\gamma = RT\sum\Gamma_i d\ln a_i \qquad (3.2)$$

Supposing that a given solution contains a single ionic surfactant in the form A^+B^-, in which B^- refers to a surface active large ion, we can write the equation as follows:

$$-\frac{d\gamma}{RT} = \Gamma_{A^+}d\ln a_{A^+} + \Gamma_{B^-}d\ln a_{B^-} + \Gamma_{H_3O^+}d\ln a_{H_3O^+}$$

$$+ \Gamma_{OH^-}d\ln a_{OH^-} \qquad (3.3)$$

where Γ and a are the surface excesses and activities of the respective ions. It is assumed here that the dissociation of water molecules takes place in the surface phase.

Taking the conditions of electroneutrality and constancy of the ionic product of water into consideration, we have

$$\Gamma_{A^+} + \Gamma_{H_3O^+} = \Gamma_{B^-} + \Gamma_{OH^-}$$

and

$$d \ln a_{H_3O^+} = -d \ln a_{OH^-}$$

Substituting these relations into Eq. (3.3), we get

$$-\frac{d\gamma}{RT} = \Gamma_{B^-} d \ln a_{A^+} a_{B^-} + (\Gamma_{A^+} - \Gamma_{B^-}) d \ln a_{A^+} a_{OH^-}$$

or

$$-\frac{d\gamma}{RT} = \Gamma_{B^-} d \ln f_{A^+} f_{B^-} m_{A^+} m_{B^-} + (\Gamma_{A^+} - \Gamma_{B^-}) d \ln f_{A^+} f_{OH^-} m_{A^+} m_{OH^-} \quad (3.4)$$

where f and m are the activity coefficients and molarities of the respective ions.

If we can arbitrarily assume for a surfactant of the strong electrolyte type that

$$\Gamma_{A^+} = \Gamma_{B^-}$$

then we obtain

$$-\frac{d\gamma}{RT} = \Gamma_{B^-} d \ln f_{A^+} f_{B^-} m_{A^+} m_{B^-} \quad (3.5)$$

Substituting the mean activity coefficient of the electrolyte, namely,

$$f_{AB} m_{AB} = (f_{A^+} f_{B^-} m_{A^+} m_{B^-})^{1/2}$$

Eq. (3.5) reduces to

$$-\frac{d\gamma}{RT} = 2\Gamma_{B^-} d \ln f_{AB} m_{AB} \quad (3.6)$$

where f_{AB} and m_{AB} refer to the mean activity coefficient and mean molarity of the electrolyte, respectively.

This last equation is a type of Gibbs equation which may be examined for experimental proof.

Suppose next that a given solution contains besides surfactant electrolyte A^+B^- an excess of a simple salt of the type A^+C^-, which has the same counter ion A^+ as that of the surfactant; then we can put the relation

$$d \ln a_{A^+} = 0$$

into Eq. (3.3), so that we obtain

$$-\frac{d\gamma}{RT} = \Gamma_{B^-} d \ln a_{B^-}$$

or

$$-\frac{d\gamma}{RT} = \Gamma_{B^-} d \ln f_{B^-} m_{B^-} \quad (3.7)$$

provided that the water dissociation is neglected.

This equation is another type of Gibbs equation amenable to examination for a surfactant of the strong electrolyte type.

If a given solution contains surfactant electrolyte A^+B^- and simple salt A^+C^- in comparable amounts, then the adsorption equation can be expressed approximately as

$$-\frac{d\gamma}{RT} = \Gamma_B - d\ln f_{AB}m_{AB} + \Gamma_A + d\ln(f_{AB}m_{AB} + f_{AC}m_{AC})$$

Since

$$\Gamma_{B^-} = \Gamma_{A^+}$$

the relation becomes

$$-\frac{d\gamma}{RT} = \left(1 + \frac{f_{AB}m_{AB}}{f_{AB}m_{AB} + f_{AC}m_{AC}}\right)\Gamma_B - d\ln f_{AB}m_{AB}$$

Substituting

$$1 + \frac{f_{AB}m_{AB}}{f_{AB}m_{AB} + f_{AC}m_{AC}} = x$$

we obtain

$$-\frac{d\gamma}{RT} = x\Gamma_B - d\ln f_{AB}m_{AB}$$

where x is a factor which has a value between 1 and 2.

When the hydrolysis of the surfactant electrolyte takes place in the bulk phase, and we can assume that

$$\Gamma_{B^-} \gg \Gamma_{A^+}$$

Eq. (3.4) becomes in approximation

$$-\frac{d\gamma}{RT} = \Gamma_B - d\ln a_{B^- a_{H_3O^+}} \tag{3.8}$$

where Γ_{B^-} represents the surface excess and $a_{B^- a_{H_3O^+}}$ the activity of the undissociated acid HB.

The derivations carried out above are principally the same as those of Pethica (20) and Cockbain (21), who discussed the derived equations on the basis of their experimental results with sodium dodecyl sulfate.

All the equations derived above are valid only for dilute solutions and not for solutions with concentrations greater than the CMC of the surfactant. For dilute solutions of a surfactant of the strong electrolyte type, we can further use the Debye-Hückel relation for f_{AB}, namely,

$$\log f_{AB} = 1 - 0.50\sqrt{m_{AB}}$$

and then Eq. (3.6) may be expressed as follows:

$$-\frac{d\gamma}{RT} = 2\Gamma_{\mathrm{B}}(1 - 0.58 \sqrt{m_{\mathrm{AB}}})d \ln m_{\mathrm{AB}} \qquad (3.9)$$

Pethica showed that the adsorption of surface active electrolytes at the air-water interface cannot be calculated from surface tension data by applying the Gibbs adsorption equation, except when excess neutral electrolyte is present in the solution. He considered that certain nonthermodynamic assumptions should be employed to estimate the adsorption from simple ionic surfactant solutions in the absence of neutral salt. Cockbain carried out the direct determination of the adsorption of sodium dodecyl sulfate at the decane-solution emulsion interface in the presence as well as absence of neutral salt (sodium chloride). From interfacial tension data he calculated the surface excess by Eq. (3.6) in the absence of neutral salt, the calculated values being found to agree with the experimental values.

The experimental results obtained by Kling and Lange (9) for a series of sodium alkyl sulfates at the solution-hexane interface in the absence of simple salt were also found to be in agreement with the theoretical values obtained from Eq. (3.6), provided that the concentration of the surfactant solutions was not very small. When the concentration was very small, and consequently the surface excess was also very small, Eq. (3.6) was found not to hold even for simple salt-free solutions. These authors considered that such deviations may be explained by the ion exchange at the interface which was assumed by Pethica (20).

The Gibbs equation in the form (3.8) was used for verification by Ter Minassian-Saraga (22) for the adsorption of dodecylcarboxylic acid at the solution-air interface in the presence of 0.01 M hydrochloric acid, the method of insoluble films being applied for the determination of the surface excess. The agreement between experiment and theory was satisfactory. The same verification procedure was applied by Zutrauen (23) to solutions of alkyl $(C_{12}-C_{18})$-trimethylammonium chlorides or bromides. The result showed that Eq. (3.6) can be applied to dodecyl compounds in the absence of inorganic salt, while the same equation can be used for other higher compounds only when the solutions contain excess inorganic salt. This latter result contradicts the considerations developed above. The author attributed this contradiction to the surface hydrolysis of the compounds in the absence of salt, on one hand, and to "doublet formation" of these higher alkyl compounds in the presence of salt, on the other.

Shinoda and Kinoshita (24) measured the interfacial tensions of several nonionic surfactants (octanol, octyl glycol ether, octyl glyceryl ether, and octyl glucoside) at the solution-air interface. The γ vs. log C curves of these surfactants significantly showed flat parts without minima, the

turning points of the curves being comparable to the CMC of the surfactants. The surface excesses and molecular surface areas were calculated by the Gibbs equation:

$$-d\gamma = RT\Gamma d \ln C \qquad (3.10)$$

where C is the molar concentration. The calculated values were found
to correspond to monolayers of almost closely packed molecules. It seems,
therefore, to be reasonable to use the Gibbs equation in the above simple
form for solutions of nonionic surfactants as long as the solutions are
dilute.

3. Radiotracer Method

For the purpose of the direct determination of the surface excess of
a surface active substance the radiotracer method seems to be a suitable
one. The method has been developed by Hutchinson (25), Dixon and co-
workers (26), Aniansson and Lamm (27), and other investigators. On
this subject there is an excellent review up to the time of 1953 by Dixon
and co-workers (28). Some more recent work will be referred to in this
section.

Sally and co-workers (29) determined the surface excess of S^{35}-labeled
sodium dioctyl sulfosuccinate at the solution-air interface and obtained
the value of 2.3×10^{-10} mole/cm^2 at an equilibrium concentration of
4×10^{-5} mole/liter in the absence of inorganic salt, while the surface
excess calculated by Eq. (3.6) gave the value of 1.2×10^{-10} mole/cm^2 over
the concentration range of 0.2–65×10^{-5} mole/liter. The discrepancy
between experiment and theory was considered to be due to the surface
hydrolysis of the surfactant electrolyte and consequently to the unreasonable use of Eq. (3.6). Nevertheless, these investigators drew a general
conclusion that for comparisons of values obtained by the radiotracer
method and those calculated from the Gibbs equation more accurate surface tension measurements are needed.

Roa and Brass (30) determined the surface excess of C^{14}-labeled
potassium palmitate in the presence of 0.1 M sodium ion and compared
the result with that calculated by Eq. (3.7). The coincidence between
the two values was fairly satisfactory.

According to Matsuura and co-workers (31), who made the determination of the surface excess of S^{35}-labeled sodium dodecyl sulfate in the
presence of 0.1–1.0 M sodium chloride, the experimental result was found
to be in accord with Eq. (3.7). It was also found that the result was independent of the nature of the added salt, when, besides sodium chloride,
potassium, magnesium, manganese, and aluminium chlorides were used.
In the absence of added salt, the experimental results were in accord
neither with Eq. (3.6) nor Eq. (3.7). These authors also measured the

velocity of adsorption of S^{35}-labeled sodium dodecyl, tetradecyl, and hexadecyl sulfates and explained the experimental results on the basis of a modified diffusion equation which contains a term for the activation energy of adsorption.

Flengas and Rideal (32) investigated the surface aging of C^{14}-labeled sodium stearate solutions by the radiotracer method and found that, with carefully examined solutions, the process was very slow and diffusion-controlled and that the process was accelerated by the presence of sodium hydroxide. They also determined the surface excess of the same sample of sodium stearate from dilute solutions and calculated the same quantity by Eq. (3.6). Comparison of experimental and theoretical values indicated that this equation was not applicable to dilute solutions in ordinary conductivity water. Also at higher concentrations, i.e., above 1×10^{-8} mole/ml, and in the presence of sodium hydroxide, the experimental values were found to be much higher than the calculated values, which was considered to be due to the surface association of the solute molecules in such solutions.

The radiotracer method is supposed to be a useful tool for the study of the adsorption of a surfactant of low surface activity if a suitable tracer element is applied. Radioactive tritium may be useful for such purposes since it emits β-rays of low energies. The method was initiated by Nilsson (33), who chose tritium-labeled sodium dodecyl sulfate for his investigation mainly for three reasons: (i) concerning this compound a large amount of data has been already accumulated; (ii) the purification procedure is simple; and (iii) this compound has a sufficiently low surface activity. This method for the surface excess determination permits an increase in accuracy and an extension of such measurements to lower values of the ratios of surface excess to concentration.

Nilsson determined the adsorption isotherms of tritium-labeled sodium dodecyl sulfate in water or in a buffer solution (pH 6.5) containing a constant excess of neutral salt (0.1 M), in the concentration range of 0–15 × 10^{-3} mole/kg of surfactant. A constant surface concentration, corresponding to a monolayer with a surface area of 33 $Å^2$ per molecule was obtained when the bulk concentration in the buffer solution had reached a value of 2×10^{-3} mole/kg. There was some evidence that micelles are formed below the CMC. The surface excess of tritium-labeled sodium dodecyl sulfate in aqueous solution was determined at a constant bulk concentration of this compound (1×10^{-3} M) and different bulk concentrations of sodium tetradecyl sulfate or decanol. It was found that sodium tetradecyl sulfate is more effective than decanol in displacing tritium-labeled sodium dodecyl sulfate from the surface.

More recently, Shinoda and Mashio (34) applied the radiotracer method in the study of selective adsorption, namely, the adsorption of

S^{35}-labeled alkali p-dodecylbenzenesulfonates or C^{14}-labeled potassium hexadecanoate at the solution-air interface from solutions of surfactant mixtures of various combinations containing either of these radioactive compounds and another nonradioactive compound in certain mole ratios.

In this investigation, the selective adsorption was determined (i) by the measurement of the ratio of counts from dried samples of collapsed foams to those from solutions, and (ii) by the measurement of the concentration of collapsed foams. The selective adsorptivity was defined by the following relation:

$$\alpha = \frac{X_a}{1 - X_a} \times \frac{1 - X_b}{X_b} \qquad (3.11)$$

TABLE 3.1

SELECTIVE ADSORPTIVITY DATA FOR SURFACTANT MIXTURES (34)

Surfactant 1[a]	Surfactant 2	Selective adsorptivity of 1 to 2	Temperature (°C)	State of solution
$R_{12}C_6H_4S^*O_3Na$	$R_{12}OSO_3Na$	35–50	25	Homogeneous
$R_{12}C_6H_4S^*O_3K$	$R_{11}COOK$	180–280	18	Homogeneous
$R_{12}C_6H_4S^*O_3K$	$R_{13}COOK$	5–6	25	Heterogeneous
$R_{15}C^*OOK$	$R_{11}COOK$	50–66	18	Homogeneous
$R_{15}C^*OOK$	$R_{13}COOK$	5–8	25	Heterogeneous

[a] Asterisk indicates labeled atom.

where X_a and X_b are mole ratios of a surfactant of higher surface activity in the adsorbed and bulk phases, respectively. This value was found for surfactant mixtures of various combinations as indicated in Table 3.1.

It is to be remarked that the selective adsorptivity defined here may be a constant over all mole fraction ranges for the respective combinations of surfactants because, if the mole fraction in bulk changes, the ratio of mole fractions of adsorbed to dissolved molecules changes, but the ratio of their mole ratios remains unchanged.

This method of investigation permits an analysis of the activities of surfactant mixtures and an understanding of the effect of a small amount of impurities. It also suggests an effective way of elimination or concentration of highly surface active substances by foam fractionation.

4. *Surface Equation of State*

The equation of state for surface phases of adsorbed layers may be expressed in its general form as follows:

$$\left(\varPi + \frac{\alpha}{\Omega^2}\right)(\Omega - \beta) = RT \qquad (3.12)$$

where Π is the surface pressure; Ω is the area of the adsorption layer per mole; R is the gas constant; T is the absolute temperature; and α and β are constants. This equation, which may be called a "two-dimensional van der Waals equation", can be written in a simpler form

$$\Pi\Omega = iRT \tag{3.13}$$

where i is given by

$$i = 1 + \frac{\beta}{\Omega} - \frac{\alpha}{\Omega RT} \tag{3.14}$$

a higher term $\alpha\beta/\Omega^2$ being neglected here.

For adsorption layers of soluble substances the surface pressure cannot be directly measured, but is indirectly determined by measuring the lowering of surface tension, and therefore we have

$$\Pi = \gamma_0 - \gamma \tag{3.15}$$

where γ_0 refers to the surface tension of pure solvent and γ to that of solution.

Assuming that adsorption layers are monolayers, we get

$$\Omega = 1/U \tag{3.16}$$

in which U is the surface concentration of adsorbed substance, which, for dilute solutions, is approximately equal to the Gibbs surface excess Γ. Consequently Eq. (3.13) reduces to

$$\gamma_0 - \gamma = iRT\Gamma \tag{3.17}$$

Differentiating this at constant temperature, i being assumed constant, we get

$$-d\gamma = iRTd\Gamma \tag{3.18}$$

Combining this equation with the Gibbs equation in the form

$$-d\gamma = RT\Gamma d \ln C \tag{3.19}$$

we obtain

$$i\frac{d\Gamma}{\Gamma} = \frac{dC}{C}$$

or

$$\Gamma = KC^{1/i} \tag{3.20}$$

where K is a constant. This relation represents an adsorption isotherm which is usually called the Freundlich adsorption isotherm.

As Γ is proportional to Π at constant temperature, we have

$$\Pi = K'C^{1/i} \tag{3.21}$$

where K' is another constant. This relation is a type of Szyszkowski equation which expresses the relation between surface tension lowering and concentration.

For surface phases of an ideal gas type, the surface equation becomes

$$\pi\Omega = RT \qquad (3.22)$$

From this equation we obtain in the same manner as above

$$\Gamma = KC \qquad (3.23)$$

and

$$\Pi = K'C \qquad (3.24)$$

These relations are of the type of the Henry equation for surface phases.

The above derivations were carried out by Tamamushi (35) in his early work, and Eq. (3.21) was tested for the experimental data obtained with a series of normal carboxylic acids with 2–9 carbon atoms. It was found that both factors K' and i are not constant over a wide range of concentration, the $\log\Pi$ vs. $\log C$ curves being more or less concave against the $\log C$—axis at middle and higher concentrations. The coefficient i is nearly equal to one at very low concentrations, while it becomes smaller than one as the concentration increases. It was also found that i is dependent on the number of carbon atoms of the acid molecules, becoming smaller as the number increases. Such deviations of i-values from one were explained from the viewpoint of the interaction between two adjacent adsorbed molecules.

Hutchinson (36) studied the state of adsorbed layers of normal carboxylic acids and normal alcohols at the oil-water interface and found that carboxylic acids with 4–14 carbon atoms gave force vs. area curves with a transition point and shape characteristic of the liquid-expanded film. This is in sharp contrast to their behavior at the air-water interface, where these compounds form imperfect gaseous films. It was suggested that lateral adhesion in films may be greater at the oil-water interface than at the air-water interface. The effects of the variation of the carbon chain length and temperature, as well as the nature of the oil, on the state of the adsorbed films were examined and discussed.

In Eq. (3.12), the term due to the surface electrical charge is not taken into consideration. This may be allowed for in the case of adsorption of normal carboxylic acids at the air-water or the oil-water interface, whose molecules are supposed to be adsorbed there as undissociated molecules, provided that the pH of the solutions is maintained on the acidic side. In such cases the Gibbs adsorption equation may also be used in the simple form (3.19), so long as the solutions are dilute.

For adsorption layers of nonionized molecules, the surface equation was presented by Guastalla (37) as well as Davies (38) in the following form:

$$\left(\Pi + \frac{400m}{A^{3/2}}\right)(A - A_0) = kT \qquad (3.25)$$

where m is the number of CH_2-groups in a normal paraffin chain compound; A is the surface area per adsorbed molecule; A_0 is the limiting area, which may be taken to be 20–30 $Å^2$ at the air-water or oil-water interface; and k is the Boltzmann constant. This equation was recently tested by Matijevic and Pethica (39) for the experimental data for n-octylcarboxylic acid at the air-water interface in the presence of 0.1 N hydrochloric acid. Figure 3.4 shows the Π vs. A curve calculated by Eq. (3.25), while the circles indicate experimental values. The coincidence between theory and experiment is quite satisfactory.

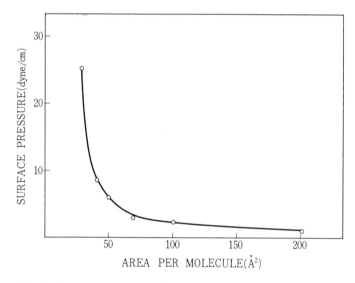

Fig. 3.4. Surface pressure vs. surface area curve for octylcarboxylic acid in the presence of hydrochloric acid at 20°C, calculated by Eq. (3.25). Circles indicate experimental values.

For ionized adsorption layers, there may be an increase in surface pressure (Π_e) resulting from the ionization of the monolayer, which may be equated with the Helmholtz free energy of formation per unit area (ΔF) of the electrical double layer. For systems involving only univalent electrolytes we have

$$\Pi_e = -\Delta F = \frac{8nkT}{\kappa}\left(\cosh\frac{e\psi}{2kT} - 1\right) \qquad (3.26)$$

where n is the number of ions of either sign per cubic centimeter of the bulk solution. k is the Boltzmann constant; κ is the Debye-Hückel characteristic reciprocal distance; e is the proton charge; and ψ is the Gouy double layer potential. Taking this additional term into consideration, the equation of state is given by

$$\left(\Pi + \frac{400m}{A^{3/2}} - \Pi_e \right)(A - A_0) = kT \tag{3.27}$$

For the solution-oil interface, where the term due to the molecular cohesion may be neglected, the equation becomes

$$\Pi = \frac{kT}{A - A_0} + \Pi_e$$

By calculating the electrical term according to Eq. (3.26), we have

$$\Pi = \frac{kT}{A - A_0} + 6.10\,C^{1/2}\left[\cos h \sin h^{-1}\left(\frac{134}{AC^{1/2}}\right) - 1 \right] \tag{3.28}$$

which becomes approximately

$$\Pi = \frac{kT}{A - A_0} - 6.10\,C^{1/2} + \frac{2kT}{A}$$

or

$$\Pi(A - A_0) = 3kT - 6.10\,C^{1/2}(A - A_0) - \frac{2kTA_0}{A} \tag{3.29}$$

When the concentration of an ionic surfactant is sufficiently small, Eq. (3.29) reduces to

$$\Pi A = 3kT \tag{3.30}$$

Equation (3.27) was tested by Matijevic and Pethica (39) for the data for n-octylcarboxylic acid solution in the presence of 0.1 N sodium hydroxide. The result is illustrated in Fig. 3.5. Curve I shows the experimental curve, while curves II and III represent the theoretical curves for higher and lower surface areas. Only qualitative agreement between theory and experiment is seen at higher surface areas. The discrepancy may be due partly to the neglect of solvation and other factors ignored in the derivation of relations (3.26) and (3.28) and partly to the non-strict equality of Π_e and $-\Delta F$.

Now, for the adsorption layers of completely ionized surfactants, the Gibbs equation can be expressed as

$$d\Pi = 2RT\Gamma d \ln C \tag{3.31}$$

in the absence of inorganic electrolyte, and as

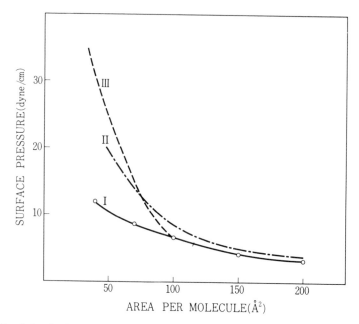

Fig. 3.5. Surface pressure vs. surface area curve for octylcarboxylic acid in 0.1 N sodium hydroxide solution at 20°C calculated by Eq. (3.27), as compared with experimental values. Curve I, experimental curve; curves II and III, theoretical curves at higher and lower surface areas.

$$d\Pi = RT\Gamma\, d \ln C \qquad (3.32)$$

in the presence of excess inorganic salt. Combining these equations with Eq. (3.30), we obtain the following adsorption isotherms:

$$\Gamma = KC^{2/3} \qquad (3.33)$$

in the absence of inorganic salt, and

$$\Gamma = KC^{1/3} \qquad (3.34)$$

in the presence of excess inorganic salt. In these relations K represents a constant.

The above derivation was performed by Davies (40), who made calculations in detail. According to his calculations, these relations are expressed in a more general form as follows:

$$n = \frac{(B_1/B_2)C \exp\left[(W - Ze\psi_0)/kT\right]}{1 + C(B_1/B_2n_0) \exp\left[(W - Ze\psi_0)/kT\right]} \qquad (3.35)$$

in which n is the amount of adsorption; C is the molar concentration of paraffin chain ions; W is the adhesion work of paraffin chain to the interface; ψ_0 is the Gouy double layer potential in the plane of the interface; e is the elementary change; z is the valence of the surfactant ion; n_0 is the adsorption density of surfactant ions in a close-packed layer; k is the Boltzmann constant; T is the absolute temperature; and B_1 and B_2 are constants. This relation represents an adsorption equation of the Langmuir type.

In the absence of inorganic salt this relation reduces approximately to

$$n = 5.35 \times 10^{13} C^{2/3} \exp\left(\frac{810m}{3RT}\right) \tag{3.36}$$

and in the presence of excess salt

$$n = 5.35 \times 10^{13} C^{1/3} C_s^{1/3} \exp\left(\frac{810m}{3RT}\right) \tag{3.37}$$

where m is the number of methylene groups in a given paraffin chain compound and C_s is the concentration of added salt ($C_s \gg C$).

These last two equations are identical with Eqs. (3.33) and (3.34) if

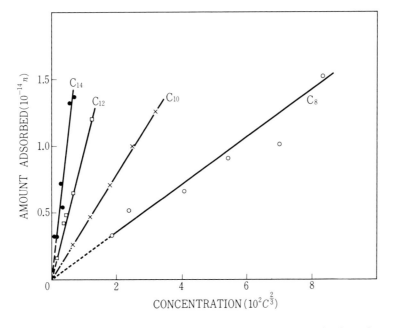

Fig. 3.6. Graph showing the relationship between amount of adsorption and concentration for sodium alkyl sulfates at the oil-solution interface in the absence of added salt. Straight lines are predicted by Eq. (3.36). Experimental data are those of Kling and Lange (9).

the numerical factors are replaced by appropriate constants.

These adsorption equations, which are theoretically valid when $\psi_0 > 100$ mv, have been examined by Davies for Kling and Lange's data for the adsorption of a series of sodium alkyl sulfates at the solution-oil interface. Fig. 3.6 indicates the result for Eq. (3.36) in the absence of added salt, and Fig. 3.7 the result for Eq. (3.37) in the presence of excess added salt.

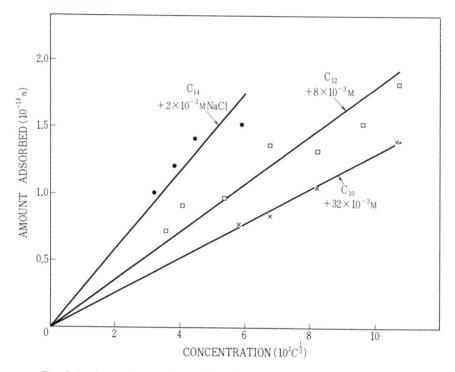

Fig. 3.7. Graph showing the relationship between amount of adsorption and concentration for sodium alkyl sulfates at the oil-solution interface in the presence of excess salt. Straight lines are predicted by Eq. (3.37). Experimental data are those of Kling and Lange (9).

The plots indicate experimental values, while straight lines are predicted by Eq. (3.36) or (3.37). The coincidence between theory and experiment is reasonably satisfactory.

The relation between surface pressure and concentration may be given in the same manner as above by

$$\Pi = K'C^{2/3} \tag{3.38}$$

in the absence of added salt, and by

$$\Pi = K'C^{1/3}C_s^{1/3} \tag{3.39}$$

in the presence of excess added salt, in which K' is a constant. Fig. 3.8 illustrates the result of the test of these relations made with Kling and Lange's data for sodium dodecyl sulfate.

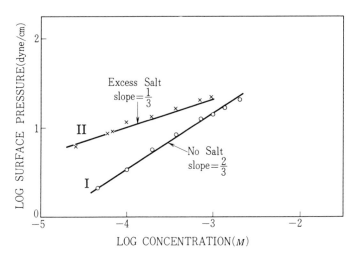

Fig. 3.8. Graph showing the relationship between surface pressure and concentration for sodium dodecyl sulfate at the oil-solution interface. Straight lines I and II are drawn by Eqs. (3.38) and (3.39), respectively. Experimental data are those of Kling and Lange (9).

So far as these results are concerned, the theory proposed by Davies seems to be satisfactory. There is, however, a difference of opinion over the applicability of Eq. (3.28) to solutions containing no added salt, and another expression has been deduced by Phillips and Rideal (41) as follows:

$$\Pi = \frac{2kT}{A - A_0} + 6.10\,C^{1/2}\left[\cosh\sinh^{-1}\left(\frac{134}{AC^{1/2}}\right) - 1\right] \tag{3.40}$$

The difference between this equation and Eq. (3.28) is the existence of the factor 2 in the first kinetic term of the right-hand side of the equation. From this equation, it follows approximately that

$$\Pi A = 4kT \tag{3.41}$$

instead of Eq. (3.30).

Haydon and Phillips (42) made an examination of these equations with their experimental data for the adsorption of dodecyltrimethylammonium bromide at the solution-petroleum ether interface, in the absence of added salt. The water used in their experiments was carefully purified, its specific conductivity being $0.55 \times 10^{-6}\,\mathrm{ohm}^{-1}\,\mathrm{cm}^{-1}$. The amount of adsorption was obtained by two independent methods: (i) by the application of the Gibbs equation in the form (3.6); and (ii) by surface potential measurements. The results of these two methods were found to be in good agreement. From the experimental data, a II vs. A curve was obtained, and this was compared with the curves calculated by Eq. (3.28) and Eq. (3.40), respectively, as illustrated in Fig. 3.9. The experimental data

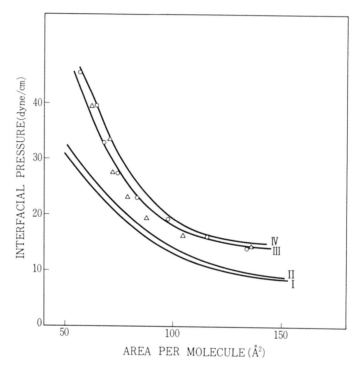

Fig. 3.9. Theoretical surface pressure vs. surface area curves obtained from Eqs. (3.28) and (3.40), as compared with experimental data, for dodecyltrimethyl-ammonium bromide at the petroleum ether-solution interface at 20°C. Curve I, Eq. (3.28), $A_0 = 25\text{Å}^2$; curve II, Eq. (3.28), $A_0 = 30\,\text{Å}^2$; curve III, Eq. (3.40), $A_0 = 25\,\text{Å}^2$; curve IV, Eq. (3.40), $A_0 = 30\text{Å}^2$. Circles indicate experimental points obtained from the Gibbs equation; triangles indicate experimental points obtained from surface potential measurements.

cover the concentration range of 0.158–0.000631 mole/liter and, consequently, the corresponding molecular surface area range of 56.7–131 Å^2. Curves I and II refer to the theoretical curves obtained by Eq. (3.28), while curves III and IV are the curves obtained by Eq. (3.40) for $A_0 =$

25 Å^2 and $A_0 = 30$ Å^2, respectively. Equation (3.40) fits the experimental data better than Eq. (3.28).

The examination was also carried out with sodium dodecyl sulfate. The experimental plots are now distributed between the two sets of theoretical curves, so that the result is still ambiguous for the choice of the two theoretical equations. Haydon and Phillips pointed out the necessity of using very carefully purified water in the experiment, especially in case of anionic surfactants.

At high surface areas per molecule, therefore, when $\Pi_e \rightarrow 0$ and $A_0 \ll A$, Eq. (3.40) becomes

$$\Pi A = 2kT \tag{3.42}$$

Matijevic and Pethica's experimental data (43) for dilute adsorption monolayers of sodium dodecyl sulfate in the presence of sodium chloride at various concentrations at the solution-air interface seem, however, not to be in accord with this equation, but rather in accord with the equation

$$\Pi A = kT \tag{3.43}$$

which follows from the Davies theory. Matijevic and Pethica consider that Eq. (3.43) may also hold in the absence of added salt, insofar as the solutions are very dilute and the relation between Π and C is linear.

From the experimental data for sodium decyl sulfate obtained by Eda and Fukuda (14), it was shown that, in the absence of added salt, the Π vs. A curves follow the ideal equation of state (3.43), while the Π vs. A curves for the same surfactant in the presence of sodium sulfate deviate from that equation—the deviation being greater, the greater the concentration of the added salt. This experimental fact suggests that the electrostatic repulsive effect between two neighboring polar groups of adsorbed ions exceeds the cohesive forces between hydrocarbon chains in the absence of added electrolyte, but that this effect may be screened by counter ions in the presence of added electrolyte.

III. Adsorption at the Solution-Mercury Interface

1. *Double Layer Capacity and Adsorption*

More than 80 years ago, Lippmann (44) showed that the interfacial tension at the mercury-aqueous electrolyte solution interface is a function of the electric potential applied across the interface and that the so-called "electrocapillary curve" which represents the relation between these two quantities is generally expressed by a continuous parabolic curve having a maximum, the so-called "electrocapillary maximum," in the middle section when the aqueous solution contains only surface inactive electrolytes, such as sodium sulfate. It was later demonstrated by Gouy

(45) that, when a small quantity of any surface active substance, such as octanol, is added to the solution, the curve changes its form, the maximum point of the curve being displaced downward as well as sideward.

The mercury-solution interface is considered to form an electric condenser consisting of an electric double layer. If we denote the applied potential by E and the electric charge density of the interface by q, q/E is the "integral capacity," while dq/dE (denoted by C) is the "differential capacity." Integrating the relation between C and E with respect to E, we obtain the relation between q and E. Integrating the latter relation with respect to E, we obtain the relation between γ and E, i.e., the electrocapillary curve. These relations are expressed by following equations:

$$-\frac{d^2\gamma}{dE^2} = \frac{dq}{dE} = C$$

or

$$\iint_{E_{ecm}}^{E} C\,dE^2 = \int_{E_{ecm}}^{E} q\,dE = \gamma_{ecm} - \gamma \qquad (3.44)$$

in which E_{ecm} and γ_{ecm} are the potential difference and the interfacial tension at the electrocapillary maximum, respectively.

In this way, the differential capacity vs. potential curve (abbreviated as the C–E curve) is transformed into the electrocapillary curve, the turning point in the latter curve being represented by a sharp peak, the so-called "desorption peak" in the former, as illustrated in Fig. 3.10 (a), (b), (c).

The lowering of the interfacial tension is a function of the surface excess of an adsorbable substance and the applied potential difference. On the assumption that the mercury surface is ideally polarizable and that the applied potential difference satisfies the condition of equilibrium, the following thermodynamic equation holds:

$$-d\gamma = q\,dE + \sum \Gamma'_i\,d\mu_i \qquad (3.45$$

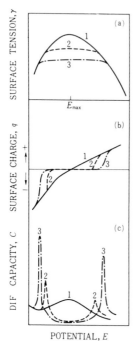

Fig. 3.10. Graph showing the relationship between electrocapillary curves and differential capacity curves: (a) illustrates a typical electrocapillary curve 1, which transforms into 2 or 3 in the presence of a surfactant like octanol; (b) the corresponding charge density vs. potential curves; (c) the corresponding differential capacity vs. potential curves.

where γ is the interfacial tension; q is the surface charge density; E is the potential difference; Γ_i is the surface excess of the ith component; and μ_i is the chemical potential of ith component. From this equation it follows that for the surface excess of a particular component denoted by a

$$\Gamma_a = -\left(\frac{\partial \gamma}{\partial \mu_a}\right)_{E,\mu_i}$$

Neglecting the difference between activity and concentration, it follows that

$$\Gamma_a = -\frac{1}{RT}\left(\frac{\partial \gamma}{\partial \ln C_a}\right)_{E,C_i}$$

where C_a is the concentration of component a.

According to Eq. (3.44) we have

$$\gamma = \iint CdE^2$$

and hence we get

$$\Gamma_a = -\frac{1}{RT}\iint_{E_0}^{E}\left(\frac{\partial C}{\partial \ln C_a}\right)dE^2 \tag{3.46}$$

in which the integration is usually performed over the range from E_0 at which $\Gamma_a = 0$ to a certain potential value E at which the surface excess is to be evaluated. In this way, the surface excess can be approximately determined from the measurement of differential capacities. The theoretical treatment of the relation between adsorption and differential capacity has been developed by Grahame (46), Delahay and co-workers (47), and Parsons (48).

The first reliable measurement of the differential capacity at the mercury-solution interface was carried out by Proskurnin and Frumkin (49). The method was improved in accuracy by Grahame (50), who applied it in an extensive study of the structure of electrical double layers as well as adsorption. The principle of the method is to use a cell consisting of a dropping mercury electrode and a reference electrode, the capacity of the mercury electrode being determined by measuring the impedance of an auxiliary electrode surrounding the mercury electrode by means of an alternating current bridge.

In recent years, the method has been widely applied not only in the study of adsorption of simple inorganic salts or organic substances, such as lower fatty alcohols (51, 52), but of polymeric or colloidal substances, such as polyacid salts (53) or proteins (54). Concerning the paraffin chain electrolytes, a systematic study has been carried out by Eda (55), whose results will be treated mainly in the present section.

2. *Structure of Adsorbed Layers*

The materials used in Eda's study (*55*) are the electrolytes having paraffin chain anions (sodium octyl, decyl, dodecyl, and tetradecyl sulfates as well as sodium octyl, decyl, and dodecyl carboxylates), on the one hand, and the electrolytes having paraffin chain cations (dodecylpyridinium, dodecyltrimethylammonium, and dodecylammonium chlorides), on the other. The differential capacity measurement method applied is in principle the same as that of Grahame (*50*), where the frequency of an

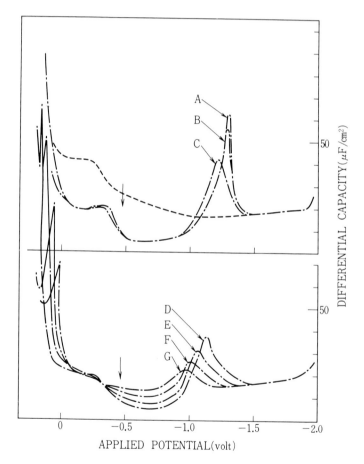

Fig. 3.11. Differential capacity vs. potential curves for sodium decyl sulfate solutions of various concentrations, containing 0.5 N sodium sulfate. (*A*) 0.1; (*B*) 0.05; (*C*) 0.025; (*D*) 0.0125; (*E*) 0.0063; (*F*) 0.0031; (*G*) 0.0016 N.

alternatingcurrent generator is usually maintained at 1 kc/sec. The measurement was carried out with solutions of different concentrations of a given chain electrolyte and of a supporting electrolyte, sodium sulfate or sodium chloride, at constant temperature (20°C). In some cases, the measurement was made at different temperatures or different alternating current frequencies.

a. Paraffin Chain Anions

Fig. 3.11 indicates the C–E curves for sodium decyl sulfate at various concentrations with sufficient supporting electrolyte (0.5 N sodium sulfate), the curve of the solution without the chain electrolyte being expressed by a broken line.

It is noted in these curves that there is a peak on the cathodic side, while on the anodic side there appears a small "hill" beside a sharp peak. The peak on the cathodic side, which has a lower slope on the left side and a sharper slope on the right, represents the desorption process of the adsorbed chain anions, its foot on the right side being in coincidence with the curve of the solution without the chain electrolyte. It is also noticeable that this peak becomes sharper and higher, as well as displaced to the more negative side, as the surfactant concentration increases, until it reaches a constant position at a certain critical concentration. The form of this peak is dependent on the concentration of the supporting electrolyte. The peak on the anodic side appears only when the solution contains the supporting electrolyte, and therefore it is considered to represent the process of replacement of the chain ions by sulfate ions at the interface. The appearance of a small hill on the anodic side may be due to a change of structure of the adsorbed layer.

Fig. 3.12 shows C-E curves for sodium decyl sulfate at constant concentration (0.02 N) and various concentrations of the supporting electrolyte. Here we note a great peak α^- on the cathodic side, which is accompanied by a small peak β^- when the concentration of the supporting electrolyte is sufficiently great, and on the anodic side two peaks, a greater one α^+ and a smaller one β^+. It is found that the height of the small peak β^- is nearly independent of the surfactant concentration or the applied frequency, whereas the great peak α^- is dependent on these factors. Moreover, the small peak β^- is dependent on temperature and disappears at temperatures higher than 40°C. With different supporting electrolytes having different counter ions, namely, Li^+, Na^+, K^+, the critical concentration of the electrolyte for the appearance of the small peak β^- is found in the order $Li^+ > Na^+ > K^+$, which is in accord with the lyotropic series of these cations (see reference 55g). The small peak β^+ on the anodic side is dependent on the surfactant concentration and appears when the bulk concentration reaches the CMC; however, it becomes

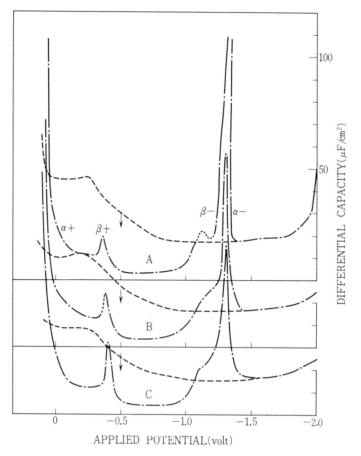

Fig. 3.12. Differential capacity vs. potential curves for 0.02 N sodium decyl sulfate solutions containing sodium sulfate in various concentrations. (A) 4.0; (B) 2.0; (C) 0.5 N.

smaller when the supporting electrolyte concentration increases, and thereby remains almost unchanged. Similar C–E curves are found for sodium dodecyl sulfates as well as tetradecyl sulfates.

These characteristic features of the C–E curves may be explained on the basis of the following assumptions for the structure of the adsorbed layer. Near the electrocapillary maximum point, the paraffin chain anions are adsorbed in a monolayer, the polar ionic group being directed toward the aqueous solution. At the cathodic side, the adsorbed monolayer may be more or less in a condensed state because the desorption peak is not so sharp as in the case of nonionic surface active substances, such as octanol. The appearance of a small peak at the foot is probably due to the phase transition of the adsorbed layer from the gaseous state to the condensed state. The condensation should be favored by the neutralization of negative ionic groups by positive counter ions. The effects of the different supporting electrolytes above mentioned can be explained from this point of view.

At the anodic side of the electrocapillary maximum, the paraffin chain anions may be adsorbed in such manner that the ionic head groups are attached to the positively charged mercury surface. Upon such a type of monolayer, a second layer may be built up by van der Waals forces between two hydrocarbon chains when the surfactant concentration is sufficiently large. The appearance of the small peak β^+ on the anodic side is considered to correspond to such a structural change, namely, monolayer $\rightarrow$ twofold layer. The fact that the longer the chain length and the smaller the hydration of counter ions the nearer is the position of this peak to the electrocapillary maximum, is in accord with this assumed mechanism. It should also be noted that this small peak appears in the electrolyte solution whose concentration is greater than the CMC. It is therefore reasonable to suppose that the building-up of the twofold layer is related in its mechanism to micelle formation in the bulk phase. The great peak is considered to correspond to the desorption process of the twofold adsorption layer.

It was found that sodium octyl, decyl, and dodecyl carboxylates give C-E curves similar to those of sodium alkyl sulfates, provided that the solution is kept strongly alkaline (ref. 55.d). When the solution becomes less alkaline, a peak appears on the cathodic side, which is supposed to be due to the penetration of the neutral molecules produced by hydrolysis into the monolayer of the chain anions. According to Lorenz (56), normal fatty acids (butyric, hexanoic, octanoic) give C-E curves in acidic media which have two peaks corresponding to the desorption processes of the undissociated acid molecules.

b. Paraffin Chain Cations

Fig. 3.13 shows the C-E curves of dodecylpyridinium chloride in the presence of sodium chloride as a supporting electrolyte. From this figure it is noted that the features of the curves of the cationic surfactant are essentially different from those of the anionic one. There appear to be no peaks on both anodic and cathodic sides, but it is to be remarked that there is a cross point of the curves on the anodic side. The dependence of the form of the curve on the surfactant concentration is rather complex, a part of the curve near the electrocapillary maximum being displaced once downward and then upward as the concentration is increased. The curve form is, however, not changed by a further increase of the

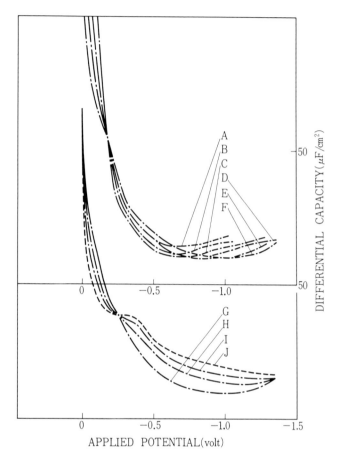

Fig. 3.13. Differential capacity vs. potential curves for dodecylpyridinium chloride solutions of various concentrations in the presence of 0.1 N sodium chloride. (A) 5-20; (B) 2.5; (C) 1.0; (D) 0.5; (E) 0.1; (F) 0.05; (G) 0.025; (H) 0.0125; (I) 0.00625; (J) 0 $(10^{-3} N)$.

concentration beyond 5.0×10^{-3} mole/liter, which probably implies saturation of adsorption.

On the cathodic side, dodecylpyridinium ions may first be adsorbed in monolayers, the positive ionic groups being attached to the negatively polarized mercury surface, and then, when the surfactant concentration is large enough, in twofold layers, the positive ionic groups being directed to aqueous solution in the second layer. The adsorbed dodecylpyridinium ions are rendered prone to electrolysis at the potential -1.2 volts before they will be desorbed. On the anodic side, the adsorbed dodecylpyridinium ions will be displaced by sodium ions at a certain potential, a process which is probably represented by the cross point of the curves.

From the characteristic features of the $C-E$ curves indicated in Fig. 3.13, it is supposed that the mechanism of the adsorption of chain cations at the mercury-solution interface should be more or less different from that of chain anions. In the case of chain anions, the adsorption will take place favorably at a positively polarized surface, whereas in the case of chain cations the adsorption will take place favorably at a negatively polarized surface. However, a simple symmetry relation does not appear

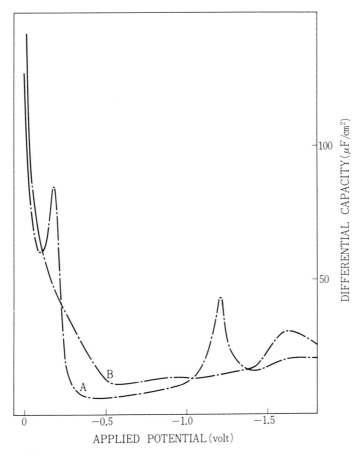

Fig. 3.14. Differential capacity vs. potential curves for 0.00015 N dodecylammonium chloride solution: (A) in the presence of 0.1 N sodium chloride and (B) in the presence of 0.1 N sodium chloride and 0.002 N hydrochloric acid.

in the $C-E$ curves in both cases, probably owing to the difference in adsorption forces in both cases. The fact that the counter ion (Cl^-) of chain cations is more specifically adsorbed on the mercury surface than the counter ion (Na^+) of chain anions may also be a cause of the different behavior of the two kinds of chain ions.

Comparing the minimum values of differential capacities at the adsorption saturation for cations and anions of the same chain length, it is found that the values for anions are generally smaller than those for cations, which suggests that anions are generally more strongly adsorbed than cations at the mercury-solution interface.

In the case of dodecylammonium chloride, which is a weak electrolyte, there appear two desorption peaks in the $C-E$ curves when the solution is slightly acidic (pH 5.8–6.0), as shown in Fig. 3.14. These peaks disappear when a small amount of hydrochloric acid is added to the solution and are therefore supposed to represent the desorption processes of the neutral chain molecules produced by hydrolysis.

c. Nonionic Paraffin Chain Compounds

The compounds so far used for the study of adsorption by the method of differential capacity are mainly compounds of low molecular weight which may be excluded in the present description. Only few experimental data concerning the compounds of high molecular weight, such as polyoxyethylene lauryl ether, are found in the literature (57).

d. Amount of Adsorption

By applying Eq. (3.46) to the adsorption of sodium octyl sulfate, for example, the surface excesses are calculated as indicated in Table 3.2 (see reference 55b).

TABLE 3.2

SURFACE EXCESS OF SODIUM OCTYL SULFATE CALCULATED FROM
DIFFERENTIAL CAPACITY AT ELECTROCAPILLARY MAXIMUM

Composition of solution	Surface excess $\times 10^{-10}$ (moles/cm²)
0.02 N Sodium octyl sulfate + 0.5 N sodium sulfate	4.0
0.01 N Sodium octyl sulfate + 1.0 N sodium sulfate	3.5
0.01 N Sodium octyl sulfate + 0.5 N sodium sulfate	3.2

From these values of the surface excess, the surface area per ion is calculated to be 41.5Å², 47.3Å², and 52.6Å², respectively, on the assumption of monolayer adsorption.

For a given surface active compound, the form of the $C-E$ curve, which is characterized by the height of the desorption peak and the depth of the foot, is a function of the amount of adsorption. Therefore, we can utilize these curves for a comparative estimation of the amount of adsorption; for example, the height of the cathodic peak of sodium dodecyl sulfate is changed by the concentration of the counter ion $[Na^+]$, on the one hand, and by the concentration of dodecyl sulfate ion $[R^-]$, on the other, in such a manner that for the same values of the product $[Na^+][R^-]$ we obtain identical curves. This means that, when $[Na^+][R^-]=$ constant or $\mu_{Na^+} + \mu_{R^-}=$ constant, in which μ_{Na^+} and μ_{R^-} refer to the chemical potential of sodium ion and dodecyl sulfate ion respectively, then $\Gamma_{R^-}=$ constant, i.e., the surface excess of the surfactant is constant. Accordingly, we can find an isoadsorption condition for varied values of the concentrations of the surfactant and the supporting electrolyte.

As noted in Fig. 3.11, the cathodic peak reaches a definite position at certain critical values of $[R^-]$ for varied values of $[Na^+]$, where the adsorption is considered to attain saturation. The figures given in Table 3.3 are the critical values of the concentration of sodium octyl sulfate for the corresponding values of the concentration of sodium sulfate.

TABLE 3.3

CRITICAL CONCENTRATION OF SURFACTANT FOR
APPEARANCE OF DEFINITE CATHODIC PEAK

Concentration of supporting electrolyte (sodium sulfate) (N)	Critical concentration of surfactant (sodium octyl sulfate) (N)
0.00	0.15
0.25	0.06
0.50	0.04
1.90	0.02

It is remarkable that these critical values are approximately in accord with the CMC values of the surfactant in the absence and in the presence of a neutral salt (58). Hence, the saturation in adsorption is supposed to be closely related to the micelle formation in the bulk phase.

e. Kinetics of Desorption

By measuring differential capacities under varied frequencies of the alternating current applied, one can get some information on the kinetic process of the desorption of adsorbed molecules or ions. According to

Frumkin and Gaikazyan (51), in the desorption of simple neutral molecules, such as butyl alcohol, the rate is chiefly determined by diffusion,
while it was pointed out by Lorenz (59) that in the case of normal hexyl,
octyl, or nonyl alcohol the desorption rate is rather determined by the
dissociation process of the associated molecules on the mercury surface.
According to Eda's study of the frequency effect on the desorption peaks
of decyl and dodecyl sulfate ions, the desorption rate is related to the
counter ion concentration (see reference 55f). At certain concentrations
of the counter ion (Na^+) the desorption rate seems to be determined not
only by diffusion but also by an activated process of molecular interaction at the mercury interface. It seems, however, that for a quantitative
analysis of the problem further study is required.

3. *Electrode Process and Adsorption*

In polarography, developed by Heyrovsky (60), electrochemical processes of some reducible or oxidizable substances in solution at the dropping mercury cathode are studied by determining the curve of current
versus voltage. As the nature of the electrical double layer at the mercury-solution interface is in general influenced by the adsorption of any
substance, the current vs. voltage curve should be changed more or less
in its features by the existence of surface active substance in solution.
It was actually demonstrated by Randles (61) that the rates of some
electrochemical processes at the mercury cathode are changed by the addition of a small amount of gelatin or methyl red to the electrolyte
solution. The effect of paraffin chain compounds on the polarographic
current-voltage curve is a problem of interest and has been reported by
some researchers in recent years.

According to Colichman (62), who studied the effect of dodecyltrimethylammonium bromide, cetyltrimethylammonium bromide, and Triton-
X-100 on the polarographic reduction curves of some metallic ions, it was
pointed out that the concentration of a chain compound just sufficient to
suppress the maximum of the curve is almost identical with the CMC
of that compound. Tamamushi and Yamanaka (63) studied the effect of
sodium dodecyl sulfate, dodecylpyridinium bromide, and polyoxyethylene
dodecyl ether on the reduction of lead, nickel, and thallium ions in a medium of 0.1 N potassium nitrate solution and found that these surfactants
are very effective in suppressing the polarographic maximum current,
the shape of the current vs. voltage curve being distorted and the so-
called half-wave potential being shifted to the more negative side. It
was also concluded from the determination of the electrocapillary curves
of these surfactants that the surface excesses are very small in the concentration range of the minimum concentration which is necessary to
suppress the maximum current. It was thus shown that the effect of

the surfactants on the polarographic current vs. voltage curve is parallel to the result of their adsorption behavior exhibited in electrocapillary curves. From the results of this study it was also concluded that sodium dodecyl sulfate, an anionic detergent, has a greater effect on the electrode process, which has a half-wave potential more positive than the electrocapillary maximum, than dodecylpyridinium bromide, a cationic detergent, and vice versa, while polyoxyethylene dodecyl ether, a nonionic detergent, is most effective in all cases. Tamamushi and co-workers (57) further studied in detail the effect of polyoxyethylene dodecyl ether on the reduction of some metallic ions and concluded that this substance can be used as an excellent suppressor in polarographic analysis. Fig. 3.15 il-

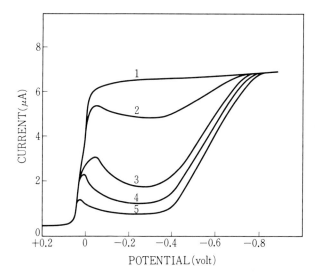

Fig. 3.15. Graph showing the effect of polyoxyethylene dodecyl ether on the polarographic reduction wave of $1\ mM$ cupric ion in $0.1\ M$ potassium nitrate solution. Curve 1, $2 \times 10^{-5}M$; curve 2, $5 \times 10^{-5}\ M$; curve 3, $1 \times 10^{-4}M$; curve 4, $2 \times 10^{-4}\ M$; curve 5, $1 \times 10^{-3}\ M$ polyoxyethylene dodecyl ether.

lustrates how current vs. voltage curves are distorted by polyoxyethylene dodecyl ether.

The inhibiting action of paraffin chain compounds, such as n-hexyl alcohol and tetrabutylammonium sulfate, on the reduction of some metallic ions, such as zinc or cadmium ion, or nonmetallic ions, such as persulfate ion $S_2O_8^{2-}$, at the mercury electrode has been studied by Russian investigators (64). In these studies the relations between the differential capacity vs. potential curve and the polarographic current vs. voltage curve for these paraffin chain compounds are investigated and discussed.

The general conclusion of their study is that the inhibiting action of a surface active substance is essentially connected with the coverage of the electrode surface by adsorbed molecules or ions.

There are some other studies published along the same line of research (65, 66). Paraffin chain compounds with high surface activity seem to provide a very efficient tool for the investigation of electrochemical processes.

In recent years a polarographic method which uses an alternating current, that is, ac polarography or "tensammetry" has been developed by Breyer (67) as well as by Doss and Gupta (68). This method is characterized by the fact that no charge transfer process, such as occurs in the case of the ordinary direct current method, is included; and, accordingly, by this method the process of adsorption or desorption at the mercury-solution interface can be more adequately analyzed than by the method of dc polarography. In fact, if we trace current vs. voltage curves in ac polarography with a solution containing any surface active substance, such as octanol, and a supporting electrolyte, such as sodium perchlorate, we obtain typical curves having two peaks, one on the negative side and another on the positive side. Such features of the curve are quite similar to those of the differential capacity vs. potential curve. Breyer suggested that this method should be useful for investigating the process of adsorption-desorption of molecules of a dipolar nature. The same author has also demonstrated the applicability of this method to various practical problems (69). It seems, however, that no systematic study on paraffin chain compounds with high surface activity has yet been made by the same method.

IV. Adsorption at the Solution-Solid Interface

1. *Adsorption Isotherms*

Adsorption at the liquid -solid interface is essentially a thermodynamic phenomenon for which the fundamental Gibbs equation should have general validity. However, the fact that it has not so far been possible to measure the liquid-solid interfacial tension directly means that, practically, its application is limited, and therefore, in this case, it is usual to determine empirically adsorption isotherms, upon the basis of which the nature and mechanism of adsorption are discussed.

The determination of the amount of adsorption is usually made by mixing an aqueous solution of a surfactant with a solid adsorbent, the mixture being kept at a constant shaking rate and at constant temperature until equilibrium is attained; then, the solution is separated from the adsorbent and its concentration is determined and compared with that of the original solution. Let N_0 be the total number of moles of the original solution, x_0 the mole fraction of the solute in that solution, x the mole fraction of the solute in the equilibrium solution, and m the mass of the adsorbent. Then $A = N_0(x_0 - x)/m$ represents the amount of adsorption, which means, however, "the apparent amount of adsorption" because the effect of solvent adsorption is thereby neglected. If we denote "the true amount of adsorption" by A_1 and that of solvent by A_2, the apparent amount of adsorption is represented by

$$A = A_1(1 - x_1) - A_2 x_1$$

where x_1 is the mole fraction of solute in the equilibrium solution. From this relation the true amount of adsorption of the solute becomes

$$A_1 = A \frac{1}{1 - x_1} + A_2 \frac{x_1}{1 - x_1}$$

which corresponds to "the surface excess" (70, 71), defined by Guggenheim and Adam (72).

Now in the case of the adsorption of highly surface active paraffin chain compounds, experiments are usually made with dilute solutions, where we can put approximately $1 - x_1 \cong 1$, so that $A_1 \cong A$, so long as A_2 is not very large. Most of the experimental data so far obtained can be treated on this assumption.

For analysis of paraffin chain electrolytes, the following methods are usually applied:

(a) *The soap antagonist method* (73)—the concentration of any paraffin

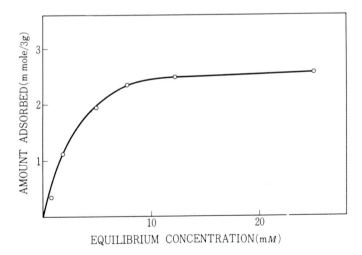

Fig. 3.16.   Adsorption isotherm for sodium dodecylcarboxylate on barium sulfate at 20°C.

chain ion is determined by titration with another paraffin chain ion of the opposite sign, using certain colored materials as indicators.

(b) *The soap titration method (74, 75)*—the displacement of the CMC of a paraffin chain compound in solution before and after adsorption is measured, and from which the amount of adsorption is calculated.

(c) *The radiotracer method (76, 77)*—a paraffin chain compound labeled with a radioisotope is used and the radioactivity of the solution before and after adsorption is determined.

The adsorption isotherms obtained for the adsorption of paraffin chain compounds are classified into several types. The experimental data for the adsorption of paraffin chain compounds with relatively low solubility, such as the higher alkyl carboxylic acids or their salts, are generally expressed by simple Langmuir-type or Freundlich-type adsorption isotherms (78). Fig. 3.16 illustrates an example of such isotherms obtained by Held and Samochwalov (79) for the adsorption of sodium dodecyl carboxylate on barium sulfate.

However, many experimental data for the adsorption of synthetic surfactants with relatively high solubility have been found not to be in accord with these simple types of isotherm, some of them being expressed by Brunauer-Emmett-Teller (BET) equations (80) and some others

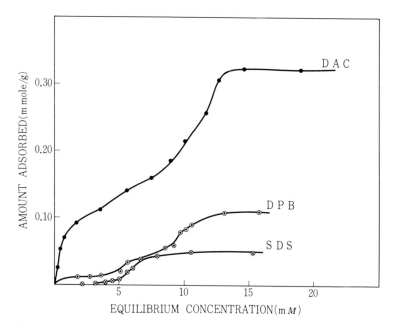

Fig. 3.17. Adsorption isotherms for sodium dodecyl sulfate, dodecylpyridinium bromide, and dodecylammonium chloride on aluminium oxide at 20°C.

exhibiting discontinuities or maxima in the isothermal curves. The adsorption isotherms of sodium dodecyl sulfate, dodecylpyridinium bromide, and dodecylammonium chloride on aluminium oxide, shown in Fig. 3.17, illustrate BET-type isotherms (*81*). Such types of isotherms have been found also for the adsorption of pentanoic or hexanoic acid on graphite or carbon black (*82*), as well as for the adsorption of dodecylammonium chloride on carbon black (*83*).

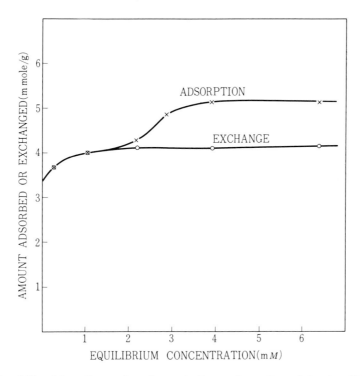

Fig. 3.18. Adsorption and exchange isotherms for sodium dodecyl sulfate on ion exchange resins, Dowex 1–X1 at 20°C.

Fig. 3.18 shows the adsorption as well as exchange isotherms of sodium dodecyl sulfate on an anion exchange resin, Dowex 1-X1, where we notice that the adsorption isotherm is of the BET type, while the exchange isotherm is of the Langmuir type. Similar isotherms were obtained for the adsorption and exchange of dodecylammonium chloride on a cation exchange resin, Dowex 50-X2. However, for the homologous compounds with alkyl groups lower than dodecyl group the adsorption isotherm was found to be coincident with the exchange isotherm, which is of the Langmuir type (*84*).

According to Cuming and Schulman (85), who studied the adsorption of sodium dodecyl sulfate on barium sulfate, the adsorption isotherm runs differently, depending on the method of observation; namely, it increases uniformly when the adsorption is measured on separate samples of solutions of different concentrations, whereas it shows a stepwise increase when the adsorption is measured in stages on one sample by successive increase of concentration, as shown in Fig. 3.19.

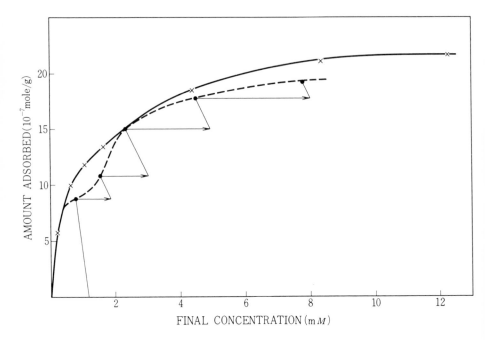

Fig. 3.19. Adsorption isotherms for sodium dodecyl sulfate on barium sulfate: (—) adsorption on separate samples from solutions of different concentrations (30 min); (- - -) adsorption in stages on one sample by successive increase of concentration (10 min between stages); (→) normal concentration increases.

Fig. 3.20 illustrates the adsorption isotherm of sodium dodecyl sulfate on graphite obtained by Corrin and co-workers (86), an example of the isotherms which have discontinuities and maxima. Similar types of isotherm have been found by several investigators for the adsorption of anionic or cationic surfactants on carbons, metals, and fibers (77, 87–89). It is to be remarked that in Fig. 3.20 the discontinuity appears at the equilibrium concentration, which approximately coincides with the CMC of the surfactant, and the maximum appears at greater concentrations, whereas in Fig. 3.17 the point of saturation is approximately equal to

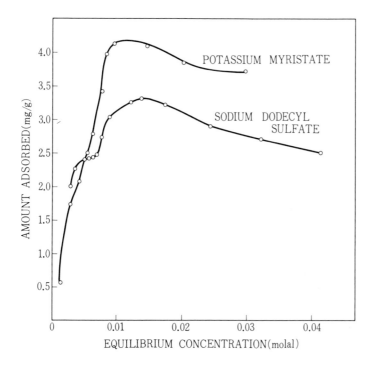

Fig. 3.20. Adsorption isotherms of sodium dodecyl sulfate on graphite at 30°C, and of potassium myristate on graphite at 35°C.

the CMC of the surfactant.

These characteristic features of adsorption isotherms will be review-ed in Section IV, 3 from the viewpoint of the mechanism of adsorption.

2. *Factors in Adsorption*

The adsorption at the solution-solid interface represents a problem of a very complex nature, which is influenced by the nature of the sub-stance to be adsorbed, the nature of the solid adsorbent, and the nature of the liquid medium. In the present case under consideration, the sub-stance to be adsorbed is a paraffin chain compound and the liquid medium is an aqueous solution, while the solid adsorbent can be of various kinds. Solid adsorbents so far studied include elementary substances like carbon or metals; inorganic compounds like aluminium oxide, tin oxide, titanium oxide, barium sulfate, calcium fluoride, and mercury sulfide; and organic or synthetic materials like fibers, plastics, and resins.

Many experimental data so far obtained can be reviewed from various points of view. However, only some typical data will be referred to in the following, from the viewpoint of the several factors which are considered to be important in governing the phenomena under consideration.

a. Effect of Temperature

The adsorption of paraffin chain compounds at the liquid-solid interface is in general decreased by an increase in temperature, as in the case of adsorption at other types of interfaces. From the experimental data for the adsorption of sodium dodecylbenzenesulfonate on cotton at 2°C and 38°C, Fava and Eyring (77) calculated the heat of adsorption ΔH_a, the mean value of which was found to be equal to~0.8 kcal/mole, while the heat of adsorption for dodecylammonium chloride on alumina was found to be equal to 4.1 kcal/mole from the adsorption data of Tamamushi and Tamaki (81). The experimental data, however, are still too meager to permit drawing any thermodynamic conclusions.

The effect of temperature on the adsorption of sodium alkyl sulfates (dodecyl, tetradecyl, hexadecyl, octadecyl) was studied by Rose et al. (90) over the range of 30-70°C, where it was found that the concentrations at which the change in slope of the adsorption curve occurs are slightly increased by increasing the temperature, which corresponds to the change in CMC of the surfactant caused by the temperature increase.

In evaluating the effect of temperature on the adsorption of a surfactant, a possible effect of the Krafft point of the surfactant, namely, the sudden increase of solubility of the surfactant at a certain temperature should also be taken into consideration.

b. Effect of Chain Length of Surfactant

It was found in the early work of Freundlich (91) that the adsorption of the homologous series of normal alkyl carboxylic acids by blood charcoal follows Traube's rule; in other words, the adsorption increases by a certain definite factor as the chain length of the acids increases by a methylene group, $-CH_2$. This rule was also found to be valid for the adsorption of the same homologs on other adsorbents, like siloxen (92); however, the validity of the rule was discussed by Hansen and Craig (82) from the viewpoint of the activity of the solute, in a study of the adsorption of alkyl carboxylic acid homologs on nonporous carbons. Traube's rule holds in this case as long as the activity of the solute is not great.

It has been noted that Traube's rule does not hold for all sorts of carbon (93). According to a recent study of Tsuruizumi and Sano (94), who investigated the adsorption of alkyl carboxylic acid homologs with various kinds of carbon, Traube's rule holds for nonporous carbons or carbons with comparatively large pores (mean diameter ~15 Å), while it does not hold for carbons with smaller pores (~8 Å).

Traube's rule has been found valid also for the adsorption of homologous sodium alkyl sulfates on carbon black (*90*), as well as for the adsorption of the homologs of alkylammonium chlorides on aluminium oxide (*81*). Fig. 3.21 shows the adsorption isotherms for dodecylammonium chloride, tetradecylammonium chloride, and hexadecylammonium chloride on aluminium oxide at 40°C.

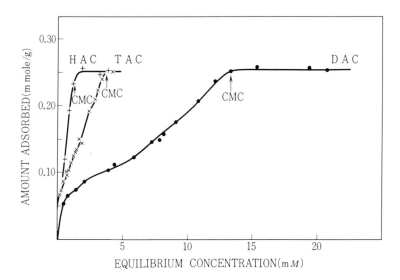

Fig. 3.21. Adsorption isotherms of dodecylammonium chloride (DAC), tetradecylammonium chloride (TAC), and hexadecylammonium chloride (HAC) on aluminium oxide at 40°C.

As this figure indicates, the longer the chain length, the lower the equilibrium concentration at which adsorption attains saturation. It is also remarkable that this equilibrium concentration for each member of the compounds is nearly equal to the CMC of that surfactant and that the amount of adsorption at saturation is independent of the chain length. If the amount of adsorption is plotted against the reduced concentration for the CMC, i.e. C/C_m, in which C is the equilibrium concentration and C_m is the CMC, a single curve is obtained for all these homologous compounds, which indicates that their isotherms are congruent functions of the reduced concentration. Such a result is considered to be an expression of Traube's rule.

Traube's rule has been found to hold as well for the adsorption of the homologous alkyl ammonium chlorides on cation-exchange resins, provided that the pore size of the resins is not too small (*84*).

c. *Effects of pH and Added Salt*

The adsorption of anionic and cationic surfactants on aluminium oxide (alumina for chromatographic use) has been found to be greatly influenced by the pH of the solution. The adsorption of cationic surfactants becomes greater as the pH increases, while that of anionic surfactants becomes greater as the pH decreases. Fig. 3.22 gives the adsorption

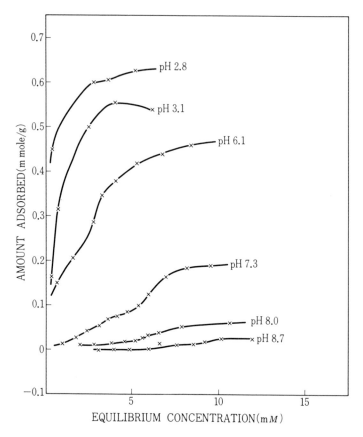

Fig. 3.22. Graph showing the effect of pH on the adsorption isotherm of sodium dodecyl sulfate on aluminium oxide at 20°C.

isotherms for the system sodium dodecyl sulfate-aluminium oxide at various values of the pH (95). For pH values greater than 8, sodium dodecyl sulfate is scarcely adsorbed by aluminium oxide. In the case of dodecylammonium chloride, not only surface effects, but hydrolysis effects, should be taken into consideration, due to the change of pH. In strongly acidic media the possibility of the chemical change of aluminium oxide itself should also be taken into consideration.

A similar effect of pH has been found for the adsorption of anionic as well as cationic surfactants on titanium oxide; but no remarkable effect on barium sulfate or calcium fluoride and only a small effect on carbons has been observed (95). A remarkable effect of pH has been found for the adsorption of sodium oleate on cotton or viscose (89), as well as for the adsorption of anionic and cationic surfactants on wool or nylon (96).

In the presence of an inorganic salt, e.g. sodium chloride, the adsorption isotherm of dodecylammonium chloride on aluminium oxide is displaced to lower equilibrium concentrations. The greater the concentration of the added salt, the greater the displacement of the isotherm, while the maximum amount of adsorption remains constant. It was also noticed that the concentration at which the adsorption attains a maximum for each isotherm coincides almost exactly with the CMC values in the presence of the salt (95). The displacement of the isotherms is therefore to be regarded as corresponding to the change of the micellar state of the solute in solution.

A similar effect of added salt has been observed for the adsorption of sodium alkyl sulfates on carbon black (90).

d. Effect of Polar Nature of Adsorbent

Solid adsorbents can be generally grouped into polar and nonpolar solids, although perfectly nonpolar solids are rarely found for practical use. Aluminium oxide is an example of a polar solid, while pure carbon black in an example of a nonpolar one. There are only a few systematic studies on the adsorption of any anionic or cationic surfactant on various kinds of solid adsorbents. However, the data obtained by Tamamushi and Tamaki (81, 83, 84, 95) for the adsorption of some anionic and cationic surfactants on aluminium oxide or carbon black illustrate how the adsorption is influenced by the polar nature of the adsorbent. From neutral solutions, a cationic surfactant, such as dodecylammonium chloride or dodecylpyridinium bromide, is more strongly adsorbed on aluminium oxide than an anionic surfactant, such as sodium dodecyl sulfate, which may be due to the negative polar character of aluminium oxide. The same aluminium oxide, when previously treated with a thorium nitrate solution, adsorbs sodium dodecyl sulfate much more strongly than dodecylammonium chloride, which suggests that the adsorption is now governed by the positive nature of the solid, whose surface is probably turned positive by adsorbed thorium ions.

If we compare the amount of adsorption of sodium dodecyl sulfate and of dodecylammonium chloride on carbon black, the difference is found to be small. Moreover, the adsorption of both these anionic and cationic surfactants on carbon black is as a whole smaller than that of these compounds on aluminium oxide. Such experimental facts indicate that nonpolar solids such as carbon black are less selective for ionic surfactants than polar solids such as aluminium oxide. According to the electrokinetic potential measurements made by Stanley (96) with textile fibers, the graph of change of charge density with concentration of paraffin chain electrolytes is found to resemble the adsorption isotherm.

TABLE 3.4

SPECIFIC SURFACE AREA OF ADSORBENTS

Adsorbent	Area obtained by N_2 adsorption (m^2/gm)	Area obtained by stearic acid adsorption from benzene (m^2/gm)
Aluminium oxide	78.8	54.8
Barium sulfate	5.9	5.55
Calcium fluoride	2.4	2.0
Titanium oxide	13.4	12.0
Carbon black A	14.6	2.9
Carbon black B	39.0	4.1

TABLE 3.5

MINIMUM AREA PER ADSORBED MOLECULE ($Å^2$)

	Sodium dodecyl sulfate	Dodecyl-ammonium chloride	Dodecyl-pyridinium bromide
Aluminium oxide	370 (pH 8.7)	24.0 (pH 6.8)	36.8 (pH 11.5)
	173 (pH 8.0)	28.2 (pH 6.3)	48.9 (pH 10.0)
	49.8 (pH 7.3)	41.8 (pH 3.8)	58.4 (pH 8.4)
	19.9 (pH 6.1)	67.8 (pH 2.9)	88.8 (pH 7.8)
	14.7 (pH 2.8)		
	17.0 (pH 3.1)		
Titanium oxide	122 (pH 3.6)		26.6 (pH 5.8)
	82.4 (pH 2.9)		23.0 (pH 7.2)
Barium sulfate	12.2	10.8	
Calcium fluoride	9.9	17.7	
Carbon black A	38.5	26.0	
Carbon black B	44.3	28.7	
Sectional area in close-packed state	20	25	72

3. *Mechanism of Adsorption*

In order to consider the mechanism of the adsorption at the liquid-solid interface, it is necessary to determine the adsorption with adsorbents of known surface areas. For the determination of the surface area of a solid adsorbent, two methods are usually applied, namely, the gas-phase adsorption method of Brunauer-Emmett-Teller (*80*) and the liquid-phase adsorption method, such as stearic acid adsorption from benzene solution (*97*). These two kinds of determination give generally identical results for nonporous adsorbents, but for porous adsorbents like alumina or carbon, the liquid-phase adsorption method usually gives smaller surface areas than the gas-phase adsorption method (*98*). In Table 3.4, the data obtained by Tamamushi and Tamaki (*95*) for several solid adsorbents are listed, by aid of which the following considerations will be discussed.

From the specific surface areas obtained above and the maximum amounts of adsorption measured, the cross-sectional areas of the molecules of some paraffin chain electrolytes are calculated on the basis of the assumption that the adsorption is of the monolayer type. Table 3.5 shows the results. In the last line the values of the sectional molecular areas of the respective compounds in the close-packed state are indicated.

It is noted in this table that the areas for sodium dodecyl sulfate and dodecylammonium chloride on barium sulfate or calcium fluoride are notably smaller than the sectional areas of these molecules corresponding to their close-packed monolayers. At certain pH values, the areas of these compounds on aluminium oxide and titanium oxide are also smaller than those corresponding to the close-packed state. The effect of solvent adsorption should be taken into account, but in the case under consideration, this is probably small owing to the strong surface activity of the solutes used. The results suggest, therefore, that the adsorption cannot be explained by the monolayer mechanism. In the adsorption of these paraffin chain electrolytes on polar solids, such as aluminium oxide, it is very probable that the first stage of the adsorption takes place in such manner that the polar heads of the chain ions are attached to the adsorbent surface by electrostatic attraction forces or chemical bonding forces. Such a type of adsorption should be specific, strongly depending on the nature of the solid surface. The fact that the adsorption on oxides such as aluminium oxide, titanium oxide, or silica is greatly influenced by the pH of the surfactant solution can be understood from the variation of the number of polar sites on the adsorbent surface. The fact that the position of the adsorption isotherms of dodecylammonium chloride and sodium dodecyl sulfate is reversed when aluminium oxide is previously treated with thorium nitrate is also in accord with this viewpoint. On polar adsorbents, when the first stage of the adsorption of the electrostatic or chemical-bonding type is completed, the second stage of adsorption due to van der Waals forces may take place, and consequently a multilayer is built up on the surface.

The possibility of such a type of twofold adsorption was first pointed out by Held and Samochwalov (79) for the adsorption of alkali carboxylates on barium sulfate or cinnabar, where the first adsorption layer is assumed to be due to the chemical reaction between barium sulfate and alkali carboxylates; for example,

$$BaSO_4 + 2NaCOOC_{12}H_{25} \rightarrow Ba(COOC_{12}H_{25})_2 + Na_2SO_4$$

A similar viewpoint was raised by Schulman and Smith (99) for the adsorption of sodium dodecyl sulfate on copper or copper minerals, where the adsorption is considered to be completed at the monolayer stage, after which it passes to the two-layer structure at the equilibrium concentration corresponding to the CMC of the surfactant. The first layer adsorption is accordingly supposed to be a type of chemisorption, while the second layer adsorption is a type of micellar adsorption. These authors further remarked that the mechanism of adsorption has an intimate relation with the flotation phenomena of the metals and minerals. The mechanism of the orientated two-layer adsorption was further supported by the recent work of Cumming and Schulman (85) for the case of adsorption of sodium dodecyl sulfate on barium sulfate, where it was proved that the effect of the precipitation of barium dodecyl sulfate can make only a very small contribution to the phenomenon.

On chromatographic alumina the first stage of adsorption may be a type of ion exchange adsorption. The alumina is normally alkaline and contains sodium ions which are exchangeable with cations in solution. Even pure alumina can adsorb cations to some extent, probably initially by aluminium-hydrogen ion exchange. The alumina can in fact function as an amphoteric ion exchanger, though its normal sodium ion content makes it more effective as a cation exchanger. The reaction of the hydrochloric acid-treated alumina with paraffin chain electrolytes is probably mainly an exchange of chlorine ions with adsorbed anions, but some covalent bonding may also take place (100, 101).

The two-layer adsorption mechanism should not be deduced simply from the data for the values of areas occupied by adsorbed molecules or ions because there may be a number of possibilities, e.g., that adsorbed molecules or ions are not oriented as in the close-packed state, or that the number of molecules in the second layer is not the same as that of the first layer. However, the fact that the saturation point of adsorption isotherms corresponds to the equilibrium concentration, which agrees with the CMC of the electrolyte, suggests that the micellar structure exists at the surface, maintaining equilibrium with micelles in solution (81).

In the case of the adsorption of paraffin chain electrolytes on nonpolar adsorbents like carbon black, it is likely that adsorption of the van der Waals type takes place to a greater extent than that of the electrostatic type or the chemisorption type, where adsorbed ions are oriented in such a manner that hydrocarbon chains are anchored to the surface of the solid. Moreover, the adsorption force may in this case not be strong enough for building up further layers. The values for the area per molecule found for sodium dodecyl sulfate or dodecylammonium chloride on carbon black are also in accord with the assumption of this monolayer adsorption mechanism. However, the possibility of multilayer adsorption on carbons can not be excluded, owing to the existence of polar sites on their surface due to ash contamination. The multilayer adsorption mechanism has been, in fact, proposed by Bartell and co-workers (102) on the basis of their experiments on the adsorption of butyric acid and other organic compounds on graphite.

As already shown in Fig. 3.18, the amount of adsorption of sodium dodecyl sulfate on an anion exchange resin, Dowex 1–X1, exceeds the amount of exchange of the same electrolyte by this resin. This characteristic fact suggests that at higher equilibrium concentrations the adsorption of the paraffin chain ions on the resin may also occur in twofold layers, namely, the first layer occurring due to an exchange mechanism and the second layer due to a van der Waals adsorption mechanism. The adsorption on ion exchange resins of compounds with alkyl chains shorter than the dodecyl group is considered to occur only in monolayer form by the exchange mechanism because the adsorption isotherm is in that case coincident with the exchange isotherm (84).

The considerations concerning the appearance of maxima in adsorption isotherms proposed by several authors will now be reviewed briefly.

Corrin and co-workers (86), who found an isotherm with a distinct maximum for the adsorption of sodium dodecyl sulfate on graphite, as shown in Fig. 3.20, considered that the maximum could be attributed to the maximum in the activity of the adsorbed single ions, as the activity of the chain ions should go through a maximum with respect to the over-all concentration of the electrolyte if the equilibrium among the single ions, counter ions, and micelles is governed by a simple form of the mass action principle. This consideration is based on the assumption that only single ions and not micelles are adsorbed at the interface. A similar point of view was raised by White and co-workers (103) for the appearance of a maximum in the adsorption isotherm of cetyltrimethylammonium bromide on cellulose.

Meader and Fries (76) assumed, on the basis of their experiments on the adsorption of sodium alkylallylsulfonate on fibers, that at higher concentrations of the surfactant the adsorption of micelles would take place as well as that of single ions and, consequently, the total adsorption should reach a maximum and then decrease as the activity of single ions continuously decreases. This mechanism was criticized by Fava and Eyring (77), who considered the possibility of the existence of micelles of various sizes and suggested that only the smallest of these micelles might be capable of being adsorbed. The effect of the hydrolysis of paraffin chain electrolytes at the solution-solid interface was also taken into consideration in explaining the maximum in the curve.

Vold and co-workers (88) found that in the adsorption of sodium dodecyl sulfate on carbons of various ash contents the amount of adsorption increases as the ash content increases, while the specific surface area of these carbons remains almost the same. From such experimental facts, they considered that, at the polar sites of the carbon surface due to ash, the paraffin chain ions are specifically adsorbed, a twofold layer being built up there. It was further considered that the adsorption should take place according to a Langmuir isotherm until the equilibrium concentration reaches the CMC and that thereafter the adsorption of micelles would take place, so that there appears to be a discontinuity in the curve at this critical point. On increasing the surfactant concentration, the ionic strength is increased and the depth of the surface double layer decreased, and the adsorbed layer will have the structure of a "surface micelle"; this transformation corresponds to the maximum in the curve. The reason why the adsorption decreases thereafter is assumed to be due to the dropping out of the surface micelles by the collision of these micelles with those in the bulk phase.

Some authors consider, however, that the mechanism of the first step of adsorption may be an ion exchange, while the further step is the formation of "ion pairs" instead of the formation of micelles (103). Other investigators, especially in the case of the adsorption of surfactants by fiber materials, have attributed the appearance of maxima to the change of the available surface of adsorbents owing to the swelling of solid materials in surfactant solutions (89).

In conclusion, the reason for the appearance of maxima in adsorption isotherms seems not to be simple, and no definite conclusion can be drawn at the present state of our knowledge of this problem.

V. Interaction of Paraffin Chain Electrolytes with Colloids

1. Interaction with Oleophilic Colloids

It is a well-known fact that hydrophobic or oleophilic colloids in an aqueous medium are sensitive to electrolytes added to the medium and that they flocculate at certain concentrations of the added electrolytes. It is further known from many experimental data concerning the stability of oleophilic colloids that the phenomenon of flocculation is ruled by two main factors: (i) the discharge effect; and (ii) the adsorption effect of added electrolytes. These two factors are generally surperimposed on each other, but in certain favorable cases either one of these factors can be followed almost independently of the other. In the early days, Matsuno (104) compared the flocculation values of cobalt complexes of various valences against arsenic sulfide sol. These values were found to decrease as the valence of the complex ions increases, the Schulze-Hardy rule (105) being typically obeyed. As the adsorbability of those complex ions is supposed to be almost the same, the difference in the flocculation values should be mainly due to the difference in the discharge effect of those ions. Freundlich and Birstein (106) compared the flocculation values of homologous sodium alkyl (C_1-C_6) carboxylates against iron oxide sol as well as of alkyl (C_2-C_{12})-substituted ammonium chlorides against arsenic sulfide sol. It was found that the flocculation value decreases regularly with the increase in the number of carbon atoms in the electrolyte molecule. Thus, Traube's rule (107) is typically followed. The results can be mainly attributed to the difference of adsorbability of these univalent organic electrolytes.

However, the latter sort of experiment was not extended to the action of longer paraffin chain electrolytes with higher solubility until such compounds became available as pure chemicals. In the last twenty years studies on the action of longer chain compounds—cationic as well as anionic surfactants—on the stability of oleophilic colloids have been made by a number of investigators in various countries (108–116).

The colloids used in these studies are divided into two groups: (i) positive colloids, such as iron oxide and aluminium oxide; and (ii) negative colloids, such as gold, arsenic sulfide, silver halides and manganese oxide.

The paraffin chain electrolytes used are divided into two groups: (i) compounds containing long chain anions, namely, alkyl carboxylates, alkyl sulfates, etc.; and (ii) compounds containing long chain cations, namely, primary, secondary, tertiary, and quarternary alkyl amine halides, alkyl pyridinium halides, alkyl quinolinium halides, etc.

Some of the characteristic results obtained from the observation of the interaction between these electrolytes and colloids are as follows.

(i) The interaction takes place more remarkably between colloids and paraffin chain ions of opposite signs, namely, between cationic surfactants and negative colloids, on the one hand, and between anionic surfactants and positive colloids, on the other.

(ii) In certain ranges of concentration of an electrolyte, flocculation of colloids occurs, the flocculation value of the electrolyte being rapidly decreased as the number of carbon atoms contained in the electrolyte

TABLE 3.6

FLOCCULATION VALUES FOR POSITIVE AND NEGATIVE SOLS

Electrolyte	Fe_2O_3 Sol (positive) (mmoles/liter)	Electrolyte	AgI Sol (negative) (mmoles/liter)
KCl	9.0^a	KNO_3	136^d
K_2SO_4	0.21	$Mg(NO_3)_2$	2.60
		$Al(NO_3)_3$	0.067
CH_3COONa	30^b		
C_3H_7COONa	11.5	$C_4H_9NH_3Cl$	21^e
$C_5H_{11}COONa$	2.5	$C_8H_{17}NH_3Cl$	1.8
		$C_{12}H_{25}NH_3Cl$	0.095
$C_4H_9OSO_3Na$	0.5^c	$C_{16}H_{33}NH_3Cl$	0.065
$C_8H_{17}OSO_3Na$	0.01	$C_{12}H_{25}(CH_3)_3NCl$	0.075
$C_{12}H_{25}OSO_3Na$	0.001	$C_{12}H_{25}C_5H_5NBr$	0.065

[a] Freundlich, H. *Z. physik. Chem.* (*Leipzig*) **44**, 151 (1903).
[b] Freundlich and Birstein (*106*).
[c] Meguro and Kondo (*110*).
[d] Kruyt, H.R., and Klompe, M.A. *Kolloid-Beih.* **54**, 484 (1942).
[e] Tamamushi and Tamaki (*115*).

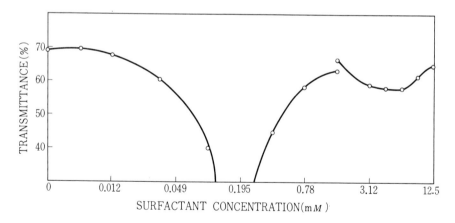

Fig. 3.23. Graph showing the change of transmittance of silver iodide sol on addition of dodecylammonium chloride in various concentrations. Wavelength, 650 $m\mu$; flocculation value of the original sol, 0.08 mmoles/liter.

molecule increases. Some of the experimental results are listed in Table 3.6, and the data for inorganic electrolytes are also included for comparison.

(iii) The flocculate thus formed is deflocculated at higher concentrations of electrolyte, provided that the electrolyte contains more than a certain number—usually 10—of carbon atoms in its molecule. In such cases, there appear flocculation and deflocculation zones, according to the concentration of the electrolyte. As an example, the change of the stability of negative silver iodide sol with increasing concentration of dodecylammonium chloride is shown in Fig. 3.23, where the change of stability was followed by measuring the transmittance of the sol by a Beckman-type photometer.

As illustrated in this figure, according to the variation of the surfactant concentration there are three distinct zones: (i) a stable zone; (ii) a flocculation zone; (iii) a deflocculation zone. Phenomena of this kind observed in the case of the interaction between oleophilic colloids and

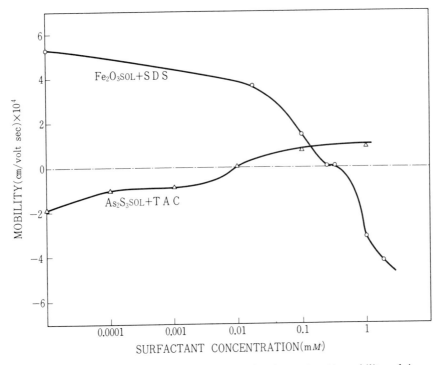

Fig. 3.24. Graph showing the change of the electrophoretic mobility of iron oxide sol by sodium dodecyl sulfate (SDS) and that of arsenic sulfide sol by dodecyltrimethylammonium chloride (TAC).

inorganic electrolytes have been known as the "irregular series" of colloidal solutions (*117*).

In the case of inorganic electrolytes, the deflocculated sol is usually flocculated again by further addition of electrolyte, and thus the second flocculation zone appears, whereas in the case of organic electrolytes the second flocculation zone does not appear distinctly as expected.

(iv) The electric charge of the original sol is reversed at the deflocculation zone, the electrophoretic mobility of colloid particles being

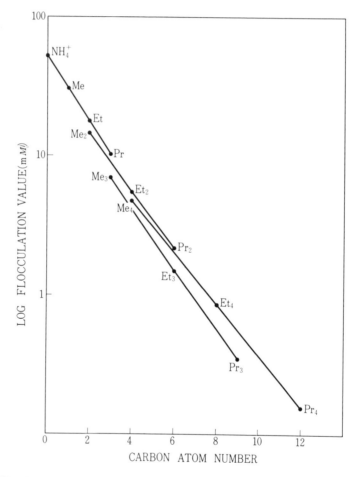

Fig. 3.25. Graph showing the relationship between logarithm of flocculation value and total carbon atom number of a surfactant molecule, obtained for the flocculation of arsenic sulfide sol by primary, secondary, tertiary, and quarternary amine chlorides. Experimental data are those of Freundlich and Slottman (*106*).

changed with the concentration of the surfactant electrolyte. As an example, the change of the mobility of iron oxide sol by sodium dodecyl sulfate as well as that of arsenic sulfide sol by dodecyltrimethylammonium chloride are illustrated in Fig. 3.24.

Now, the dependence of the flocculation or deflocculation value of a surfactant electrolyte on the length of the paraffin chain or the total number of carbon atoms contained in the electrolyte molecule may be presented in more detail.

In the interaction of a series of sodium alkyl sulfates with positive iron oxide sol, it was found that the flocculation values of sodium butyl, octyl, and dodecyl sulfates are 500, 10, and 1 mmoles/liter, respectively, (110), while in the interaction of a series of primary alkyl amine chlorides with negative silver iodide sol, the flocculation values of butyl, octyl, and dodecylamine chlorides are 21, 1.8, and 0.095 mmoles/liter, respectively (115). According to Hazel and Strange (112), who studied the interaction of sodium alkyl (C_{10}–C_{16}) sulfates or potassium alkyl (C_8–C_{14}) carboxylates with iron oxide sol and that of alkyl (C_8–C_{16}) amine chlorides or alkyl (C_8–C_{16}) pyridinium chlorides with manganese oxide sol, the logarithm of the flocculation value has a linear relationship with the number of carbon atoms of the surfactant molecule; in other words, there exists the following relation for a homologous series of electrolytes:

$$\log (\text{FV}) = A + Bn$$

where FV is the flocculation value; n is the number of carbon atoms; and A and B are constants. All these results demonstrate that Traube's rule (107) is obeyed in the flocculating action of the homologous paraffin chain electrolytes.

There are, however, some other structural factors which act on flocculation as well as deflocculation, as demonstrated by the following experimental data. Fig. 3.25 shows the relation between the logarithm of the flocculation value and the carbon atom number obtained for the flocculation of arsenic sulfide sol by the action of primary, secondary, tertiary, and quarternary alkyl amine chlorides. Fig. 3.26 shows the corresponding relation for the flocculation of negative silver iodide sol by the action of primary, secondary, tertiary, and quarternary alkyl amine chlorides (118).

It is noted in these figures that: (i) the flocculation value decreases linearly as the carbon atom number increases for each type of amine compound; (ii) the flocculation values of compounds of the same carbon atom number and of different structures are in the order, primary > secondary > tertiary, quarternary; and (iii) the flocculation values of electrolytes containing more than 12 carbon atoms are almost constant for any of these types of compounds.

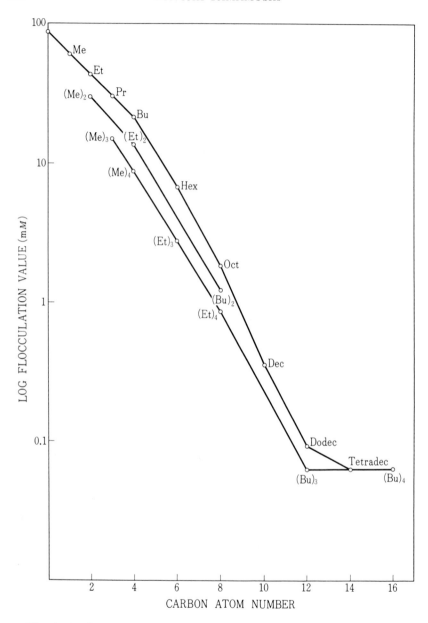

Fig. 3.26. Graph showing the relationship between logarithm of flocculation value and total carbon atom number of surfactant molecule, obtained for the flocculation of silver iodide sol by primary, secondary, tertiary, and quarternary alkyl amine chlorides.

In the interaction of alkyl amine compounds with silver iodide sol, it has been found that the deflocculation value is also dependent on the number of carbon atoms contained in the surfactant molecules, and it becomes constant when the number reaches a certain value (C_{14}). The deflocculation values of the compounds containing the same number of carbon atoms are found to be different according to the type of the compound, namely, they are in the order, primary < secondary < tertiary, quarternary. It should be noted here that this order is the reverse of that found for the flocculation values.

Comparing the flocculation values or the deflocculation values of dodecylamine chloride, bromide, and iodide for silver iodide sol, it is found that neither the flocculation values nor the deflocculation values are sensibly influenced by the nature of the counter ions. Tetrabutylammonium chloride ($C_4H_9)_4NCl$ and tetrabutylammonium dodecyl sulfate ($C_4H_9)_4NC_{12}H_{25}OSO_3$, which have the same cationic group and a different anionic group, have almost the same flocculation values, while they have different deflocculation values, the deflocculation value of the latter compound being distinctly smaller than that of the former. Moreover, the sol stabilized by this latter compound is negatively charged.

Another remarkable fact found in these studies is that the flocculation value as well as the deflocculation value are dependent on the sol concentration. The flocculation value of electrolytes containing less than 4 carbon atoms decreases with an increase in sol concentration, whereas that of the electrolytes with more than 6 carbon atoms is either almost independent of the sol concentration or increases with an increase in the sol concentration. The deflocculation value, on the other hand, generally increases with an increase in the sol concentration.

The experimental relationships described above may be discussed from the viewpoint of the mechanism of the action of paraffin chain electrolytes on the stability of oleophilic colloids. Concerning the action of simple inorganic electrolytes on oleophilic colloids, there are well-known empirical laws—Schulze-Hardy's law and Burton-Bishop's law (119). According to the former law, the flocculation of colloids is chiefly governed by the valence of ions charged oppositely to the colloid particles; and according to the latter law, the flocculation value of electrolytes depends on the sol concentration and, for univalent electrolytes, the flocculation value generally decreases with the increase of the sol concentration.

The stability of oleophilic colloids is chiefly governed by the electrokinetic potential of the colloid particles, the flocculation being the result of the compression of the double layer (in other words, the lowering of the electrokinetic potential of colloid particles). Now the added ions are subjected to two influences: in the first place, their Brownian motion causes them to tend to diffuse away from the surface of the colloid particles;

and secondly, they are attracted to the surface by Coulomb forces. These two opposed influences lead to a distribution equilibrium characterized by certain mean distances between the ions and the surface of colloid particles. This mean distance is a function of electrolyte concentration, on the one hand, and sol concentration, on the other. It is very probable that, under certain conditions, the shortening of this distance (i.e., the compression of the double layer), may be more pronounced for more concentrated sols. Burton-Bishop's law is understood from this point of view. In order to explain the law of Schulze-Hardy it is usually sufficient to suppose that ions of different valences have different discharge effects, the effect being doubled when the ionic charge is doubled, and it is not necessary to suppose that the ions have different adsorbability (120).

The action of large organic ions like paraffin chain ions on oleophilic colloids may be very different from that of simple ions. For the distribution of ions in solution and, accordingly, for the stability of colloids in such cases, the surface activity of large organic ions may have a paramount importance. According to the law of adsorption, surface active large ions will be very effectively concentrated at the surface, and consequently colloid particles will be discharged at very low equilibrium concentrations of electrolyte. Moreover, paraffin chain ions may be adsorbed at the solid-liquid interface in such a manner that the polar ionic group is attracted to the solid surface and the nonpolar hydrocarbon chain is directed towards liquid medium. As the result of such oriented adsorption, colloid particles not only lose their electrical charge but also change the nature of their surface, making it strongly oleophilic, so that the tendency for flocculation will be much accelerated. This is evidenced by the fact that the flocculate thus formed can be removed by benzene from the aqueous phase.

The above-mentioned experimental facts, namely, that the flocculation values and the deflocculation values of paraffin chain electrolytes are dependent on the molecular size or structure of the electrolyte on one hand, and that they obey the reverse relation of Burton-Bishop's law on the other, are reasonably explained by the strong surface activity of those compounds.

A further analysis of this viewpoint may be added here. Suppose that the adsorption of the surfactant ions takes place according to the Freundlich equation, namely,

$$x/m = k(C - x)^n \tag{3.47}$$

where x is the amount of adsorption; m is the mass of adsorbent, which can be replaced in this case by the sol concentration; C is the concentration of electrolyte at which flocculation or deflocculation occurs and is therefore the equilibrium concentration; and both k and n are constants. Assuming that the flocculation or deflocculation occurs at a certain definite amount of adsorption per particle, we can put

$$x/m = k'$$ (3.48)

where k' is a constant.   From Eq. (3.47) and (3.48), we obtain

$$C - km' = (k'/k)^{1/n} = C_0$$

or

$$C = C_0 + k'm$$ (3.49)

where C_0 is another constant.   The last equation shows that C, namely, the flocculation or deflocculation value, is a linear function of m, i.e., the sol concentration.

Such a point of view has been proved to be in accord with a direct determination of the amount of adsorption of paraffin chain ions on silver iodide particles.   The silver iodide sol used in that study was nearly monodisperse, the mean diameter of particles being determined by electron microscope to be 36 $m\mu$.   As the amount of adsorption varies in the range of 0.01–0.045 mmoles/gram or 300–1400 ions particle, the area per adsorbed ion varies in the range of 150–700 Å^2.   It is suggested by this result that adsorption takes place only at certain specific sites on the surface of the colloid crystals.   The adsorbed paraffin chain ions are supposed to be orientated in such a way as to direct their polar heads to the solid surface and their hydrocarbon chains towards the liquid phase.

In the state of deflocculation, direct measurement of the amount of adsorption also indicates that adsorption takes place only at certain

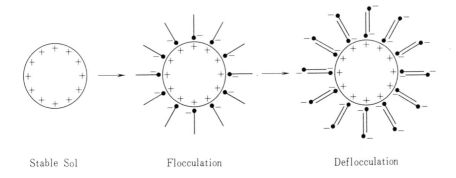

Stable Sol   Flocculation   Deflocculation

Fig. 3.27.   Schematic diagram showing the mechanism of flocculation and deflocculation.

specific sites of the surface.   From the fact that in the deflocculated state
the colloid particle has an electrical charge of the same sign as that of
the paraffin chain ion used for flocculation, it is very probable that in
that state adsorption will take place in such a way that the chain ions
are attracted to the primarily adsorbed ions by van der Waals forces
between two paraffin chains, the secondarily adsorbed ions being oriented in just the opposite way from those primarily adsorbed.   This mechanism represents a certain type of "twofold layer" adsorption.   Fig.
3.27 shows a schematic diagram for such a mechanism of flocculation and
deflocculation.

    The experimental result, i.e., that the deflocculating effect of elect-
rolytes of various structures having the same number of carbon atoms

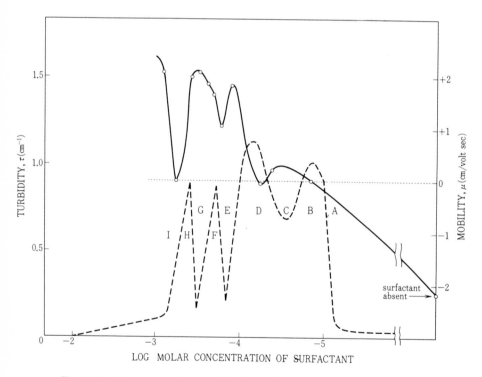

Fig. 3.28.   Curves showing mobility (o-o-o) and turbidity (- - -) of silver iodide
sol vs. logarithm molar concentration of dodecylpyridinium iodide.   Turbidity values
are taken 1 min after mixing sol and surfactant.   Sol concentration, 5×10^{-4} M.

are in the order, primary > secondary > tertiary, quarternary, can be attributed to the stronger van der Waals forces between two normal paraffin chains as compared to those between two branched chains. It is a remarkable fact that the above-mentioned order is reversed for the flocculating action. This, however, can be understood if we assume that at the liquid-solid interface normal chain compounds are less surface active than branched chain compounds.

Independent of the study made by Tamamushi and collaborators referred to above, studies along the same line have been carried out by Ottewill and co-workers (113, 114), who investigated the influence of cationic surfactants on the formation of negative silver halides sols by means of spectrophotometry, microelectrophoresis, and electronmicroscopy. Their study is characterized by the fact that the phenomena were observed in sols in *statu nascendi*, in other words, in the process of growing colloid crystals, whereas the studies made by the former investigators refer to "prepared" sols. For the system silver bromide and dodecyltrimethylammonium bromide or dodecylpyridinium bromide and for the system silver iodide and dodecylpyridinium iodide, a very remarkable phenomenon, i.e., a periodic change of flocculation and stabilization, has been observed as the molar concentration of the surfactant changes. Fig. 3.28 illustrates how the electrophoretic mobility or turbidity of silver iodide sol changes with the surfactant concentration.

It is noted in this figure that the maximum in the turbidity curve corresponds to the minimum in the mobility curve, while the minimum of the turbidity curve corresponds to the maximum of the mobility curve. The former corresponding points represent the state of flocculation, while the latter represent the state of deflocculation. These periodic curves were found to be influenced by the sol concentration, on the one hand, and by the observation time after initiation of sol formation, on the other, although the general features of the curves are maintained. With the system of silver chloride and dodecylpyridinium chloride, there appears only one broad maximum, which is similar to the phenomenon observed with "prepared" sols, as already shown in Fig. 3.23.

A comparison of the electrophoretic mobility curve and the turbidity curve indicates that a maximum in turbidity corresponds to virtually uncharged particles, while a minimum in turbidity corresponds to charged particles. From this relation it is suggested that the turbidity maximum corresponds to the point where the monolayer adsorption of chain ions occurs on the initially negatively charged particles, while the turbidity minimum corresponds to the point where twofold layer adsorption takes place, providing the particles with positive charge. The appearance of the periodic maxima and minima shown in Fig. 3.28 has been attributed by the investigators to competition between the two rate processes, namely, particle formation and adsorption. The electron micrographs taken with the system silver iodide and dodecylpyridinium iodide give clear evidence that the resultant particle size decreases with increasing surfactant concentration. The total solid phase area exposed is thus increasing; hence, a greater concentration of chain ions is needed for monolayer or twofold layer adsorption. Depending on the ratio of the total particle area to the surfactant concentration, a series of conditions will occur in which either a complete or incomplete monolayer or a twofold layer is possible. As the decrease of particle size does not appear to be a continuous function of the surfactant concentration, a periodic change of the formation of adsorbed layers, and consequently of flocculation and stabilization, may result. Such considerations raised in these studies seem also to support the adsorption theory developed above for the change of stability of oleophilic sols by paraffin chain electrolytes.

In their extended work, Ottewill and co-workers (116, 121) have recently developed a theory on the subject under consideration from the viewpoint of the potential energy of the interaction between colloidal particles, which gives a quantitative relation between the flocculation value and the electrochemical free energy of adsorption of the surfactant electrolytes.

2. *Interaction with Hydrophilic Colloids*

The interaction of paraffin chain electrolytes with another type of colloids (i.e., hydrophilic colloids, including proteins) has also been a subject of interest in recent years and has been extensively studied by many researchers (122–130). In this section, however, only a few data concerning this problem will be referred to insofar as they suggest a viewpoint similar to that for the problem of oleophilic colloids.

Kuhn and co-workers (122) showed in their study on cationic soaps that the disinfecting action of these soaps on bacteria can be attributed to the combining power of these compounds with cell proteins, and they further showed that the action of cationic soaps on bacteria or proteins is parallel with the surface activity of these compounds. It is observed that proteins are precipitated by cationic soaps only in their anionic forms, the precipitates being redissolved at higher concentrations of the soaps. Similar phenomena are observed in the interaction of proteins with anionic surfactants. Putnum and Neurath (123, 124), who studied the interaction between sodium dodecyl sulfate and horse serum albumin, ascertained that the precipitation reaction takes place in the region of pH below 4.75, i.e., the isoelectric point of this protein, and the precipitate is redissolved in an excess of sodium dodecyl sulfate. Analogous relations are found in the interaction between sodium dodecyl sulfate and egg albumin, between sodium cetyl sulfate and hemoglobin, between sodium dodecyl sulfate and gelatin, etc. (125–130).

Pankhurst and Smith (125, 126) assumed, basing their assumption on their investigation of complex formation between gelatin and sodium dodecyl sulfate, that precipitation takes place when the monolayer of dodecyl sulfate ions is formed at the basic groups of the gelatin molecules and that the precipitate is led to dissolve when the second adsorption layer is built up. Tamamushi and Tamaki (129) showed in their study of the interaction between gelatin and sodium dodecyl sulfate or dodecylammonium chloride that the precipitation zone is greatly influenced by the pH of the mixed solution and that, in case of the gelatin–dodecylammonium chloride system, the precipitation zone is displaced toward the higher ratio of surfactant to protein as the pH becomes greater, while in case of the gelatin–sodium dodecyl sulfate system, the precipitation zone is displaced toward the higher ratio of surfactant to protein as the pH becomes smaller. In both cases, it is remarked that maximum precipitation and complete dissolution of precipitate take place at a definite ratio of surfactant concentrations, which is approximately equal to 1:2. Such a relation is also found in the case of the sodium dodecyl sulfate–egg albumin system (128). As the maximum values of a surfactant combined at each pH are equal to the combining power of the gelatin molecule with hydronium ion or hydroxyl ion, it is evident that the first polar combination between gelatin and surfactant is accomplished at the point of maximum precipitation. The first layer adsorption is therefore in this case a type of chemisorption, while the second layer adsorption is a type of van der Waals physical adsorption.

The gelatin–sodium dodecyl sulfate complexes formed by primary adsorption at the minimum water solubility are separated as oil-soluble complexes, which indicates their strong oleophilic character. Such oleophilic character of the complexes of gelatin–sodium dodecyl sulfate or gelatin–dodecylammonium chloride is also proved by measuring water vapor sorption capacity of these complexes (129).

The effect of the chain length of surfactant ions on complex formation is also evident in this case, the surfactant/gelatin ratio required for the separation of complexes being decreased by a definite ratio as the chain length increases, which bears out Traube's rule (125).

Cationic surfactants interact also with organic colloids, such as ligninsulfonic acid, alginic acid, starch, and glycogen, where precipitates result at certain pH ranges and certain surfactant/colloid ratios (130). The interaction in these systems may also be a type of chemisorption, insofar as the primary interaction is concerned.

3. *Dispersion of Solid Particles in Aqueous Media*

Paraffin chain electrolytes are used for preparing suspensions of solid materials like pigments in an aqueous medium. The mechanism of the dispersing action is probably due to two main factors: (i) increase of the electrokinetic potential at the solid-liquid interface; and (ii) gain of hydrophilic nature of the solid surface as a result of the oriented adsorption of long chain ions. Some experimental data have been discussed, chiefly from the viewpoint of the former factor (*131, 132, 134*). Experimental results which suggest the importance of the second factor may be given in the following (*134–136*).

Rouge, titanium white, and yellow ocher, which are not dispersed in water, are dispersed in solutions of some inorganic electrolytes of high valence, such as iron chloride or aluminium chloride, over a certain range of concentration; for example, rouge and yellow ocher are dispersed in 10–50 mM solutions of iron chloride, and titanium white in 5–10 mM solutions of aluminium chloride, the resultant suspensions being stable for three days. Now, if sodium dodecyl sulfate is added to the suspensions thus prepared, flocculation will occur at a certain range of surfactant concentration (5–20 mM). The flocculate thus formed is highly oleophilic; it can be removed into benzene from the aqueous phase by shaking. The flocculates are, however, dispersed again by adding further quantities of the same surfactant used in the flocculation or by other ionic or nonionic surfactants. For example, the flocculate of rouge or yellow ocher formed by sodium dodecyl sulfate can be dispersed by the addition

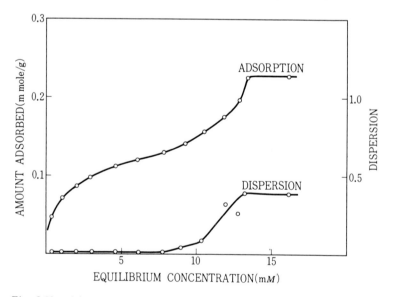

Fig. 3.29.   Adsorption and dispersion curves for the system dodecylammonium chloride and carbon black in aqueous medium.

of sodium dodecyl sulfate, or dodecylpyridinium bromide, or polyoxyethylene dodecyl ether at certain concentrations. The suspensions thus
prepared are very stable, the suspension prepared by the addition of
nonionic surfactant being proved especially insensitive against the further
addition of simple electrolytes (135).

Carbon black can also be dispersed in water by adding a certain
amount of paraffin chain electrolytes. The following experiments made
by Tamaki (136) illustrate the condition for dispersion. Under violent
shaking 0.5 gm carbon black, previously treated to remove ash and oil
contaminations, is mixed with 10 cc of surfactant (sodium dodecyl sulfate,
dodecylpyridinium bromide, dodecylammonium chloride, dodecyltrimethylammonium chloride) solution of a certain concentration (2–20 mM),
the mixture being kept at rest and observed after one hour. At lower
concentrations of surfactant, carbon black sediments, the sedimentation
volume first decreasing and then increasing gradually with increasing
concentration of surfactant. When the equilibrium concentration reaches
a certain value (10–15 mM), the suspension becomes so stable that carbon
particles cannot be separated from the liquid medium by centrifugation
at 14,000 rpm.

The stability of the suspension seems to have a close relationship

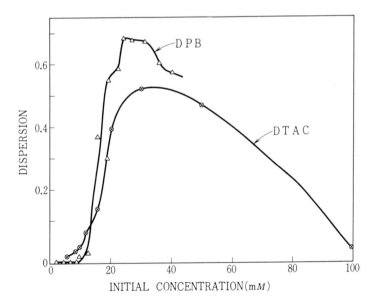

Fig. 3.30. Curves showing the relationship between dispersion and surfactant
concentration for carbon black in aqueous medium. Curve I, for dodecylpyridinium
bromide (DPB); curve II, for dodecyltrimethylammonium chloride (DTAC).

with the amount of adsorption of the surfactant. Fig. 3.29 gives the dispersion and adsorption curves of dodecylammonium chloride for carbon black; the amount of adsorption is determined by ordinary methods, and the dispersion is determined by nephelometry.

As this figure indicates, the curves for adsorption and dispersion do not run completely parallel to each other. Nevertheless, it is remarked that the dispersion increases rapidly when the amount of adsorption reaches a certain value, which, from the shape of the adsorption isotherm, seems to correspond to the transition stage from monolayer to twofold layer adsorption. It is noted further that the dispersion approaches a maximum when the adsorption reaches the saturation point; the equilibrium concentration corresponding to these maxima is approximately equal to the CMC of the surfactant. Similar relations are observed also for the system carbon black–sodium dodecyl sulfate. From such relations, it is very probable that at the stage of maximum dispersion, carbon particles become strongly hydrophilic, owing to the oriented adsorption of paraffin chain ions on the solid surface.

Fig. 3.30 shows the change of dispersion over a wider range of surfactant concentration for dodecylpyridinium bromide and dodecyltrimethylammonium chloride, which indicates that there is an optimum condition for dispersion, the dispersion being maximum in the initial concentration range of 20–30 mM. The dispersion is gradually decreased at higher concentrations of surfactant. An analogous relation has been pointed out by Vold and co-workers (132).

References

1. Adam, N. K., and Shute, H. L. *Trans. Faraday Soc.* **32**, 653 (1936).
2. McBain, J. W., and Mills, G. F. *Repts. Progr. in Phys.* **5**, 30 (1939).
3. Miles, G. D., and Shedlovsky, L. *J. Phys. Chem.* **48**, 57 (1944).
4. Reichenberg, D. *Trans. Faraday Soc.* **43**, 467 (1947).
5. Hutchinson, E. *J. Colloid Sci.* **3**, 413 (1948).
6. Brady, A. P. *J. Phys. & Colloid Chem.* **53**, 56 (1949).
7. Ward, F. A. H., and Tordai, L., *Nature* **154**, 146 (1944); *J. Chem. Phys.* **14**, 453 (1946).
8. Pethica, B. A. *Trans. Faraday Soc.* **50**, 413 (1954).
9. Kling, W., and Lange, H. *In* "Surface Activity: Proceedings of the Second International Congress, London, 1957" (J. H. Schulman, ed.), Vol. 1, p. 295. Academic Press, New York, 1958.
10. Harold, S. P. *J. Phys. Chem.* **63**, 317 (1959).
11. Haydon, D. A., and Phillips, J. N. *Nature* **178**, 813 (1956).
12. Clayfield, E. J., and Matthews, J. B. *In* "Surface: Activity: Proceedings of the Second International Congress, London 1957" (J. H. Schulman, ed.), Vol. I, p. 172. Academic Press, New York, 1958.

13. Sutherland, K. L., *Australian J. Chem.* **12**, 1 (1958).

14. Eda, K., and Fukuda, J., *J. Chem. Soc. Japan,* **79**, 1088 (1958). (In Japanese.)

15. Eda, K. *J. Chem. Soc. Japan* **80**, 8 (1959). (In Japanese.)

16. Addison, C. C., and Elliott, T. A. *J. Chem. Soc.* p. 2789 (1949); 3090 (1950).

17. Garner, F. H., and Mina, P. *Trans. Faraday Soc.* **55**, 1016, 1067. (1959).

18. Brady, A. P., and Brown, A. G. *In* "Monomolecular Layers" (H. Sobotka, ed.), pp. 33–62. American Association for the Advancement of Science, Washington, D.C., 1954.

19. Guggenheim, E. A. "Thermodynamics," p. 367. North-Holland Publ., Amsterdam, 1957.

20. Pethica, B. A. *Trans. Faraday Soc.* **50**, 413 (1954).

21. Cockbain, E. G. *Trans. Faraday Soc.* **50**, 874 (1954).

22. Ter Minassian-Saraga, L. *J. Chem. Phys.* **52**, 99 (1955).

23. Zutrauen, H. A. *J. Chem. Phys.* **53**, 54 (1956).

24. Shinoda, K., and Kinoshita, K. *J. Phys. Chem.* **63**, 648 (1959).

25. Hutchinson, E. *J. Colloid Sci.* **4**, 599 (1949).

26. Dixon, J. K., Weith, A. J., Argyle, A. A., and Sally, D. J. *Nature* **163**, 845 (1949).

27. Aniansson, G., and Lamm, O. *Nature* **165**, 357 (1950).

28. Dixon, J. K., Judson, C. M., and Sally, D. J. *In* "Monomolecular Layers" (H. Sobotka, ed.), pp. 63–106, American Association for the Advancement of Science, Washington, D. C., 1954.

29. Sally, D. J., Weith, A. J., Argyle, A. A., and Dixon, J. K. *Proc. Roy. Soc.* **A203**, 42 (1950).

30. Roa, C. P., and Brass, P. D. *J. Am. Chem. Soc.* **76**, 4703 (1954).

31. Matsuura, R., and Kimizuka, H., Miyamoto, S., and Shimozawa, R. *Bull. Chem. Soc. Japan,* **31**, 532 (1958); **32**, 404 (1959); Matsuura, R., Kimizuka, H., and Yasunami, K. *ibid.* **32**, 646 (1959).

32. Flengas, S. N., and Rideal, E. K. *Trans. Faraday Soc.* **55**, 339 (1959).

33. Nilsson, G. *J. Phys. Chem.* **61**, 1135 (1957).

34. Shinoda, K., and Mashio, K. *J. Phys. Chem.* **64**, 54 (1960).

35. Tamamushi, B. *Bull Chem. Soc. Japan* **8**, 120 (1933); **2**, 363 (1934); *Kolloid-Z.* **71**, 150 (1935).

36. Hutchinson, E. *J. Colloid Sci.* **3**, 219, 235 (1948).

37. Guastalla, J. *J. chim. phys.* **43**, 184 (1946).

38. Davies, J. T. *Proc. Roy. Soc.* **A208**, 224 (1951); *J. Colloid Sci.* **11**, 377 (1956).

39. Matijevic, E., and Pethica, B. A. *Croat. Chem. Acta* **29**, 431 (1957).

40. Davies, J. T. *Proc. Roy. Soc.* **A245**, 417, 429 (1958).

41. Phillips, J. N., and Rideal, E. K. *Proc. Roy. Soc.* **A232**, 159 (1955).

42. Haydon, D. A., and Phillips, J. N. *Trans. Faraday Soc.* **54**, 698 (1958).

43. Matijevic, E., and Pethica, B. A. *Trans. Faraday Soc.* **54**, 1382 (1958).

44. Lippmann, G. *Poggendorf's Ann.* [2| **149**, 547 (1873); *Ann. chim. phys.* [5] **5**, 494 (1875); **12**, 265 (1877).

45. Gouy, L. *Ann. chim. phys.* [7] **29**, 149 (1903); [8] **8**, 291 (1906).

46. Grahame, D. C. *Chem. Revs.* **41**, 441 (1947).

47. Berzins, T., and Delahay, P. *J. Phys. Chem.* **59**, 906 (1955); Breiler, M., and Delahay, P. *J. Am. Chem. Soc.* **81**, 2938 (1959).

48. Parsons, R. *Trans. Faraday Soc.* **55**, 999 (1959).
49. Proskurnin, M. A., and Frumkin, A. N. *Trans. Faraday Soc.* **31**, 110 (1935).
50. Grahame, D. C. *J. Am. Chem. Soc.* **68**, 301 (1946); **71**, 2975 (1949).
51. Frumkin, A. N., and Melik-Gaikazyan, V. I. *Doklady Akad. Nauk S. S. S. R.* **77**, 855 (1951); Melik-Gaikazyan, V. I. *Zhur. Fiz. Khim.* **26**, 560, 1184 (1952).
52. Hansen, R. S., Minturn, R. E., and Hickson, D. A. *J. Phys. Chem.* **60**, 1185 (1956).
53. Miller, I. R., and Grahame, D. C. *J. Am. Chem. Soc.* **78**, 3577 (1956); **79**, 3006 (1957); Miller, I. R. *In* "Surface Activity: Proceedings of the Second International Congress, London, 1957" (J. H. Schulman, ed.), Vol. III, p. 34. Academic Press, New York, 1958.
54. Gupta, S. L. *Kolloid-Z.* **137**, 86 (1954).
55. (a) Eda, K. *J. Chem. Soc. Japan* **80**, 343 (1959); (b) *ibid.* p. 347; (c) *ibid.* p. 349; (d) *ibid.* p. 461; (e) *ibid.* 465; (f) *ibid.* p. 708; (g) *ibid.* **81**, 689, (1960); (h) *ibid.* p. 875. (In Japanese.)
56. Lorenz. W. *Z. Elektrochem.* **62**, 192 (1958).
57. Tamamushi, R., Yamamoto, S., Takahashi, A., and Tanaka, N. *Anal. Chim. Acta* **20**, 486 (1959).
58. Hutchinson, E., and Melrose, J. C. *Kolloid-Z.* **2**, 363 (1954).
59. Lorenz, W., and Mockel, F. *Z. Electrochem.* **60**, 507, 939 (1956).
60. Heyrossky, J. *Trans. Faraday Soc.* **19**, 692 (1924); *Rec. trav. chim.* **44**, 488 (1925).
61. Randles, J. E. B. "Electrode Processes," *General Discussions Faraday Soc.* p. 11 (1947).
62. Colichman, E. L. *J. Am. Chem. Soc.* **72**, 4036 (1950).
63. Tamamushi, R., and Yamanaka, T. *Bull. Chem. Soc. Japan,* **28**, 673 (1955).
64. Frumkin, A. N. *In* "Surface Activity: Proceedings of the Second International Congress, London, 1957" (J. H. Schulman, ed.), Vol. III, p. 578. Academic Press, New York, 1958.
65. Schmid, R. W., and Reilley, C. N. *J. Am. Chem. Soc.* **80**, 2087 (1958).
66. Kolthoff, I. M., and Okinaka, Y. *J. Am. Chem. Soc.* **81**, 2296 (1959).
67. Breyer, B. "Report of the 28th Meeting, Australian and New Zealand Association for the Advancement of Science," p. 192. Brisbane, Australia, 1951; Breyer, B., and Hacobian, S. *Australian J. Sci. Research* **A4**, 500 (1952).
68. Doss, K. S. G., and Gupta, S. L. *Proc. Indian Acad. Sci.* **A36**, 493 (1952).
69. Breyer, B. *In* "Surface Activity: Proceedings of the Second International Congress, London, 1957" (J. H. Schulman, ed.), Vol. III, p. 157. Academic Press, New York, 1958.
70. Ostwald, W., and Izaguirre, D. *Kolloid-Z.* **30**, 279 (1922).
71. Bartell, F. E., and Sloan, C. K. *J. Am. Chem. Soc.* **51**, 1637 (1929).
72. Guggenheim E. A., and Adam, N. K. *Proc. Roy. Soc.* **A139**, 218 (1933).
73. Tschoegl, N. W. *Revs. Pure and Appl. Chem. (Australia)* **4**, 171 (1954).
74. Willson, E. A., Miller, J. R., and Rowe, E. H. *J. Phys. & Colloid Chem.* **53**, 357 (1949).
75. Maron, S. H., Elder, M. E., and Ulevitch, L. N. *J. Colloid Sci.* **9**, 89, 104, 263, 347, 353, 382 (1954); Maron, S. H., Bobalek, E. G., and Fok, S. *ibid.* **11**, 21 (1956).

76. Meader, A. L., and Fries, B. A. *Ind. Eng. Chem.* **44**, 1636 (1952).
77. Fava, A., and Eyring, H. *J. Phys. Chem.* **60**, 890 (1956).
78. Bikerman, J. J. "Surface Chemistry," p. 206. Academic Press, New York, 1958.
79. Held, N. A., and Samochwalov, K. N. *Kolloid-Z.* **72**, 13 (1935); Held, A. N., and Khainsky, I. A., *ibid.* **76**, 26 (1936).
80. Brunauer, S., Emmett, P. H., and Teller, E. *J. Am. Chem. Soc.* **60**, 309 (1938); Brunauer, S. "The Adsorption of Gases and Vapors," Vol. I, p. 285. Princeton Univ. Press, Princeton, New Jersey, 1943.
81. Tamamushi, B., and Tamaki, K., *In* "Surface Activity: Proceedings of the Second International Congress, London, 1957" (J. H. Schulman, ed.), Vol. III, p. 449. Academic Press, New York, 1958.
82. Hansen, R. S., and Craig, P. *J. Phys. Chem.* **58**, 211 (1954).
83. Tamaki, K. *Kolloid-Z.* **170**, 113 (1960).
84. Tamamushi, B., and Tamaki, K. *Trans. Faraday Soc.* **55**, 1013, (1959).
85. Cuming, B. D., and Schulman, J. H. *Australian J. Chem.* **12**, 413 (1959).
86. Corrin, M. L., Lind, E. L., Roginsky, A., and Harkins, W. D. *J. Colloid Sci.* **4**, 485 (1949).
87. Aikin, R. A. *J. Soc. Dyers Colourists* **60**, 60 (1944).
88. Vold, R. D., and Phansalkar, A. K. *Rec. trav. chim.* **74**, 41 (1955); Sivarama Krishnan, N. H. *J. Phys. Chem.* **62**, 984 (1958).
89. Evans, H. C. *J. Colloid Sci.* **13**, 537 (1958).
90. Rose, G. R. F., Weatherburn, A. S., and Bayley, C. H. *Textile Research J.* **22**, 797 (1951).
91. Freundlich, H. *Z. physik. Chem. (Leipzig)* **57**, 385 (1907).
92. Kautsky, H., and Blinoff, *Z. physik. Chem. (Leipzig)* **139**, 497 (1928).
93. Nekrassow, B. *Z. physik. Chem. (Leipzig)* **136**, 379 (1928); Dubinin, M. M. *ibid.* **140**, 81 (1929).
94. Tsuruizumi, A., and Sano, S. Report at Colloid Chemistry Symposium of the Chemical Society of Japan, Sendai, 1958. (In Japanese.)
95. Tamamushi, B., and Tamaki, K. *Trans. Faraday Soc.* **55**, 1007 (1959).
96. Stanley, J. S. *J. Phys. Chem.* **58**, 533 (1954).
97. Hutchinson, E. *Trans. Faraday Soc.* **43**, 439 (1947).
98. Tamaki, K. *J. Chem. Soc. Japan, (Pure Chem. Sect.)* **78**, 1151 (1957). (In Japanese.)
99. Schulman, J. H., and Smith, T. D. *Kolloid-Z.* **126**, 20 (1952).
100. Cummings, T., Garven, H. C., Giles, C. H., Rahman, S. M. K., Sneddon, J. G., and Stewarts, C. E. *J. Chem. Soc.* p. 535 (1959).
101. Giles, C. H. Private communication.
102. Hansen, R. S., Fu. Y., and Bartell, F. E. *J. Phys. & Colloid Chem.* **53**, 769 (1949).
103. White, H. J., Gotshal, Y., Rebenfeld, L., and Sexsmith, F. H. *J. Colloid Sci.* **14**, 598, 619, 630 (1959).
104. Matsuno, K. *J. Coll. Sci. Imp. Univ. Tokyo* **41**, Art. 11 (1921).
105. Schulze, H. *J. prakt. Chem.* [2] **25**, 431 (1882); **27**, 320 (1883); Hardy, W. B. *Proc. Roy. Soc.* **66**, 110 (1900).
106. Freundlich, H., and Birstein, V. *Kolloidchem. Beih.* **22**, 95 (1926); Freundlich, H., and Slottman, G. N. *Z. physik. Chem. (Leipzig)* **129**, 305 (1927).

107. Traube, I. *Liebigs Ann.* **265**, 27 (1891).

108. Lottermoser, A., and Steudel, R. *Kolloid-Z.* **82**, 319 (1938); **83**, 37 (1938).

109. Tamamushi, B. *In* "Colloid Symposium Monograph" (J. Samejima, ed.), Vol. I, p. 63, Tokyo, 1948. (In Japanese); *Kolloid-Z.* **150**, 44 (1957).

110. Meguro, K., and Kondo, T. *J. Chem. Soc. Japan* **76**, 642 (1955); **77**, 77 (1956). (In Japanese.)

111. Takemura, T. Report, Faculty of Liberal Arts, Shinshu University, Japan (November, 1957).

112. Hazel, J. F., and Strange, H. O. *J. Colloid Sci.* **12**, 529 (1957); *J. Phys. Chem.* **61**, 1281 (1957).

113. Matijevic, E., and Ottewill, R. H. *J. Colloid Sci.* **13**, 242 (1958).

114. Horne, R. W., Matijevic, E., Ottewill, R. H., and Weymouth, J. W. *Kolloid-Z.* **161**, 50 (1958).

115. Tamamushi, B., and Tamaki, K. *Kolloid-Z.* **163**, 122 (1959).

116. Ottewill, R. H., Rastogi, M. C., and Watanabe, A. *Trans. Faraday Soc.* **56**, 854, 866, 880 (1960).

117. Freundlich, H. "Kapillarchemie" Vol. II, p. 135. Akademische Verlagsges., Leipzig, 1932; Kruyt, H. R. "Colloid Science" Vol. I, p. 314. Van Nostrand, Princeton, New Jersey, 1952.

118. Tamaki, K. *Kolloid-Z.* **170**, 113 (1690).

119. Burton, E. F., and Bishop, E. *J. Phys. Chem.* **24**, 701 (1920).

120. Freundlich, H. "Kapillarchemie" Vol. II, Akademische Verlagsges., Leipzig, 1932; Verwey, E. J. W., and Overbeek, J. Th. G. "Theory of the Stability of Lyophobic Colloids," Elsevier, Amsterdam, 1948.

121. Ottewill, R. H., and Watanabe, A. *Kolloid-Z.* **170**, 38, 132 (1960).

122. Kuhn, R. and Bielig, H. J. *Ber. deut. chem. Ges.* **73**, 1080 (1940); **74**, 941 (1941); **75**, 1942 (1942).

123. Putnum, F. W., and Neurath, H. *J. Am. Chem. Soc.* **66**, 692 (1944).

124. Putnum, F. W. *Advances in Protein Chem.* **4**, 79 (1948).

125. Pankhurst, K. G. A., and Smith, R. C. M. *Trans. Faraday Soc.* **40**, 565 (1944); **41**, 630 (1945); **43**, 506 (1947); **43**, 511 (1947).

126. Pankhurst, K. G. A. "Surface Chemistry," p. 109, Butterworths, London, 1949.

127. Elkes, J., and Fineau, J. B. "Surface Chemistry" (Special Supplement to *Research*), p. 281. Butterworths, London, 1949.

128. Aoki, K., Hori, J., Sakurai, K., and Suzuki, Y. *Bull. Chem. Soc. Japan* **29**, 104 (1956); **29**, 369 (1956); **29**, 758 (1956); **30**, 53 (1957).

129. Tamamushi, B., and Tamaki, K. *Bull. Chem. Soc. Japan* **28**, 555 (1955); **29**, 731 (1956).

130. Sato, K. Reports at the Colloid Chemistry Symposium of the Chemical Society of Japan, Tokyo (1946), Kanazawa (1957). (In Japanese.)

131. Urbain, W. M., and Jensen, L. B. *J. Phys. Chem.* **40**, 821 (1936).

132. Vold, R. D. and Greiner, L. *J. Phys. Colloid Chem.* **53**, 67 (1949); Vold, R. D., and Konecny, C. C. *ibid.* **53**, 1262 (1949).

133. Doscher, T. M. *J. Colloid Sci.* **5**, 100 (1950).

134. Ray, L. N., and Hutchison, A. W. *J. Phys. Colloid Chem.* **55**, 1334 (1951).

135. Meguro, K. *J. Eng. Chem.* **58**, 905 (1955). (In Japanese.)

136. Tamaki, K. *J. Japan Oil Chemists' Soc.* **9**, 426 (1960). (In Japanese.)

CHAPTER FOUR

MONOMOLECULAR LAYERS

TOSHIZO ISEMURA

I. Introduction

Amphipathic compounds which have a lipophilic, nonpolar group at one end and a hydrophilic, polar, or ionizable group at the other end, such as the higher fatty acids or alcohols, can be readily adsorbed on the surface of their solutions. As Traube indicated, the lowering of surface tension by substances in a homologous series of some fatty compounds increase as a function of the length of the hydrocarbon chain. Gibbs first derived thermodynamically the quantitative relation between the adsorption and the lowering of surface tension of a solution as early as 1878. The surface of a solution of a surface active solute will be covered completely by solute molecules when the concentration of the solution reaches a certain limit, which is lower the greater the hydrophobicity of amphipathic substances. If the hydrocarbon chain is sufficiently long, the surface of an aqueous phase would be completely covered with the adsorbed layer of solute, of which the concentration in solution is practically null. This is the case encountered with lauric acid.

It was found by Pockels (1) and Rayleigh (2) that a lowering of surface tension of water was caused by putting a minute amount of oil on the water surface. They studied the surface tension of oil films on water as a function of surface concentration. Langmuir (3) first introduced the concept of surface pressure, which is based on the spreading of insoluble substances such as oil along the water surface. The surface pressure corresponds to the difference of surface tension between a clean and an oil-covered surface of water. Langmuir devised a surface balance which can measure this two-dimensional spreading pressure directly. By studying chemically definite substances instead of rather indefinite oil, he was able to analyze his results in the light of the chemical structure of the molecule. It can be said that his success in this field of science is the basis of the present-day development of the surface chemistry of monolayers.

Since Langmuir's pioneer work, Adam, Rideal, Marcelin, Harkins, and many other investigators have carried out a great number of studies concerning monolayer behavior, especially with long chain fatty acids, alcohols, esters, and amines.

The present status of knowledge on films at oil-water interfaces is insufficient compared with the detailed knowledge of films at the air-water interface, because substances such as fatty acids and alcohols, which had been studied extensively at the air-water interface, can hardly be spread as a monolayer at the oil-water interface, owing to their solubility in either phase. On the other hand, some ionic surface active agents, such as sodium octadecyl sulfate and some polymers, have balanced affinities to both phases, and relatively stable interfacial films can be obtained.

The present chapter attempts to survey and to summarize not only certain aspects of the behavior of synthetic surface active materials at the air-water interface as well as at the oil-water interface, but also those of polymers, especially synthetic polymers which have recently been developed. A knowledge of surface films contributes to an understanding of the role played by surface active materials at gas-liquid or liquid-liquid interfaces in relation to the formation and destruction of foam, emulsion, and other disperse systems. Therefore, it is expected that work along these lines will have useful suggestions to offer with respect to the application of surface active agents.

II. General Aspects of Monolayers

Many surface active substances spread at the air-water or oil-water interfaces show on compression a surface pressure-area-temperature (Π–A–T) diagram which is analogous to the pressure-volume-temperature (P–V–T) diagram of real gases. In general, if the area occupied by a molecule in the monolayer is very large, the molecule behaves just like

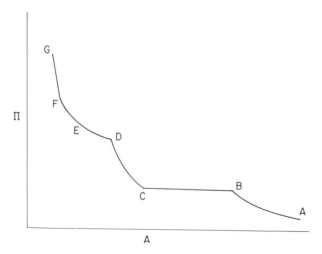

Fig. 4.1. Typical surface pressure vs. area relationship.

a gaseous molecule. At sufficiently large areas (10,000 Å^2/molecule), a relation similar to the ideal gas law

$$\Pi A = kT \tag{4.1}$$

is obeyed, where Π is the surface pressure; A, the area occupied per molecule; k, the Boltzmann constant, and T, the absolute temperature. Then the film is compressed successively, and the surface density of film-forming molecules is increased, the monolayer begins to assume the nature of a real gas.

As a result of compression, the Π A curve breaks at certain points, where the surface film suffers phase changes. These phase changes of monolayers are related to the discontinuity of the first, second, or third derivatives of free energy with respect to surface pressure. These phase changes are called transformations of the first, second, or third order, respectively, according to Ehrenfest(4).

Substances spread at the interface do not always show this typical surface pressure-area relation. Some substances, particularly polymers, give monotonic curves of the type encountered above the critical temperature, as shown by curve I in Fig. 4.2; still other curves fail to show

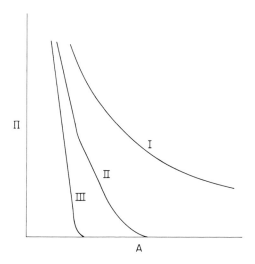

Fig. 4.2. Various types of surface pressure vs. area curves.

any appreciable low pressure region unless a specially made, high sensitivity surface balance is used; they rise rather steeply from the beginning, as shown in curves II and III. Certain types of curves are affected by various conditions, such as temperature, substrate, chain length of the hydrocarbon tail, and nature of the polar or ionic group. In Fig. 4.3,

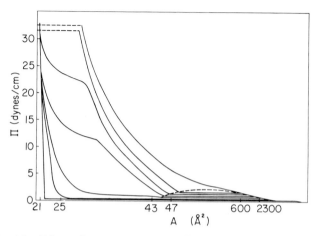

Fig. 4.3. Effect of temperature on surface pressure vs. area curve.

the effect of temperature in determining the type of surface pressure vs. area curve is shown (5).

The type of monolayer produced by ionic surface active agents is markedly affected by the presence of salt in the substrate, i.e., by the state of ionization. The low pressure limb of the gaseous film gives a

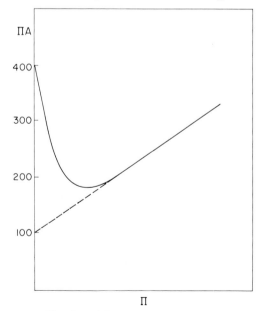

Fig. 4.4. Diagram of ΠA vs. Π.

straight line in the πA vs. π diagram, as shown in Fig. 4.4; $(\pi A)_0$, which can be obtained by extrapolating the πA vs. π diagram to $\pi = 0$, is a measure of the molecular weight of the film-forming substances. Although sodium dodecyl sulfate and cetyl sulfate cannot be spread as monolayers on a neutral subphase without salt, even sodium dodecyl sulfate can be spread on a neutral aqueous subphase containing salt. A πA vs. π diagram results, which is linear at pressures of about two dynes or larger; $(\pi A)_0$ obtained from this straight line corresponds to a low polymeric molecular weight. At lower pressures, however, there is a steep upward curvature rising to an intercept corresponding to the true monomeric molecular weight.

It seems that monolayers of polymers do not form the so-called solid film which is encountered with monolayers of stearic acid on a substrate containing calcium ion. Relatively simple single chain compounds show a distinct collapse pressure of the film beyond which the surface pressure does not rise and beyond which collapse of the monolayer occurs. On the other hand, polymer monolayers do not give a distinct collapse point because the polar and nonpolar groups of the film substance are removed gradually by compression from the interface if the surface pressure exceeds a value which gives the minimum compressibility of the film, so that parts of the polymer molecule stand out of or sink into substrate.

Surface potential, the difference of contact potentials between the interfaces with or without film at the interface, and surface viscosity, the change in viscosity of the surface layer produced by the insoluble layer at the interface, reflect the phase changes in the monolayer. Surface potential-area and surface viscosity-area relations are also very useful in elucidating the nature of the monolayer.

In the spread monolayer of relatively small molecules, such as stearic acid or docosyl sulfate, all the molecules orient statistically in the same way in the monolayer. However, large molecules, such as proteins or other polymers, in definite conformation do not have all their polar groups in one plane; accordingly, there occurs the straying of polar groups above the surface when the molecule is spread in a round folded form. In this case, the surface moment per residue calculated from the observed surface potential is small, owing to the intramolecular cancellation of dipole moment in the monolayer. The difference in behavior of the monolayers between polymers and other rather small molecules which can be easily oriented lies in this point.

III. Experimental Techniques

1. Surface Pressure

Insoluble films at interfaces are generally studied by three different methods, namely, by the measurement of surface pressure, surface potential, and surface viscosity. Among these, the measurement of surface pressure has been carried out for many years by a number of investigators. Langmuir first measured the surface pressure of an insoluble monolayer by directly weighing with a balance the force exerted by the film-forming substance on a floating barrier. Guastalla (6) devised a method which can measure surface pressures as low as 0.001 dyne/cm. The surface balance consists of a pendulum, the deviation of which, caused by surface pressure change, is reflected by an optical lever. The film-forming substance is usually spread from petroleum ether solution or some other volatile water-insoluble solvent, using a micrometer syringe with which the applied volume, and hence the number of molecules put on the surface, are readily known. The succesive injection method using a micrometer syringe is also applied for changing the concentration of the film-forming substance at the interface. The latter procedure for changing the surface concentration is used especially at the oil-water interface rather than the procedure using constraining barriers. However, both methods have some disadvantages. Thus, the constraining barrier method has the possibility of leaks, particularly at the oil-water interface where manipulation is difficult. On the other hand, there does seem to be reason for doubting whether complete spreading always occurs at higher film concentrations when the successive injection method is used.

Surface pressure can also be measured by the Wilhelmy method for measuring surface tension. This method can be applied also to the measurement of interfacial pressure at the oil-water interface (7). Using a torsion balance, such as is used in DuNouy's tensiometer, instead of a chemical balance, a very simple and convenient surface balance was constructed by Sasaki (8). It seems experimentally difficult to obtain really high sensitivity with this type of surface balance. Nevertheless, Inokuchi (9) described a surface balance of the hanging-plate type which has a double torque system. Inokuchi insists that it can measure surface pressures as low as 0.001 dyne/cm. However, it is very doubtful that measurement of such a low pressure by the hanging-plate method is significant because the temperature of the trough can hardly be maintained sufficiently constant to avoid such a small surface tension change. On the other hand, it seems to be possible theoretically to measure extremely low surface pressures by a surface balance of the float type because the surface pressure is measured in this case as a difference of surface tensions between film-free and film-covered surfaces. Allan and Alexander (10) described a very sensitive surface balance of the float type, although considerable difficulties were experienced with the Wilhelmy plate balance in attaining a stable zero position for the vertical glass slide, owing to changes in contact angle, evaporation, and drainage effects. The thickness of the threads which are sealed to the float and the edge of the trough to confine the monolayer affect the sensitivity of the balance. Terylene monofilament 0.01 mm in diameter was reported to satisfactory.

Another type of surface balance was described by Puddington (11), who used a two-dimensional analog of the aneroid barometer. Dervichian first described an apparatus which automatically records surface pressure (12). Figure 4.5 is the diagram of the barrier drive and kynograph

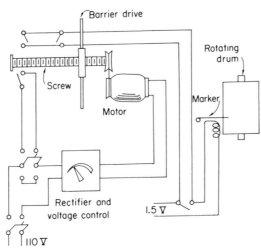

Fig. 4.5. Automatic driving unit for barrier (by Brady).

circuit for an automatic recording surface balance built by Brady (13). The compression was automatically driven by arms riding on a helical screw driven by an adjustable speed dc shunt motor. These arms also operated switches near the start and end of the compression that made reference marks on the kynograph sheet which ran during the experiment.

2. Surface Potential

Surface potential is measured by two different procedures. One method uses the ionization air electrode, and the other uses a vibrating air electrode, originated by Zisman and Yamins (14). Owing to the progress of electronics, the latter method is now widely practiced. The former was first used by Schulman and Rideal (15) who determined surface potential by measuring the electromotive force of a cell which is crossed by an air-water interface covered with a spread monolayer. As an air electrode, a metal rod, e.g. zinc, on which a radioactive substance such as polonium is deposited, is usually used. The polonium ionizes the air so as to conduct the current.

The ionizing air electrode method cannot be applied to the oil-water interface. On the other hand, the vibrating air electrode method is suitable for measurements at air-water interfaces as well as at oil-water interfaces.

3. Surface Viscosity

Surface viscosity is determined by various methods, one of which is based on the measurement of the rate of flow of the film through a narrow slit or canal, and the other on the damping of a rotatory oscillation of a disc, ring, or vane, attached to a vertical torsion wire and resting on the surface. The former method is suitable for films of low viscosity, as encountered in the gaseous and expanded states, and the latter for films in the condensed state, where the viscosity may rise to quite high values. A two-dimensional modification of the Couette instrument was also used to measure the surface viscosity (16). Recently, Davies and his collaborator (17) have proposed a new surface viscometer

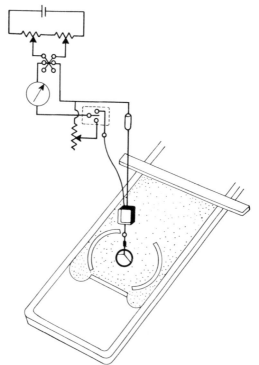

Fig. 4.6. Schematic illustration of surface rheometer (by Inokuchi).

which can apply to both air-water and oil-water interfaces. It consists of two circular rings of stainless steel wire (0.064 mm in diameter) held concentrically in the interface. These rings are both held stationary in the interface, while the liquids are rotated in a Pyrex dish placed on a turntable. The retardation of talc particles sprinkled on the interface in the canal between rings is a measure of the viscosity.

As will be seen later, the flow properties of polymer monolayers are very specific, depending on the nature of the polymers. Studies along these lines were conducted by Tachibana and Inokuchi (18), who measured the viscoelasticity of surface films of polymers by applying Schwedoff and Hatschek's method (19), converted from the bulk phase to the surface. Later, Inokuchi (20) constructed an electromagnetically driven surface rheometer such as is illustrated in Fig. 4.6.

IV. Monolayer Studies of Surface Active Agents

Classic studies on monolayers were chiefly carried out with long chain fatty acids, alcohols, and esters. Surface active agents, especially those of practical interest, are generally soluble to some extent in water. The force-area diagram for films of soluble surface active agents on water cannot be studied by the ordinary film balance techniques because of the tendency of the film to leave the surface and dissolve into the subphase when the film is compressed. Sodium octadecyl sulfate, a surface active agent which has a relatively long hydrocarbon chain, is fairly soluble in pure water. Hence, monolayer experiments are precluded unless some salt is added to the aqueous subphase.

Accordingly, instead of the spread monolayer, the adsorbed layer is often studied, using aqueous solutions of surface active agents. However, we can apply the monolayer technique to study surface active agents by modifying the experimental conditions, e.g., by changing the concentration of salt in the aqueous subphase, the rate of film compression, or the chain length of hydrocarbon chain of the surface active agent. As a matter of fact, to eliminate this difficulty, the higher, insoluble homologs of the compound of interest is generally used, or else salt is added to the substrate to reduce the solubility of the film-forming substance. In this section, the results of the studies using the monolayer technique as well as those obtained by measurements on adsorbed layers will be described.

While octadecyl sulfate is fairly soluble in pure water, as mentioned above, it spreads as a monolayer on the top of solutions which contain sodium chloride in amounts greater than only 10^{-3} M. As octadecyl sulfuric acid is more insoluble than its sodium salt, it forms a stable monolayer on a solution of hydrochloric acid of concentration greater than 10^{-2} M. Some typical force vs. area curves for sodium octadecyl sulfate are illustrated in Fig. 4.7.

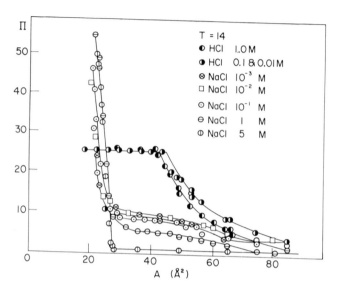

Fig. 4.7. Force vs. area curves for octadecyl sulfate monolayers.

The monolayer is liquid or gaseous under all the conditions shown, except possibly on 5 M NaCl, when it is either a fragile solid or a viscous liquid. On 5 M NaCl the surface active agent is suppressed in its dissociation and tends to form micelles in the film. Accordingly, the film forms islands at areas above ca. 20 Å² per long chain. This fact is suggested by the fluctuation of surface potential in this region. On hydrochloric acid solutions, the monolayer is markedly expanded, as shown in Fig. 4.7. Pethica and Few (21) suggested that the sulfate monolayer is stabilized in the expanded state on acid solution by hydrogen bonding. It collapses at 45 Å² per long chain. Phillips and Rideal also spread sodium octadecyl and docosyl sulfate at both air-water and oil-water interfaces from a 50% petroleum ether + 49% isopropyl alcohol + 1% water solution and found that a stable, reproducible film formed on a number of solutions (22). It would appear that the spreading difficulties encountered earlier by Stenhagen (23) with docosyl sulfate at the air-water interface were due to the poor spreading solvent used, namely, ethyl alcohol.

On the other hand, Brady (13) employing an apparatus mentioned above (Section III, 1), showed that the rapid compression of a film, with sufficiently high concentration of salt permits the measurement of surface pressure for fairly soluble detergents, since they are nearly in-soluble under rapid compression. Most films of alkyl sulfonates and sulfates, with the exception of the C_{16} and C_{18} alkyl sulfates are of the expanded type, as shown in Fig. 4.8. Adam (*24*) has reported that even

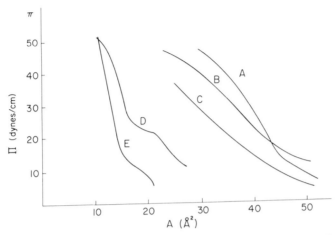

Fig. 4.8.   Force vs. area curves for some sulfates and sulfonates. (*A*) Aerosol OT (sodium dioctyl sulfosuccinate); (*B*) C_{12} sodium sulfonate; (*C*) C_{14} sodium sulfo-nate; (*D*) C_{16} sodium sulfonate; (*E*) C_{18} sodium sulfonate.

the 20- or 22-carbon homologs of straight chain pyridinium bromide or trimethylammonium iodide, which are insoluble enough to be examined by the monolayer technique, give expanded films.

According to Brady, if the salt concentration in the substrate is reduced, the force vs. area curves move to the right, whereas the salt concentration is decreased to the point where the film becomes appreciably soluble at high pressures; the curve actually moves to the left at high pressures. In relatively short aging periods (1–10 min), no effect on the force vs. area curve was observed. However, aging for two hours caused a change in character of the force vs. area curves of C_{16} and C_{18} sulfates. The film is more expanded and the plateau in the force vs. area curves has disappeared, as shown in Fig. 4.9. Brady concluded that the plateau was not caused by a phase change but only by imperfect orientation, and probably results from a sliding of one layer of molecules over another.

When calcium chloride was substituted for sodium chloride added to the substrate to reduce the solubility of surface active agents, such a substitution had only a minor influence on the force vs. area curves for the lower alkyl sulfates and Aerosol OT, but the curves for higher

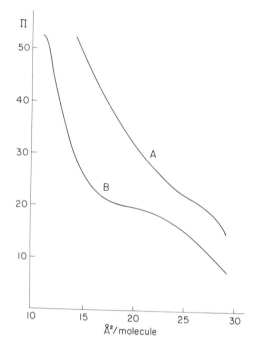

Fig 4.9. Effect of aging the film. Sodium cetyl sulfate: (*A*) surface aged 2 hours; (*B*) surface aged 1–10 min. Substrate, 16.6% NaCl.

alkyl sulfates changed and were quite similar to those obtained for the aged films on sodium chloride.

Although the influence of substrate electrolyte on the properties of monolayers is very complex, monolayers of uncharged molecules usually exist at air-water interfaces as condensed or liquid expanded films. The effect of ions in the substrate on surface energy is obscured because of the powerful cohesional energy between neighboring hydrocarbon chains. At the oil-water interface the effect of cohesion on the surface pressure is considerably reduced. However, it is very difficult to study the effect of ions on monolayers at the oil-water interface, as few uncharged molecules can be efficiently spread owing to their lipoid solubility. Davies found (*25*) that an equimolar mixture of cationic and anionic surface active agents, such as octadecyltrimethylammonium chloride and sodium docosyl sulfate, can be spread without dissolution on distilled water as well as at an oil-water interface. It was observed by Phillips and Rideal (*22*) that on dilute (10^{-2} *M*) substrates the Π vs. *A* relationship is constant and independent of the nature and concentration of the substrate. The film obeyed the simple equation for films with no interaction, namely,

$\Pi(A - A_0) = kT$, where A_0 is the cross-sectional area per hydrocarbon chain.

Concerning adsorbed layers of ionic surface active agents, it might be necessary to consider multicomponent adsorption of surfactant ion, counter ion, hydrogen ions, and hydroxyl ions. The question as to whether the Gibbs equation

$$\Gamma = -\frac{1}{RT}\frac{d\gamma}{d\ln c} \quad \text{or} \quad \Gamma = -\frac{1}{2RT}\frac{d\gamma}{d\ln c}$$

applies to the surface of detergent solutions is of some interest. A factor of 2 in the Gibbs equation, although predicted (26) on the assumption that both anion and cation contribute to the surface tension, has never been found experimentally. Davies also confirms that the 1 kT equation can be applied to the ionized film of hexadecyltrimethylammonium bromide at the oil-water interface (26).

Hutchinson (27) studied mixed monolayers of dodecyl sulfate and octyl alcohol adsorbed at the air-water interface. For the system water, octyl alcohol, and sodium dodecyl sulfate, the following relations were derived according to the Gibbs theorem, assuming the solutions to be ideal, and defining the position of the Gibbs surface in such a way that $\Gamma_1 = 0$ is a suitable convention,

$$\Gamma_2 = -\frac{N_2}{RT}\frac{\partial\gamma}{\partial N_2}$$

$$\Gamma_3 = -\frac{N_3}{2RT}\frac{\partial\gamma}{\partial N_3}$$

where N is the molar fraction; Γ, the surface excess; and γ, the surface tension of the solution. Subscripts 1, 2, and 3 refer to water, octyl alcohol, and sodium dodecyl sulfate, respectively; Γ_2 and Γ_3 can be calculated; and the slope of the γ vs. N curves can be obtained experimentally. As the area per molecule is given by $A = 1/N_0(\Gamma_2 + \Gamma_3)$, where N_0 is the Avogadro constant, force vs. area curves can be obtained. In Fig. 4.10 are given the force vs. area curves for the adsorbed mixed film containing both components in 1 : 1 proportion.

The force vs. area curve for sodium dodecyl sulfate shows that this compound forms a gaseous film with a roughly constant value for the product $(\Pi \cdot A) \sim 800$–900. For the film adsorbed from approximately equimolar solutions, it is seen that the film has properties intermediate between the condensed film of the alcohol and gaseous film of sodium dodecyl sulfate. Hutchinson found that even when the bulk concentration of the alcohol is only one-fifth that of the sodium dodecyl sulfate, there are rather more molecules of alcohol in the film. Reasons are adduced to explain "type III" surface tension curves for this type of

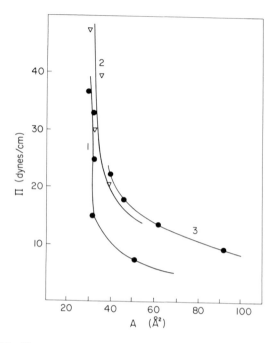

Fig. 4.10.   Force vs. area curves for a mixed film and its components.

surface active agent.

Surface potentials of surface active agents were first studied by Schulman and Hughes (28), and later by Cassie and Palmer (29), Davies (30), and other investigators. Davies studied hexadecyl-, octadecyl-, and ceryltrimethylammonium halide monolayers in regard to the variation of surface potential ($\varDelta V$) with both electrolyte concentration and film area. In Figs. 4.11 and 4.12 are shown the $\varDelta V$ vs. A curves for octadecyl sulfate spread at the air-water and at the oil-water interface as measured by Phillips and Rideal (22).

Schulman and Hughes suggested that in the case of a charged film the relationship between the surface potential and the film area would be expressed by the equation

$$\varDelta V = \frac{4\pi\mu_D}{A} + \psi \tag{4.2}$$

where μ_D represents the vertical component of the dipole moment and ψ the potential drop between the surface and bulk phase due to the separation of the film and counter ions. Davies substituted the theoretical Gouy potential ψ_0 for ψ in the above equation and derived

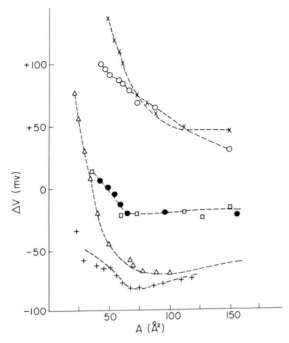

Fig. 4.11.   Relationship between ΔV and A for sodium octadecyl sulfate at the air-water interface at 20°C.   Spread on $1M$ HCl [radioactive electrode (re) technique] ($\bigcirc$); $1\,M$ NaCl (re technique) ($\times$); $10^{-1}M$ HCl (re technique) ($\square$); $10^{-1}M$ HCl (vibrating plate condenser technique); ($\bullet$); $10^{-2}M$ HCl (vp technique) ($+$); $10^{-2}M$ NaCl (vp technique) ($\triangle$).

$$\Delta V = \frac{4\pi\mu_D}{A} + \frac{2kT}{e}\,\sinh^{-1}\frac{134}{A\sqrt{c}} \qquad (4.3)$$

for a subphase at 20°C containing a 1 : 1 electrolyte, where e is the electronic charge, and c the concentration of aqueous phase.

This relationship was confirmed by Davies from studies on hexadecyl, octadecyl, and ceryltrimethylammonium halide monolayers at the air-water and oil-water interfaces. Phillips and Heydon showed it can be applied to the film of dodecyltrimethylammonium bromide at the oil-water interface.

As shown in Fig. 4.12, at the oil-water interface the ΔV vs. A relationships for the octadecyl sulfate film seem fairly normal in that the surface potential is hardly influenced by the nature of the substrate and $(\partial \Delta V/\partial \log c)_A$ is reasonably close to the theoretical value of 57.5 mv, (kT/e), within the range 10^{-2} to 10^{-1} M. However, the surface potential

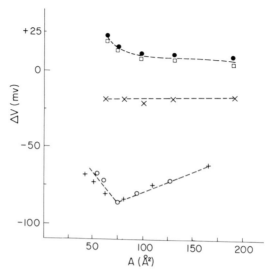

Fig. 4.12. Relationship between ΔV and A for sodium octadecyl sulfate at an oil-water interface at 20°C. Spread on $1\,M$ HCl ($\bullet$); $1\,M$ NaCl; ($\square$); $10^{-1}M$ HCl; ($\times$); $10^{-2}M$ HCl ($\bigcirc$); $10^{-2}M$ NaCl ($+$).

on a $1\,M$ substrate is considerably less positive than would have been expected from the values on the more dilute solutions. Pethica and Few (21) gave 5-10 mv as the surface potential of an octadecyl sulfate monolayer on $1\,M$ NaCl at an area of 60 Å² per molecule. There is a considerable discrepancy between their results and those reported by Phillips and Rideal for the same system. According to Cockbain, the film of sodium dodecyl sulfate, which is fairly soluble, gives surface potentials approximately 40-100 mv more negative than its C_{18} insoluble analog under corresponding conditions.

The surface moments of various alkyl sulfates, μ_D, calculated from Eq. 4.3 are plotted as a function of the film area, as shown in Fig. 4.13. The differences in surface moment of these alkyl sulfates may be explained in terms of the orientation of the polar head at the interface. Different configurations of the sulfate ion relative to the alkyl chain are possible if there is restricted rotation about the C-O bond linking the alkyl and sulfate groups. The same is not true for the symmetrical quarternary ammonium ion, however, and this may explain the constancy in surface potential of films of this type of surface active agent.

For the study of the surface viscosity of detergent solutions, the slit and canal viscometer developed for the study of insoluble monolayers cannot readily be applied. Brown et al. (31) devised a surface viscometer

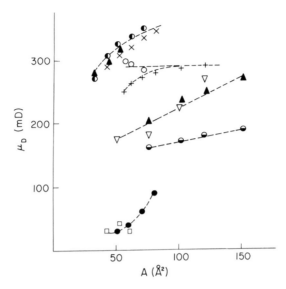

Fig. 4.13. Relationship between μ_D and A for sulfate films at 20°C. Sodium dodecyl sulfate: in aqueous solutions at the oil-water (O/W) interface (●); on 1.0 M NaCl or HCl at O/W (□). Sodium octadecyl sulfate: on 0.1 M NaCl or HCl at O/W (◕); on 0.01 M NaCl or HCl at O/W (▼); 0.01 M NaCl or HCl at O/W (▽); on 1.0 M NaCl at the airwater (A/W) interface (○); on 1.0 M HCl at A/W (+). Sodium docosyl sulfate: on 1.0 M HCl at A/W; (×); on 0.01 M HCl at A/W (◑) on 0.003 M HCl at the A/W (△).

based on the Coutte-type rotational viscometer and adapted for two-dimensional research. Both Newtonian and plastic behavior of the film can be examined by this instrument.

The surface viscosity of solutions of sodium dodecyl sulfate is reported to be 2×10^{-3} surface poises for the solution containing 0.1 gm/ 100 ml, and 4×10^{-3} surface poises for a 0.5 gm/100 ml solution. However, if the sodium dodecyl sulfate is extremely pure, the surface viscosity of the solutions is much less than the above-mentioned values, namely, of the order of magnitude of 1.5×10^{-5} surface poise (32). The high surface viscosity of the sodium dodecyl sulfate solution is attributed to contamination by a trace of dodecyl alcohol. The surface film of this detergent gives no surface yield value. Small amounts of dodecyl alcohol have a striking effect in increasing the surface viscosity of sodium dodecyl sulfate, as shown in Table 4.1. It is very interesting that a greater ratio of dodecyl alcohol is required to produce appreciable viscosity when the sodium dodecyl sulfate concentration is above that for micelle formation than when this concentration is below the CMC.

TABLE 4.1

SURFACE VISCOSITY AND SURFACE YIELD VALUES FOR SOLUTIONS OF PURE
SODIUM DODECYL SULFATE CONTAINING ADDED DODECYL
ALCOHOL AND FOR DODECYL ALCOHOL ALONE

Concentration (gm/100 ml)		Surface viscosity $\times 10^3$ (surface poises)	Surface yield value $\times 10^3$ (dynes/cm)
Sodium dodecyl sulfate	Dodecyl alcohol		
0.1		2	0
0.1	0.001	2	0
0.1	0.003	2	0
0.1	0.005	32	54
0.1	0.008	32	62
0.5		4	0
0.5	0.005	3	0
0.5	0.015	3	0
0.5	0.025	24	29
0.5	0.040	31	82
	(Standard)	41	82

This may be caused by the reduction of the activity of dodecyl alcohol by solubilization in the micelles of sodium dodecyl sulfate. Brady and Brown (33) calculated the bulk viscosity corresponding to the monolayer data for the dodecyl alcohol, and compared it with an experimentally determined bulk viscosity of 0.2 poise at 25°C. The value so computed corresponds to a plastic material with a "plastic viscosity" of 2.5×10^5 poises. The notable difference may be caused by coherence in the monolayer produced by the surface orientation of the molecules.

As mentioned above, sodium dodecyl sulfate yields an expanded film, in which coherence should be very poorly developed. However, if a small amount of dodecyl alchohol is present in the film, it acts as a condensing agent. The first small quantities increase the viscosity, but the Newtonian character is maintained, whereas additional quantities produce a plastic structure with true yield value, and still further amounts mainly increase the yield value.

Blakey and Lawrence (34) showed that the surface viscosity of hexadecyl alcohol monolayers increases with an increase in concentration of surface active agents such as tetradecyl-, hexadecyl-, and octadecyl-trimethylammonium bromide in the substrate up to a maximum in the neighborhood of the CMC and decreases rapidly beyond the CMC because of the solubilization of hexadecyl alcohol into the bulk of the substrate. In Fig. 4.14, the surface viscosity of a monolayer of hexadecyl alcohol

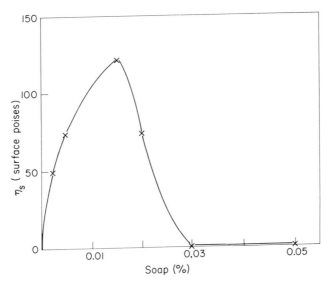

Fig. 4.14. Surface viscosity of hexadecyl alcohol monolayer on surfactant solutions of various concentrations.

at 25 $Å^2$ per molecule is plotted against concentration of hexadecyltrimethylammonium bromide. Surface viscosity increases up to the CMC and then decreases due to the solubilization of monolayer in bulk solution.

Davies and Mayers (17) have recently determined the interfacial viscosity of a monolayer of sodium dodecyl sulfate adsorbed from its 4×10^{-3} M solution in redistilled water at the interface with pure benzene. These viscosities are only slightly lower than those for films of the same substances at the air-water interface, as shown in Table 4.2. For a mixed adsorbed film of hexadecyl alcohol and sodium hexadecyl

TABLE 4.2

INTERFACIAL VISCOSITIES OF MONOLAYERS ADSORBED FROM SODIUM DODECYL SULFATE AT THE BENZENE-WATER INTERFACE

Temperature (°C)	Surface viscosity $\times 10^4$
18	1.7
20	1.5
22	1

sulfate, the interfacial viscosity is very high unless the temperature exceeds about 26°C.

V. Surface Activity of Protein

It is a well-known fact that proteins are often denatured on the surface of their solutions and are readily denatured by shaking or bubbling the solutions. This suggests that proteins are surface active and can be adsorbed at the interface between air and solution. It was Devaux who first showed that soluble proteins could be spread as monolayers on water surfaces in much the same way as Pockels had spread oil on water surfaces (35). Later, systematic work was carried out by the schools of Gorter and Rideal, who showed that by spreading from aqueous solutions very many soluble proteins formed stable monolayers at both air-water and oil-water interfaces.

The earlier detailed work was carried out on monolayers of gliadin (36). However, before about 1940, the technique of spreading protein monolayers was not well established. Accordingly, we cannot rely too much on results of monolayer studies of proteins reported before that time. Ställberg and Teorell showed that 60% n-propyl or isopropyl alcohol with sodium acetate added in a concentration of 0.5 moles/liter is a suitable solvent for a protein-spreading solution (37). This solvent does not cause denaturation of most proteins, and protein is rapidly spread by the aid of the surface active alcohol and subjected to surface denaturation before the protein is dissolved. Dervichian (38) is of the opinion that the quantity of alcohol added to the spreading solution is sufficient in amounts as low as 0.5% and that amyl alcohol, butyl acetate, and butyl propionate may be used as a substitute for propyl alcohol. The concentration of protein in these solvents should be less than 0.05%, otherwise insufficient spreading often results. Moreover, it is desirable that the surface concentration of protein put on the surface not exceed 0.5 mg/m^2 in order to ensure complete spreading and to give reproducible results.

Although there are many varieties of proteins, their force vs. area curves are all very similar. The limiting area is about 1 m^2/mg irrespective of the kind of protein. Globular proteins such as are used in surface chemical investigations consist of a single or few polypeptide chains containing no or few prosthetic groups, and the chains are folded in a proper manner so as to present the polar or ionic groups on the outside of the molecule and make it soluble in water. Proteins, as is well known, are made from about twenty kinds of amino acid residues. All the proteins have a residue weight of about 120 on the average. Even though proteins are by no means typical polymers, small residues which may be soluble as a single amino acid are generally insoluble in polypeptide chains as is the soluble monomer in other polymers. This may be the reason why proteins spread as monolayers with similar force vs. area curves, having similar limiting areas per residue. When the protein molecules are put on the surface, they are unfolded so as to present the polar or ionic groups to water and assume the β-configuration. Consequently, we cannot obtain much information concerning the structure of protein molecules by studying the force-area relationships.

From this point of view, studies by surface viscosity measurements indicate differences between proteins far better because surface viscosity is remarkably dependent on the kind of protein and also on the nature of the subphase. A typical force vs. area curve is shown in Fig. 4.15.

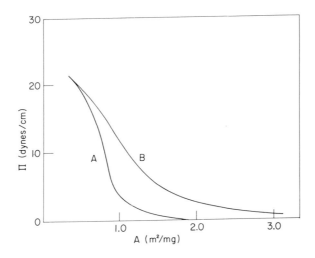

Fig. 4.15. Force vs. area curves of protein (serum albumin). (A) Air-water interface; (B) oil-water interface.

The limiting area per amino acid residue is about 15–20 Å^2. If the protein molecule assumes the β-keratin configuration in the monolayer, and if the side chains project alternately from the polypeptide backbone into air and into water, each side chain in air occupies 30–40 Å^2. At the collapse point of the film, it occupies an area of about 0.1 m^2/mg. Assuming the average residue weight to be 120, the area would be 10–12 Å^2 per residue. If the protein is spread in the β-keratin form as mentioned above, a residue on one side (in air or in water) occupies 20–22 Å^2. These limiting values are very similar to those for mesophase films and for condensed films of fatty acid.

As we have mentioned above, the limiting area per residue for protein monolayers is about 15–20 Å^2. The monolayer of a synthetic polypeptide such as poly-DL-norleucine, which has a residue weight of 113, resembles a protein monolayer in its force-area relation (*39*). The film should consist of the extended form of the polypeptide and has a limiting area of 15 Å². The correspondence of limiting area per residue supports the inference that the protein assumes a configuration of the β-keratin type, namely, the extended form at the interface.

If a protein is spread at an oil-water interface, the monolayer is considerably expanded (*40*). This expansion of the film is caused by the reduction of van der Waals interaction between nonpolar side chains, due to the intervention of hydrocarbon molecules. The polypeptide backbone remains at the interface owing to the hydrophilic character of the peptide bonds and the polar and ionic side chains.

Surface potential of protein monolayers is greatest on acid substrates, whereas it is the smallest on alkaline substrates. Since it is well known that the surface potential tends generally toward negative values when the carboxyl group ionizes, whereas the surface potential is hardly affected by the salt formation of amines, the change of surface potential of protein monolayers with pH change seems to be chiefly related to the dissociation of the carboxyl group (*41*).

The relationship of maximum surface potential (ΔV_{max}) at the collapse point of a monolayer of bovine serum albumin to the pH value of the substrate on which the monolayer is spread is shown in Fig. 4.16. In

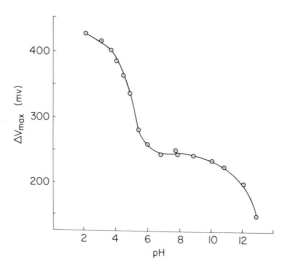

Fig. 4.16. Maximum surface potential and pH. Monolayer of bovine serum albumin.

both pH ranges 3.5–6.5 and 10–13, remarkable changes of surface potential were observed. The change observed in the pH range 3.5-6.5 should be attributed to the ionization of the carboxyl group and that in the pH range 10-13 to the neutralization of the cationic amine group. The general shape of the ΔV_{max} vs. pH curve resembles closely the titration curve of globular protein in bulk solution. Despite the resemblance to the titration curve as a whole, the curve shifts markedly to the high pH region as compared with the titration curve. The neutralization of the imidazole $=NH^+-$ group of histidine is not shown by changes in surface potential(42). Despite the similarities in their Π vs. A curves, different proteins are clearly differentiated by their mechanical properties and by the hysteresis phenomena which these films usually manifest.

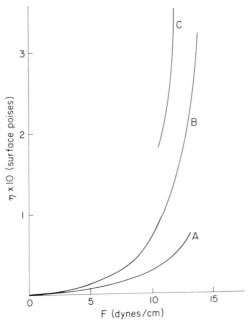

Fig. 4.17. Relationship between surface pressure and surface viscosity (gliadin film). (A) Spread at 0.7-2.8 dynes/cm; (B) spread at 5.5-8 dynes/cm; (C) spread at 11 dynes/cm.

Figure 4.17 shows the curves for surface viscosity vs. surface pressure for the wheat gliadin monolayer on $N/100$ HCl at 21°C. Joly (43) has indicated that the surface viscosity of the protein monolayer depends on the mode of spreading. The protein film which is spread on a sufficiently large free surface gives a film which Joly called an A-film, which is stable and of low surface viscosity. On the other hand, the film which is spread against some finite surface pressure is very viscous and shows aging phenomena. This film is called a B-film by Joly. When the protein film is spread completely, the surface viscosity is independent of velocity gradient below a definite surface pressure Π_n. If the monolayer is compressed further, the film will gel at another definite surface pressure, Π_g. Between Π_n and Π_g, the film flows as a non-Newtonian liquid. The Π_n and Π_g values of various proteins on 0.01 N HCl at 17°C are listed in Table 4.3. It is very interesting that proteins show surface viscosities

TABLE 4.3

VALUES OF Π_n AND Π_g OF VARIOUS PROTEINS ON N HCl AT 17°C

Protein	Π_n (dynes/cm)	Π_g (dynes/cm)
Horse pseudoglobulin	2	3
Beef hemoglobin	3	8
Ovalbumin	4	7
Beef serum albumin	4	10
Horse serum albumin	10	—
Gliadin	16	—

of the same order of magnitude, irrespective of the kind of protein, at the point where the flow begins to change from Newtonian to non-Newtonian.

Knowing the size and shape of protein molecules, we can estimate the surface viscosity of a protein monolayer. According to Joly (44), such calculation leads to an abnormally high value of surface viscosity. Accordingly, the flow unit must be not a whole molecule but a small segment of the molecule. He concluded that the unit occupies some 90 Å^2 and has a mass of about 900.

VI. Surface Activity of Synthetic Polymers

Most synthetic linear polymers consist of a chain in which nonpolar and polar parts repeat alternately, or of a long chain with a number of polar or nonpolar side chains. Such compounds are amphipathic and generally surface active. If a small portion of a solution of these substances is put on water, it spreads as a thin film. The surface chemical method for studying monolayers might prove to be very useful to obtain some information on the properties of polymers.

Before the end of War II, only a few studies had been carried out with high polymer films other than on protein films. Among these we can cite the work on the polymer of ω-hydroxydecanoic acid by Harkins et al. (45) and on Buna-N by Suzuki (46). Since the war, various kinds of polymers have been easily available. For this reason, surface films of polymers have attracted the attention of a number of investigators.

Polyvinyl acetate can be easily spread on water from its solution in benzene. The force-area relation is perfectly reproducible if the film is spread first on a sufficiently large area of water surface. The force vs. area curve of this polymer is of an expanded type, as shown in Fig. 4.18. On the other hand, polyvinyl stearate in which the acetate

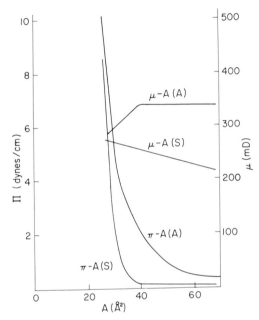

Fig. 4.18. Force vs. area curves and surface moment vs. area curves for polymer films. (A) Polyvinyl acetate; (S) polyvinyl stearate.

groups are replaced by stearate groups gives a film of the condensed type. The limiting area for polyvinyl stearate was found always to be 25 Å^2 per monomer unit, while that for polyvinyl acetate was 60 Å^2 per monomer unit. From these facts it is reasonable to suppose a linear polymer, such as polyvinyl acetate or stearate, should assume a monomolecular layer.

The condensation of the surface film of polyvinyl stearate may be caused by van der Waals interaction of massive side chains, since all other conditions excepting the stearate group are the same in comparison with polyvinyl acetate. If polyvinyl stearate is spread at the interface between petroleum ether and water, the van der Waals forces between long hydrocarbon chains of stearate groups are released by intervention of petroleum ether between the hydrocarbon chains. It is very interesting that the surface film of polyvinyl stearate expands at the oil-water interface and that its force vs. area curve overlaps the curve of polyvinyl acetate at the air-water interface. On the other hand, the force vs. area curve of polyvinyl acetate is independent of the nature of the interface, whether it is spread at the air-water or at the oil-water interface. This fact indicates the importance of the nature of the side chain for the expansion and condensation of the monolayer, as already stated in connection with films of proteins. Although polyvinyl acetate gives a film of expanded type, the film of its copolymer with vinyl stearate is considerably condensed even if it contains only 10% vinyl stearate. It is clear that the cohesion between nonpolar groups makes a film condensed, as mentioned above.

Polymethacrylic acid, polmethyl methacrylate, polyvinyl acetate, and polyvinyl stearate have a specific limiting area depending on the nature of the side chain lying at the interface, although the main chain of all these polymers is the same. They have a common limiting area (about 10 $Å^2$ per residue) in the case of no side chain lying at the interface. The disposition of the side chain, whether at the interface or not, is more important with copolymers than with homopolymers; that is, the copolymers of vinyl acetate and vinyl stearate which lay their side chains at the interface give irregular results and have a smaller limiting area than that of polyvinyl stearate itself, whereas the methacrylic acid–diethylaminoethyl vinyl ether copolymers which lay no side chain at the interface, give reproducible results and have the same limiting area as that of polymethacrylic acid under the condition of no effective charge. The latter area is also nearly equal to that of polyacrylonitrile at the oil-water interface (47).

As already stated, most proteins give similar Π vs. A curves, from which we cannot obtain much information concerning protein structure. However, it is very elegant to study protein films by comparing them with a monolayer of a synthetic polypeptide of known structure. Cumper and Alexander (48), Isemura, et al. (49), Davies (50), and others studied monolayers of synthetic polypeptides. Figure 4.19 shows a typical Π vs. A curve for poly-DL-α-aminocaproic acid (poly-DL-norleucine), which apparently resembles that for protein. However, if the polypeptide has side chains of more than six carbon atoms, the force vs. area curve is entirely different from those of proteins. As shown in the figure, the Π vs. A curve has a region of remarkable compressibility. Nylon 6 (amilan) gave an entirely different Π vs. A curve from that for protein, notwithstanding the fact that it has the same composition as poly-DL-norleucine, indicating the significance of polypeptides of α-amino acids.

Poly-DL-norleucine has a limiting area of about 15 $Å^2$ per residue. The limiting area recalculated per milligram polypeptide is 0.8 m^2 which

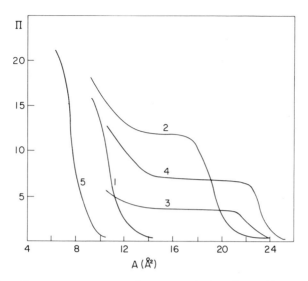

Fig. 4.19. Force vs. area curves of some synthetic polypeptide monolayers. (1) Poly-DL-α-aminocaproic acid; (2) poly-DL-α-aminocaprylic acid; (3) poly-DL-α-aminocapric acid; (4) poly-DL-α-aminolauric acid; (5) poly-γ-methyl-L-glutamate.

corresponds well to that for protein. These polypeptides spread as a monolayer in which they lie flat in the β-keratin form at the interface. The area per residuce, 15 Å^2, is in good agreement with the area calculated from X-ray data, where the length of the repeating unit is 3.32 Å and the distance between chains 4.4 Å. From surface viscosity-area relation, Cumper and Alexander found 14.7 Å^2 and 14.4 Å as the limiting areas for polyalanine and polyphenylalanine, respectively. The area per phenylalanine residue determined by the surface pressure-area relation is somewhat larger than 15 Å^2. The phenyl group may occupy a larger area than a single hydrocarbon chain.

The surface pressure at which the monolayer shows a characteristic, high compressibility decrease with the length of side chain if the temperature is maintained constant, while it decreases with a rise of tempreature with the same polypeptide film. If the polypeptide film contains side chains of nonpolar hydrocarbon, its force vs. area curve is not affected by the pH of the subphase. However, if the polypeptide has side chains which are electrolytic in nature, the force-area and viscosity-area relations are profoundly affected by the pH of the substrate. In Fig. 4.20 are shown the effects of the pH of the substrate on a film of a copolypeptide of glutamic acid, leucine, and lysine. At the isoelectric point of this copolypeptide, the limiting area per residue is a maximum.

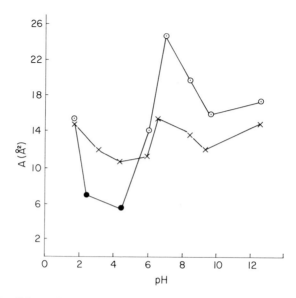

Fig. 4.20. Effect of pH on force vs. area and viscosity vs. area relationship. (1) Area at minimum compressibility against pH; (2) area at $\eta = 2 \times 10^{-2}$ surface poises against pH.

At either side of the isoelectric point the film contracts somewhat. The contraction may be caused by a decrease of interchain salt linkages. The force vs. area curves are of the condensed type on substrates of which the pH value lies in the range between 5.8 and 9.4, but changes to the expanded type if the substrate becomes more alkaline or more acidic than either end of this pH range. The relation of area per residue at constant viscosity (2×10^{-2} surface poises) to the pH of the substrate is also W-shaped, as shown in Fig. 4.20. These results may be interpreted in terms of an excess of either species of ion in the copolypeptide chain.

The polypeptide films are generally of the condensed type unless the polypeptide dissociates to an appreciable extent. The reason why they yield a condensed film is that they form interchain hydrogen bonds between peptide chains. The prolyl residue, which has no hydrogen atom to provide hydrogen bonding, causes the film to expand. A poly-L-proline film is accordingly of the expanded type. Owing to the spatial configuration, no two prolyl residues in the polyproline monolayer can exist in an equivalent manner when it is spread at the interface. Under these conditions no carbonyl groups can orient in the same direction, and the surface moment is low, owing to the intrachain cancellation of dipole moment. Poly-L-proline is known to exist in either configuration I or II. The former is partly, and the latter easily, soluble in water. The peptide bonds in poly-L-proline II are planar *trans*, whereas in poly-L-proline I might be *cis*. The effect of the substrate on the expansion of a film could be caused by *cis-trans* isomerization (*51*).

On the other hand, the tyrosyl group has a phenolic hydroxyl group which binds to the peptide bond in the main chain by hydrogen bonding. If poly-L-tyrosine is spread from solution in pyridine, which does not affect the hydrogen bond, the spread film occupies a far smaller area than other polypeptide films. However, the film occupies nearly the same area as other polypeptides when the poly-L-tyrosine is spread from 3olution in a hydrogen bond-breaking agent, such as dichloroacetic acid. Poly-O-benzyl-L-tyrosine in which the phenolic hydroxyl is etherized by the benzyl group gives a film of the condensed type with a rather larger area per residue. All this evidence shows the importance of hydrogen bonding for condensing the film, especially that of polypeptide (52).

Poly-γ-benzyl-L-glutamate, poly-β-benzyl-L-aspartate, and copoly 1 : 1 (γ-benzyl-L-glutamate, β-benzyl-L-aspartate) give monolayers of the condensed type for which the limiting areas per residue are all about 22 Å². This larger limiting area than that for polypeptides with side chains of nonpolar straight hydrocarbon may be attributed to the bulky side chains in these benzyl compounds. Even though they have almost the same limiting area, the compressibility is in the order poly-β-benzyl-L-aspartate > copoly-(β-benzyl-L-aspartate, benzyl-L-glutamate) > poly-γ-benzyl-L-glutamate.

One of the features of these polypeptide monolayers is that the surface moment of the polypeptide films is considerably higher than that of the polypeptides containing nonpolar side chains, for example poly-DL-alanine. Polar bonds in the side contribute to the surface moment as well as those in the main chain. It is very noteworthy that the surface viscosity of poly-β-benzyl-L-aspartate is manifest first in the high surface pressure region. In general, the surface viscosity of a monolayer in the condensed state is already high at an area where surface pressure is sufficiently low, and the surface viscosity of a monolayer in the expanded state is detected at an area where surface pressure is quite high. In other words, the surface viscosity of a condensed film is actually measured for the monolayer, but that of the expanded film is presumably for a folded monolayer. This characteristic difference between the surface viscosities of condensed and expanded films is observed not only with the copolypeptide films mentioned above but also for every other polymer film. Although the surface viscosity of poly-β-benzyl-L-aspartate is just like that for an expanded film, the force vs. area curve of this polypeptide is of the condensed type. More-

over, the surface viscosity of this polypeptide shows a positive temperature coefficient, while the expanded film usually has a negative temperature coefficient. The difference between poly-γ-benzyl-L-glutamate and
poly-β-benzyl-L-aspartate films, and especially the anomalous properties
of poly-β-benzyl-L-aspartate, is caused by the disposition of polar groups
in the side chains. The carbonyl group on the side chain may be far
from the aqueous surface but that of poly-γ-benzyl-L-aspartate is in
contact with the aqueous surface and scarcely distinguished from the
carbonyl group on the main chain. Accordingly, the configuration of
poly-β-benzyl-L-aspartate will be less stable owing to possible hydrogen
bonding of the carbonyl group on the side chain with the amino group
of the main chain. This might be the reason why the poly-β-benzyl-L-
aspartate film shows anomalous behavior in surface viscosity and has a
relatively high surface compressibility (53).

Poly-γ-benzyl-L-glutamate can be reduced to remove the benzyl group
in an anhydrous state, forming poly-L-glutamic acid. Poly-L-aspartic
acid was reported by Frankel and Berger (54) to be formed in the same
way. However, Noguchi (55) insisted that Berger's poly-L-aspartic acid
might be polyanhydro-L-aspartic acid, namely, the copolymer of aspartic
and its anhydride. Monolayers studies suggested polyanhydro-L-aspartic
acid should be the copolymer of aspartic acid and succinimide, while
polyanhydroglutamic acid, which was prepared by dehydrating poly-L-
glutamic acid with acetic anhydride, resembles polysuccinimide in its
monolayer properties. Polyanhydroglutamic acid may be identical with
polyglutarimide, which has a rigid folded configuration even in the
monolayer (56).

Since the ring of glutarimide can be cleaved by dilute alkali, rings
of polyanhydroglutamic acid might be cleaved to various extents when
it is spread as a monolayer on alkaline substrates of various pH values.
Poly-L-glutamic acid produced by cleavage of the ring of polyanhydroglutamic acid does not cause expansion of the film but gives a condensed
film of a smaller limiting area. This suggests that the poly-L-glutamic
acid thus formed should be composed of both α- and γ-peptide bonds,
as poly-γ-L-glutamic acid does not form a monolayer on aqueous subphases
of various compositions (57).

As mentioned in Section II, the molecular weight of a film-forming
substance can be determined from the ΠA vs. Π curve. If we apply
this method to polymers such as polyvinyl acetate, which give monolayers of the expanded type, the molecular weight obtained is usually
far less than the true molecular weight because the kinetic unit of the
molecule may be the smaller segments. On the other hand, it is well
known that the viscosity of a polymer solution is a function of molecular
weight. Accordingly, Isemura and Fukuzuka (58) examined whether

the surface viscosity (η) changes with the molecular weight (M) or not. It was found that the following relation holds with a polymer film such as polyvinyl acetate under relatively high surface pressure

$$\log \eta = A\sqrt{M} + B$$

where A is a constant, and B is dependent on temperature and surface pressure. The equation is formally identical to the viscosity formula for the melt of some long chain esters.

VII. Interaction at Interface

Interaction between the oriented molecules in monolayers and reagents dissolved in the underlying liquid can be studied by changes in surface pressure, the area occupied at constant surface pressure, and surface potential. Schulman and his collaborators found that, if a very dilute solution of certain types of compounds is injected under a monolayer, a change in surface pressure or an expansion of the monolayer and a change in surface potential are observed, due to interaction between the two molecular species. Further, if the van der Waals forces of attraction between the nonpolar parts of the two compounds are sufficiently strong, a rapid penetration of the monolayer by the injected substance occurs, irrespective of the inital surface pressure of the monolayer, giving a mixed monolayer containing the two reactants in a definite stoichiometric ratio (59).

With a monolayer of cholesterol confined by a suitable barrier by a thread compressed from outside by a triolein piston which is not penetrated by the injected material, the injection of a dilute solution of digitonin causes an immediate expansion of the monolayer to twice the area. The previously liquid cholesterol film turns in to a solid film. The compressive pressure of triolein is not changed by the injection of digitonin. If, instead of digitonin, hexadecyl sulfate in suitable concentration is injected and if oleic acid is employed as the piston oil, the area increase is only 50% instead of 100%. Since the molecular areas of cholesterol, digitonin, and hexadecyl sulfate are 40 Å^2, 40 Å^2, and 20 Å^2, respectively, this suggests that a 1:1 complex should be formed. Replacing oleic acid by triolein of lower spreading pressure, it was found that on injection of hexadecyl sulfate there was an immediate expansion of 50%, forming the 1:1 complex. This was followed by a further slow expansion at this lower pressure, indicating the formation of a less stable complex of the composition cholesterol and hexadecyl sulfate (1:2). If dodecyl sulfate is used instead of hexadecyl sulfate, only a very weak 1:1 complex can be formed. Thus, van der Waals forces play a great role in the formation of the complex in this case.

Relatively simple acids, such as *p*-cresol, resorcinol, and benzoic acid, react weakly with alkyl amine films. In the case of octadecyl-amine hydrochloride films on an underlying solution containing benzoic acid, there are no breaks in the Π vs. A or ΔV vs. A curves and no evidence of stoichiometric complex formation. The interaction between the molecules in the monolayer and compunds present in the subphase can vary in strength between wide limits.

When proteins such as bovine serum albumin or γ-globulin are injected into a substrate on which cardiolipin or sodium behenyl sulfate is spread, expansion of the film is observed under constant surface pressure, and an increase in surface pressure is observed at constant area if the monolayer is oppositely charged (*60*). Bull studied the interaction of sodium dodecyl sulfate with egg albumin by spreading mixtures of these substances of various composition, prepared beforehand. If the underlying solution contains 35% ammonium sulfate, even pure sodium dodecyl sulfate can spread as a stable monolayer up to high surface pressures. Figure 4.21 shows the areas in square meters per milligram

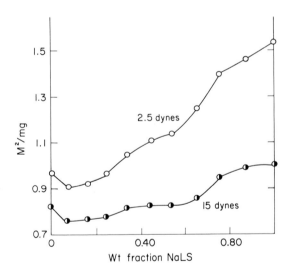

Fig. 4.21. Interaction of sodium dodecyl sulfate with egg albumin.

of the mixtures, plotted against the weight fraction of sodium dodecyl sulfate at 2.5 and 15 dynes/cm. The results shown in this figure indicate extensive and complicated interaction between egg albumin and sodium dodecyl sulfate. Bull has calculated the percentage of the area of the protein in the film which is covered by sodium dodecyl sulfate, using certain assumptions. These percentages are plotted against the weight fraction of sodium dodecyl sulfate in Fig. 4.22, which indicates three

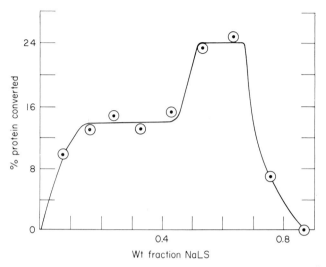

Fig. 4.22. Percentage of protein film covered with sodium dodecyl sulfate.

distinct steps in the interaction between the protein and sodium dodecyl sulfate as the weight fraction of the detergent is increased (*61*).

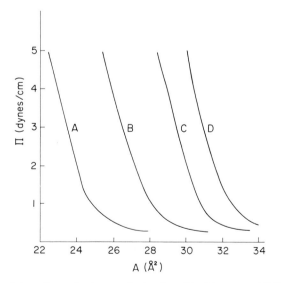

Fig. 4.23. Interaction of poly-α-aminolauric acid with urea. (*A*) Distilled water; (*B*) 10% urea; (*C*) 20% urea; (*D*) 30% urea solution.

Polypeptide monolayers interact with urea in the substrate. The monolayers of polypeptides are expanded considerably in the presence of urea in the substrate, as shown in Fig. 4.23. The greater the concentration of urea in the subphase, the more the monolayer expands. However, the number of molecules is not changed by the interaction with urea as is sometimes encountered in protein denaturation. Accordingly, the molecular weight of a polypeptide determined by surface pressure measurements on the substrate with or without urea is the same, although the co-area of the molecule is increased by increase of urea concentration. Urea may be bound to the peptide bonds in the backbone by hydrogen bonding. Although salt affects the Π vs. A curves of electrolyte polymers profoundly, as described above, it scarcely affects those of nonelectrolyte polypeptide films (62).

VIII. Equation of State of Ionized Monolayers

As already mentioned in Section II, the monolayer behaves just like an ideal gas if the surface concentration of spread material is sufficiently small, and the surface pressure-area relation is expressed fairly well by an equation of the ideal gas type, i.e.,

$$\Pi A = kT$$

However, if the monolayer is compressed moderately, it deviates from this ideal gas relation. In this case, the behavior of the monolayer is expressed by the relation which can be applied to a real gas, and we thus have a two-dimensional analog of the van der Waals equation.

Langmuir has shown that this type of equation, namely,

$$(\Pi - \Pi_0)(A - A_0) = kT$$

can be applied to expanded films too. It was later shown that the same equation can be applied experimentally to liquid condensed films as well as to liquid expanded films (63). In this equation, A_0, the co-area, corresponds to the constant b and $-\Pi_0$ to a/A^2, the term due to the coherence of molecules in the van der Waals equation. Nakagaki calculated A_0 assuming the molecule to be a rigid rod and to be in a specific orientation at the interface, namely, flat, vertical, with definite inclination, or freely oriented in the interface. He succeeded in explaing quantitatively the monolayer behavior of some fatty acids by this treatment (64).

It is well known that the presence of an electrical charge on a monolayer greatly affects the behavior of the film. If a fatty acid film is spread on an alkaline subphase, the film markedly expands, suggesting a great diminution of the net lateral adhesion. The ionized films dissolve more readily, and their surface pressure, surface potential, and surface viscosity vary with the pH and salt content in the subphase, which influence the degree of ionization and the structure of the diffuse ionic layer in the subphase. The effect of ionization of the monolayer was first studied by Adam (65) and later by a number of investigators.

Cassie and Palmer (66) proposed the following equation

$$\Pi^{\pm}(A - A_0) = 1.5\,kT \tag{4.5}$$

where $\Pi^{\pm}$ is the film pressure of either a positively or a negatively charged film. Equation (4.5) gives values of the product $\Pi^{\pm}\,(A - A_0)$ which are usually far too low, especially for charged films at the oil-water interface. On the other hand, Brady and Brown have reported that $2kT$ values for the product $\Pi^{\pm}(A - A_0)$ hold for films of sodium dodecyl sulfate adsorbed at the air-water interface (67) though their range of A is small, whereas Pethica finds that the product is less than $1\,kT$ for films of the same surface active agent also at air-water interfaces when 0.145 M NaCl is present. A value of 3 kT for the product was put forward by Davies for a charged film at oil-water interfaces for low salt concentration (68). He correlates the effect encountered in a charged monolayer with the surface potential quantitatively predicted from the equation of Gouy. This potential is given at 20°C by the expression

$$\psi_0 = \frac{2kT}{e}\,\sinh^{-1}\frac{134}{A\sqrt{c}}$$

where ψ_0 is expressed in millivolts, A is the area in Å^2 per charged group in the monolayer, and c is the concentration of univalent electrolyte in the solution.

The cohesion of the monolayer is reduced, owing to the repulsion between the similar ions when electrolytic dissociation takes place. Davies calculated the repulsion due to the potential by means of the Gouy theory and reached the result

$$\Delta\Pi = 6.1\sqrt{c}\left(\cosh\frac{e\psi_0}{2kT} - 1\right) \tag{4.6}$$

The actually observed surface pressure of a charged monolayer is the sum of this pressure and that which the monolayer would have if uncharged. The total surface pressure $\Pi^{\pm}$ is given by

$$\Pi^{\pm} = \Pi_c + \Pi_s + \Delta\Pi \tag{4.7}$$

where Π_s is the kinetic pressure, Π_c is the cohesive pressure, and $\Delta\Pi$ the pressure caused by ionization. Inserting the cohesive pressure

$$\Pi_c = \frac{400\,n}{A^{2/3}}$$

where n is the number of methylene groups in each long chain ion, at the air-water interface the surface pressure is expressed by

$$\Pi = \frac{3kT}{A - A_0} - \frac{400\,n}{A^{3/2}} - 6.1\sqrt{c} - \frac{2kT\,A_0}{(A - A_0)A} \qquad (4.8)$$

Further approximation leads to the equation,

$$(\Pi^{\pm} - \Pi_s - \Delta\Pi)(A - A_0) = kT$$

At the oil-water interface Π_s, the second term on the right side of Eq. (4.8) may be omitted. Then, if A is sufficiently large, the equation tends to

$$\Pi^{\pm}(A - A_0) = kT$$

On the other hand, Phillips and Rideal gave the general equation of state for a gaseous monolayer from the thermodynamic standpoint

$$\Pi + E_R + \frac{AdE}{dA} - E_V - \frac{AdE_V}{dA} + \frac{kT}{C_s^{R+}}\frac{dC_s^{R+}}{dA} + \frac{kT}{C_s^{X-}}\frac{dC_s^{X-}}{dA} = 0 \quad (4.9)$$

where E_R and E_V represent the electrical repulsion energy and the cohesive attraction energy per unit area of the interface, and C_s^{R+} and C_s^{X-} represent the surface concentration of the film and counter ions, respectively, expressed as mole fractions. Assuming an ionized film to correspond to an ideal planar charge and applying the ideal Gouy theory,

$$E_R = \frac{e\psi_0}{A} - F$$

where F is the total free energy of the double layer. In the case of a $1:1$ electrolyte, the equation of state for an ionized monolayer becomes, under ideal conditions, where $E_V = 0$

$$\Pi = \frac{2kT}{A - A_0} - 6.1\sqrt{c} - \frac{2kT\,A_0}{(A - A_0)A} \qquad (4.10)$$

This differs from the ideal expression derived by Davies by a term kT/A, due to neglect of the counter ion contribution to the surface energy.

Ikeda and Isemura (69) showed that the same results can be derived from simpler thermodynamic considerations as well as from the electrostatic theory. They assumed that an insoluble monolayer is a two-dimensional solution in a surface phase, in which the monolayer substance behaves as a solute, apart from its nonpolar side chains. It exerts a surface pressure for maintaining thermodynamic equilibrium with the bulk phase. Thus, for an electrolyte monolayer it may be assumed that its ionized groups are dissolved uniformly in a "surface phase" with a definite thickness δ, and ions of salt in the aqueous subphase are distributed between the surface and bulk phases, counter ions being concentrated in the surface phase and co-ions being repelled from there into the bulk phase. The distribution of ions between the two phases is first evaluated by analogy with membrane equilibrium and then by an improved aproximation. The difference in ionic concentrations between the two phases, resulting from the ionization of a monolayer, contributes to the surface pressure. These contributions were calculated by means of thermodynamic procedures.

It is assumed that the boundary between the surface and bulk phases behaves like a semipermeable membrane in osmotic equilibrium in a colloidal solution. The electrochemical potential of each diffusible ion in both phases should be equal. Furthermore, it is assumed that the surface phase remains electrically neutral. Then, the surface pressure $\Delta\Pi$ due to the ionization of the monolayer can be expressed by

$$\Delta\Pi = 2kT\left\{-\frac{4n}{\kappa} + \left[\frac{1}{A^2} + \left(\frac{4n}{\kappa}\right)^2\right]^{1/2}\right\} \tag{4.11}$$

where n is the concentration of ion in the bulk phase and κ the Debye-Hückel parameter. If $\delta = 2/\kappa$, the relation is just the same that obtained by Davies. Instead of assuming electroneutrality in the surface phase, they assume that the surface phase deviates slightly from electroneutrality. In this case the "λ-method" for solving the problem of polyelectrolyte solutions (69) is applied; λ is a parameter indicating the deviation from electroneutrality. By this procedure, the surface pressure due to the ionization of the monolayer can be expressed by the equation

$$\Delta\Pi = 2kT\left\{-\frac{4n}{\kappa} + \left[\frac{1}{A^2} + \left(\frac{4n}{\kappa}\right)^2\right]^{1/2} - \frac{1}{A^2}\frac{<\lambda>}{[|(1/A^2) + (4n/\kappa)^2]^{1/2}}\right\} \tag{4.12}$$

Applying this equation to the data of octadecyltrimethylammonium

TABLE 4.4

SURFACE PRESSURE OF AN UNCHARGED MONOLAYER OF OCTADECYLTRIMETHYL-
AMMONIUM CHLORIDE ON NaCl AT 20°C

n (moles/liter)	$\Delta\Pi$	Π	Π_0
0.033	3.87	5.8	1.93
0.100	2.99	5.3	2.31
0.50	1.40	3.8	2.40
2.0	0.34	2.7	2.36

chloride obtained by Davies, the surface pressure of the uncharged film
was calculated. The results are listed in Table 4.4. The surface pressures of uncharged films are independent of salt concentration and are
always positive. Equation (4.12) is superior to other equations because
it gives positive surface pressures for an uncharged film, while the others
always give negative pressures.

References

1. Pockels, A. *Nature* **43**, (1891).
2. Rayleigh, W. *Proc. Roy. Soc.* **A48**, 127 (1890).
3. Langmuir, I. *J. Am. Chem. Soc.* **38**, 2221 (1916).
4. Ehrenfest, P. *Communs. Kamerlingh Onnes Lab. Univ. Leiden, Suppl.* **No. 75b** (1933).
5. Harkins, W. D., Young, T. F., and Boyd, E. *J. Chem. Phys*, **8**, 954 (1940).
6. Guastalla, J. *Compt. rend. acad. sci.* **206**, 993 (1938).
7. Cheesman, D. F. *Arkiv Kemi. Mineral. Geol.* **B** , 221 (1946).
8. Sasaki, T. *J. Chem. Soc. Japan* **62**, 796 (1941). (In Japanese.)
9. Inokuchi, K. *Sci. to. Ochanomizu Univ.*, **4**, 92 (1953).
10. Allan, A. J., and Alexander, E. A. *Trans. Faraday Soc.* **46**, 316 (1950).
11. Puddington, I. E. *J. Colloid Sci.* **1**, 505 (1946).
12. Dervichian, D. G. see Bruun, H. H. *Acta Akad. Aboensis* **No. 75** (1954).
13. Brady, A. P. *J. Colloid Sci.* **4**, 417 (1949).
14. Zisman, W. A., and Yamins, H. G. *J. Chem. Phys.* **1**, 656 (1933).
15. Schllman, J. H., Rideal E. K. *Proc. Roy. Soc.* **A130**, 259, 270, 284 (1930).
16. Moquin, H., and Rideal, E. K. *Proc. Roy. Soc.* **A114**, 690 (1927).
17. Davies, J. T., and Mayers, G. R. A. *Trans. Faraday Soc.* **56**, 656 (1960).
18. Tachibana, T., and Inokuchi, K. J. *Collid Sci.* **8**, 341 (1953).
19. Hatschek, V. E., and Jans, R. S. *Kolloid-Z.* **39**, 300 (1926).
20. Inokuchi, K. *Bull. Chem. Soc. Japan* **27**, 433 (1954).
21. Pethica, B. A., and Few, A. W. *Discussions Faraday Soc.* **18**, 258 (1954).
22. Phillips, J. N., and Rideal, E. K. *Proc. Roy. Soc.* **A232**, 159 (1955).
23. Stenhagen, E. *Trans. Faraday Soc.* **36**, 496 (1940).
24. Adam, N. K. "Physics and Chemistry of Surfaces." Oxford Univ. Press, London and New York, 1941.
25. Davies, J. T. *Trans. Faraday Soc.* 1052 (1952).
26. Guggenheim, E. "Thermodynamics." Elsevier, Amsterdam, 1949.
27. Hutchinson, E, *J. Colloid Sci.* **3**, 413 (1948).
28. Schulman, J. H., and Hughes, *Proc. Roy. Soc.* **A138**, 480 (1932).
29. Cassie, A. B. D., and Palmer, R. C. *Trans. Faraday Soc.* **37**, 156 (1941).
30. Davies, J. T. *Proc. Roy. Soc.* **A208**, 224 (1951)
31. Brown, A. G., Thuman, W. C., and McBain, J. W. *J. Colloid Sci.* **8**, 491 (1953).
32. Mysels, K. J., Shinoda, K., and Frankel, S. "Soap Films," p. 87. Pergamon, New York, 1959.
33. Brady, A. P., and Brown, A. G. *In* "Monomolecular Layers" (H. Sobotka, ed.),

p. 33. American Association for the Advancement of Science, Washingon, D. C., 1954.

34. Blankey, B. C., and Lawrence, A. S. C. *Discussions Faraday Soc.* **18**, 268 (1954).

35. Devaux, H. *Procès-verbaux séances soc. sci. phys. et nat. Bordeaux* (November, 19, 1903).

36. Rideal, E. K., and Hughes, H. A. *Proc. Roy. Soc.* **A 137**, 62 (1932, Mitchell, J. S. *Trans. Faraday Soc.* **33**, 1129 (1937), Schulman, J. H., and Cockbain, E. G. *ibid.* **35**, 1266 (1939).

37. Ställberg, S., and Teorell, T. *Trans. Faraday Soc.* **35**, 1413 (1939).

38. Dervichian D. G. *Nature* **114**, 629 (1938).

39. Isemura, T., and Hamahuchi, K. *Bull. Chem. Soc. Japan* **25**, 40 (1952).

40. Alexander, A. E., and Teorell, T. *Trans. Faraday Soc.* **35** 727 (1939).

41. Hughes, H. A., and Rideal, E. K. *Proc. Roy. Soc.* **A130**, 70 (1932).

42. Dogan, M. Z., and Glazer, J. *Nature* **170**, 417 (1952).

43. Joly, M. *J. chim. Phys.* **36**, 285 (1939).

44. Joly, M. "Surface Chemistry." Butterworths, London, 1949.

45. Harkins, W. D., Carman, E. F., and Ries, H. E. *J. Chem. Phys.* **3**, 692 (1935).

46. Suzuki, K. *Discussions Colloid Sci. (Japan)* **1**, 63 (1947). (In Japanese.)

47. Isemura, T., Hotta, H., and Miwa, T. *Bull. Chem. Soc. Japan* **26**, 380 (1953); Isemura, T., Hotta, H. and Otsuka, S. *Bull. Chem. Soc. Japan* **27**, 93 (1954).

48. Cumper, C. W. A., and Alexander, E. A. *Trans. Faraday Soc.* **46**, 235 (1950).

49. Isemura, T., and Hamaguchi, K. *Bull. Chem. Soc. Japan* **25**, 40 (1952); **26**, 425 (1953); **27**, 125, 339 (1954); Isemura, T., and Ikeda, S. *ibid.* **33**, 659 (1959); **34**, 137 (1960); Isemura, T., and Yamashita, T. *ibid.* **33**, 1 (1959).

50. Davies, J. T. *Trans. Faraday Soc.* **49**, 949 (1953); *Biochim. et Biophys. Acta* **11**, 165 (1953).

51. Harrington, W. F., and Sela, M. *Biochim. Biophys. Acta,* **27**, 24 (1958).

52. Isemura. T., and Yamashita, T. *Bull. Chem. Soc. Japan* **33**, 1 (1959).

52. Ikeda, S., and Isemura, T. *Bull. Chem. Soc. Japan* **34**, in press (1961).

54. Frankel, M., and Berger, A. *J. Org. Chem.* **16**, 1513 (1951); Berger, A., and Katchalski, E. *J. Am. Chem. Soc.* **73**, 4084 (1951).

55. Noguchi, J. *J. Chem. Soc. Japan, Pure Chem. Sect.* **81**, 622 (1960).

56. Ikeda, S., and Isemura, T. *Bull. Chem. Soc. Japan* **34**, in press (1961).

57. Isemura, T., and Yamashita, T. Unpublished data.

58. Isemura, T., and Fukuzuka, K. *Mem. Inst. Sci. and Ind. Research, Osaka Univ.* **13**, 137 (1956); **14** (1957).

59. Schulman, J. H., Stenhagen, E., and Rideal E. K. *Nature* **141**, 785 (1938); Cockbain, E. G., and Schulman, J. H. *Trans. Faraday Soc.* , 716 (1939).

60. Matalon, R., and Schulman, J. H. *Discussions Faraday Soc.* **6**, 27 (1949).

61. Bull, H. B. *J. Am. Chem. Soc.* **67**, 10 (1945).

62. Isemura, T., Hamaguchi, K., and Kawasato, H. *Bull. Chem. Soc. Japan* **38**, 185 (1955).

63. Akamatsu, H., and Nakagaki, M. *Bull. Chem. Soc. Japan* **23**, 232 (1950).

64. Nakagaki, M. *Bull. Chem. Soc. Japan* **32**, 1231 (1959).

63. Adam, N. K. *Proc. Roy. Soc.* **A101**, 516 (1922); "Physics and Chemistry of Surfaces," pp. 72, 129. Oxford Univ. Press, London and New York, 1941.

66. Cassie, A. B. D., and Palmer, R. C. *Trans. Faraday Soc.* **37**, 156 (1941).

67. Brady, A. P., and Brown A. G. *In* "Monomolecular Layers," p. 33. (H. Sobotka, ed.), American Association for the Advancement of Science, Washington, 1954.

68. Davies, J. T. *Proc. Roy. Soc.* **A208**, 224 (1951).

69. Ikeda, S., and Isemura, T. *Bull. Chem. Soc. Japan* **34**, 131 (1960).

AUTHOR INDEX

Numbers in parentheses are reference numbers, and are inserted to assist in locating a reference when the author's name is not cited at the point of reference in the text. Numbers in italic refer to the page on which the full reference is listed.

SUBJECT INDEX

A

Absorption spectra, of dye, 10, 100–102, 109, 126, 156–158
of solubilizate, 140
Acetic acid, analogy with micelle formation, 6
Activation energy of adsorption, 192
Activity, change with concentration, 36, 130
of gegenion, 16
of solute, 3, 7, 27, 35, 100, 187
Activity coefficient, 27, 33, 188
Adhesion work, 198
Adsorbed layers, structure at mercury-solution interface, 206–214
Adsorption, at air-hydrocarbon interface, 4
at air-solution interface, 181–187
apparent amount of, 217
effect of chain length, 222–223
at liquid-solid interface, 216–230
at solution-mercury interface, 203–216
at solution-oil interface, 181–187
true amount of, 217
Adsorption isotherm (see also Gibbs adsorption isotherm), 216–221
Aerosol (see Sulfosuccinate)
Aggregation number (see Micellar weight)
Aging phenomenon, at surface, 182–187
Alcohol, effect on the cloud point, 148
effect on the CMC, 69–74, 147
Alkane tricarboxylate, 43–46
Alkylammonium carboxylate, 83, 86–87
Alkylammonium halide (see also under individual substances, such as dodecylammonium halide), adsorption of, 218, 223
CMC of, 43, 54
flocculation value of, 232
monolayer of, 282

Alkylbenzene sulfonate, CMC of, 43, 50
effect on cloud point of nonionic agent, 139
micellar weight, 21
selective adsorption of, 79
Alkyl glucoside, CMC of, 3, 43–44, 55, 105–106, 112
micellar region, 8
surface tension, 26, 160
Alkyl malonate, CMC of, 43–46
Alkyl sulfate (see also under individual substances, such as sodium dodecyl sulfate), adsorption at oil-solution interface, 200
CMC of, 43, 48–49, 55–57, 124
heat of micellization, 31
heat of solution, 8
micellar weight of, 124
monolayer of, 261, 263, 281–285
surface moment of, 266
Alkyl sulfonate, CMC of, 43, 56
electrical conductance of, 25
force area curve, 261
heat of micellization, 31
Alkyltrimethylammonium halide, CMC of, 54, 128
monolayer of, 261, 263–265, 288
surface viscosity of, 268–269
Ammonium fluoroalkanoate, 53
Amylopectin, 159
Amylose, 159
Analysis, of nonionic agent, 159, 172–175
of paraffin chain salt, 217
Aniline blue, 100
Arsenic sulphide sol, electrophoretic mobility of, 233
flocculation of, 231
Arylstearate soap, micellar weight of, 83–86
Athermal mixing, 65
Axial ratio, 118, 123
Azobenzene, solubilization of, 5